S0-ABY-276

FOUNDATIONS OF MATHEMATICS FOR TOMORROW:

AN INTRODUCTION
si metric

FOUNDATIONS OF MATHEMATICS FOR TOMORROW:
AN INTRODUCTION
SI METRIC EDITION

"The Metric Commission has granted use
of the National Symbol for Metric Conversion"

FMT
AN INTRODUCTION
si metric

Dino Dottori B.Sc., M.S.Ed.
Head, Mathematics Department
Glendale Secondary School
Hamilton, Ontario

George Knill B.Sc., M.S.Ed.
Head, Mathematics Department
Sir Allan MacNab Secondary School
Hamilton, Ontario

James Stewart Ph.D.
Associate Professor
Department of Mathematics
McMaster University
Hamilton, Ontario

McGRAW-HILL RYERSON LIMITED

Toronto Montreal New York St. Louis San Francisco
Auckland Bogotá Düsseldorf Johannesburg London
Madrid Mexico New Delhi Panama
Paris São Paulo Singapore Sydney Tokyo

FOUNDATIONS OF MATHEMATICS FOR TOMORROW:
AN INTRODUCTION

Copyright © McGraw-Hill Ryerson Limited, 1977

All rights reserved. No part of this publication may be reproduced, stored in a retrieval system, or transmitted in any form or by any means, electronic, mechanical, photocopying, recording, or otherwise, without the prior written permission of McGraw-Hill Ryerson Limited.

ISBN 0-07-082529-7

4 5 6 7 8 9 0 BP 6 5 4 3 2 1 0 9

Illustrations by Henning Christensen

Printed and bound in Canada

Canadian Cataloguing in Publication Data

DOTTORI, DINO, 1937—
    FMT

(THE RYERSON MATHEMATICS PROGRAM)
INCLUDES INDEX.
ISBN 0-07-082529-7

1. MATHEMATICS — 1961—   I. KNILL, GEORGE, 1938—
II. STEWART, JAMES.   III. TITLE.   IV. TITLE:
FOUNDATIONS OF MATHEMATICS FOR TOMORROW.

QA39.2.D682   510   C77-001547-6

THE RYERSON MATHEMATICS PROGRAM
CORE TEXTS
MATHEMATICS FOR TODAY AND TOMORROW

FOUNDATIONS OF MATHEMATICS FOR TOMORROW: AN INTRODUCTION
FOUNDATIONS OF MATHEMATICS FOR TOMORROW: INTERMEDIATE
FOUNDATIONS OF MATHEMATICS FOR TOMORROW: SENIOR

APPLIED MATHEMATICS FOR TODAY: AN INTRODUCTION
APPLIED MATHEMATICS FOR TODAY: INTERMEDIATE
APPLIED MATHEMATICS FOR TODAY: SENIOR

COMPANION BOOKLETS

MATHEMATICS SKILLBUILDING
MATHEMATICS FOR ENRICHMENT
BUSINESS MATH EXERCISES
TECHNICAL MATH EXERCISES

Contents

Mathematics is not a spectator sport.   *Anonymous*

REVIEW AND PREVIEW TO CHAPTER 1

EXERCISE 1
ADDITION AND SUBTRACTION

1. Add

(a) $3x + 4y$
$\underline{2x + 5y}$

(b) $4x^2 + 3x$
$\underline{7x^2 + 10x}$

(c) $7xy + 5w$
$\underline{20xy - 2w}$

(d) $5x - 6y$
$\underline{2x + 5y}$

(e) $3x^2 - 12x$
$\underline{7x^2 - 5x}$

(f) $4x^2 - 8x + 5$
$\underline{7x^2 + 11x - 7}$

(g) $3w - 7x + 4y \, ; 6w - 5x - 8y$
(h) $2m^2 - 3m - 9 \, ; m^2 - m + 6 \, ; 2m^2 + 6m - 3$
(i) $6x^2 - 5 + 4x \, ; 6x - x^2 + 7 \, ; 10 - 3x^2 + 9x$
(j) $9x^2 - 6xy + 4y^2 \, ; 7x^2 + 6xy - y^2 \, ; -8x^2 - 10xy - 7y^2$
(k) $6x - 3y \, ; 4m + 5n$

2. Subtract the first polynomial from the second.

(a) $2x + 3y \, ; 5x + 6y$
(b) $3w + 2x + 5y \, ; 7w + 11x + 9y$
(c) $7x - 4y \, ; 11x + 2y$
(d) $3x^2 + 2x - 4 \, ; 2x^2 - 4x - 2$
(e) $4w - 3x - 5y \, ; 2w - 9x - 5y$
(f) $5x^2 - 6x + 4 \, ; -3x^2 + 2x - 8$
(g) $6x - 5x^2 + 8 \, ; 4 - 3x + 2x^2$
(h) $3y - 4w - 2x \, ; 6w - 5y + 7x$
(i) $x^2 - 3xy + y^2 \, ; 5xy$
(j) $4m - 3n \, ; -2$

A book contains 200 leaves. On which leaf is page 51?

EXERCISE 2
SUBSTITUTION

1. If $w = 3$, $x = 2$ and $y = 4$, evaluate

(a) $2xy$
(b) $3wxy$
(c) $3x + 4w + 5y$
(d) $3x - 2y$
(e) $w^2 + x^2 + y^2$
(f) $w - x - y$
(g) $2x^2 - 3x - 4$
(h) $wx - xy - 2wy$
(i) $3x^2 - 2xy - y^2$
(j) $4(3x - 2y)$
(k) $2w^2x - 3xy^2$
(l) $w^3 - x^4 - y^2$
(m) $3x(w - x - y)$
(n) $3w^2 - 2w - 4$
(o) $-x^2(x - 2)$

2. If $w = -1$, $x = -2$ and $y = 3$, evaluate

(a) $3w + 2x + 4y$
✓(b) $5x - 3y$
(c) $3wxy$
✓(d) $-4wxy$
(e) $w - x - y$
(f) $w^2 + x^2 + y^2$
(g) $x^2 - w^2 - y^2$
(h) $3wx - xy + y$
(i) $3w^2x^2 - 4xy^2$
(j) $w^5 - 2x^3 - 7$
(k) $-2(w^3 - 3w^2)$
(l) $4w(x - y - w)$
(m) $w^2x^2 - 3wxy$
(n) $w^7 - w^6 + w^5$
(o) $-7 - 4w - 5x - 3y$

EXERCISE 3

MULTIPLICATION

1. Simplify

(a) $(3xy)(4w)$ (b) $(-2x)(5w)$ (c) $(-8x)(-5y)$

(d) $(2x^2)(4x)$ (e) $(-2w^3)(-3w^2)$ (f) $(2x^5)(-6x^4)$

(g) $(2x^5)(3x^2)(2x)$ (h) $(-2x^2y)(3x^4)$ (i) $(5wx)(2y^2)$

(j) $(3m^2n)(-5m^3n^2)$ (k) $(0.5y^5)(-8x^6)$ (l) $(-3x)(xy)(-4y)$

(m) $(7wx^3)(wx)(-2w^3)$ (n) $(10xy^5)(-0.2x)$ (o) $(8x^2y^7)(-5x^6)(-2xy^7)$

(p) $(-8xy^2)(-5x)(-6)$ (q) $(6st)(-11s^2t)$ (r) $-(-2x^2y)(-xy^4)$

2. Expand

$$a(b+c)$$
$$= a(b+c)$$
$$= ab + ac$$

(a) $3(x+5)$ (b) $2(x-7)$ (c) $(2m-1)9$

(d) $-3(x-6)$ (e) $-(x+5)$ (f) $7(3x-2y-8)$

(g) $-2(2x^2-5x-1)$ (h) $x(3x-8)$ (i) $2x(x^2-x+9)$

(j) $-4x(x^2-3xy-y^2)$ (k) $2xy(3x-5y)$ (l) $3t^3(5t^2-4t+2)$

(m) $-3w(4w^2-3w+4)$ (n) $-3xy(x^2-4xy-2y^2)$ (o) $3t(7x-3y+11)$

(p) $st(-4s^2-5st+3t^2)$ (q) $-wxy(3x-y-w)$ (r) $5x^6(2x^5-5x^3-9x)$

CHAPTER 1

Algebra and Matrices

Mathematics is the predominant science of our time; its conquests grow daily, though without noise; he who does not employ it *for* himself will someday find it employed *against* himself.

J. F. Herbart

Evariste Galois (1811–1832)

In spite of the fact that Galois had one of the most brilliant mathematical minds of all time, he got very low marks in mathematics in high school. He created new and original mathematical ideas by the time he was 17, but he found it difficult to explain these ideas to others, and his teachers never understood him. He twice failed the entrance examination to the Ecole Polytechnique, and when he submitted his brilliant discoveries to the French Academy of Sciences, they lost his papers.

Galois became involved in the 1830 revolution and spent some time in jail. Later he was challenged to a duel over a woman named Eve, his first (and last) love. (It is thought that the duel was promoted by the authorities to get rid of Galois.) The duel was to take place the next day, and Galois knew he would die in the duel, so he stayed up all night feverishly writing down all his mathematical discoveries in a letter which was forwarded to the leading mathematical authorities of the day. Early in the morning of May 30, 1832, the duel took place. It was with pistols at 25 paces. Galois was killed at the age of twenty.

What was in the letter? When mathematicians finally were able to decipher and understand it, the genius of Galois was finally recognized. The letter contained the beginnings of the theory of groups. It also contained the solution of a problem that had bothered mathematicians for two thousand years. From the time of Euclid many of the best minds had tried to find a way of trisecting angles using only ruler and compasses. Galois proved that it is *impossible* to trisect angles in this way!

1.1 PRODUCT OF POLYNOMIALS.

Before dealing with the product of polynomials we will review some of the terminology of algebra.

A term is a mathematical expression using numbers and/or variables to indicate a product or a quotient. Examples of terms are:

$$5x, \quad 7, \quad -4y^2, \quad 3xy$$

The numerical part of a term is called the *coefficient*. A term may also have a variable part. A variable is a symbol which may represent any member of a particular set.

Term

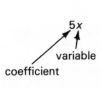

$5x$

variable

coefficient

The degree of a term is the sum of the exponents of its variables.

$$3y^4 \text{ is a term of degree 4.}$$
$$-5x^2y^1 \text{ is a term of degree 3.}$$

We classify algebraic expressions by the number of terms in the expression.

$$5x \;:\; \text{one term: monomial}$$
$$2x + 3y \;:\; \text{two terms: binomial}$$
$$4x^2 - 3x + 7 \;:\; \text{three terms: trinomial}$$

The degree of a polynomial is the greatest degree of its terms.

$5x - 4$ is a first degree polynomial or *linear* polynomial.
$3y^2 - 2y + 2$ is a second degree polynomial or *quadratic* polynomial.
$2t^3 - 5$ is a third degree polynomial or *cubic* polynomial.

Terms that have the same variable factors such as $5xy$ and $9xy$ are called *like terms.* The distributive property is used to *simplify* polynomials containing like terms.

$$5xy + 9xy = (5 + 9)xy = 14xy$$

Polynomials are in simplest form when like terms have been collected.
We use the distributive property to multiply polynomials.

$$(x + 3)(2x - 1) = x(2x - 1) + 3(2x - 1)$$
$$= 2x^2 - x + 6x - 3$$
$$= 2x^2 + 5x - 3$$

> To find the product of two polynomials, multiply each term of one of the polynomials by each term of the other and then add the products.

EXAMPLE 1. *Expand and simplify*
$$2(2x + 1)(x - 3) - 4(x + 5)$$

Solution
$$2(2x + 1)(x - 3) - 4(x + 5) = 2(2x^2 - 6x + x - 3) - 4(x + 5)$$
$$= 2(2x^2 - 5x - 3) - 4(x + 5)$$
$$= 4x^2 - 10x - 6 - 4x - 20$$
$$= 4x^2 - 14x - 26$$

The following are examples of three special cases of binomial products.

$(a + b)^2 = a^2 + 2ab + b^2$

$$(x + 5y)^2 = (x + 5y)(x + 5y)$$
$$= x^2 + 5xy + 5xy + 25y^2$$
$$= x^2 + 10xy + 25y^2$$

$(a - b)^2 = a^2 - 2ab + b^2$

$$(2x - 3)^2 = (2x - 3)(2x - 3)$$
$$= 4x^2 - 6x - 6x + 9$$
$$= 4x^2 - 12x + 9$$

$$(2x - 3y)(2x + 3y) = 4x^2 + 6xy - 6xy - 9y^2$$
$$= 4x^2 - 9y^2$$

$$\boxed{(a - b)(a + b) = a^2 - b^2}$$

EXAMPLE 2. *Expand and simplify*
$$2(3x + 2)(2x + 1) - (3x - 4)^2$$

Solution

$$2(3x + 2)(2x + 1) - (3x - 4)^2 = 2(6x^2 + 3x + 4x + 2) - (9x^2 - 24x + 16)$$
$$= 2(6x^2 + 7x + 2) - (9x^2 - 24x + 16)$$
$$= 12x^2 + 14x + 4 - 9x^2 + 24x - 16$$
$$= 3x^2 + 38x - 12$$

EXAMPLE 3. *Expand and simplify*
$$(2x - 1)(x^2 - 4x - 3)$$

Solution

$$(2x - 1)(x^2 - 4x - 3) = 2x^3 - 8x^2 - 6x - x^2 + 4x + 3$$
$$= 2x^3 - 9x^2 - 2x + 3$$

EXERCISE 1.1

A **1.** Expand

(a) $2(x - 5)$ (b) $4(2x - 3)$ (c) $7(1 - 3x)$

(d) $(3y - 4)6$ (e) $-2(4x + 5)$ (f) $-9(2y - 1)$

(g) $-(x - 8)$ (h) $4(2x - 5y)$ (i) $-3(x^2 - 3x - 2)$

(j) $4x(2x + 3y)$ (k) $-6m(2m - 3n)$ (l) $-3y(3x - 4y + 2)$

2. Expand

(a) $(x + 1)(x + 2)$ (b) $(x + 2)(x + 3)$ (c) $(x + 4)(x + 2)$

(d) $(x - 1)(x - 3)$ (e) $(x - 3)(x + 5)$ (f) $(x + 2)(x - 1)$

(g) $(y - 5)(y - 4)$ (h) $(t + 7)(t + 8)$ (i) $(m - 4)(m + 9)$

(j) $(n - 2)(n - 9)$ (k) $(x + 8)(x - 7)$ (l) $(y + 1)(y - 7)$

(m) $(x + 7)(x + 6)$ (n) $(t - 5)(t - 9)$ (o) $(m - 6)(m - 11)$

3. Expand

(a) $(x + 3)^2$ (b) $(x - 2)^2$ (c) $(x + 5)^2$

(d) $(x - 4)(x + 4)$ (e) $(y + 2)^2$ (f) $(m - 7)^2$

(g) $(t + 5)(t - 5)$ (h) $(x + 6)(x - 6)$ (i) $(y + 1)^2$

(j) $(x - 9)^2$ (k) $(x + 10)^2$ (l) $(x - 7)(x + 7)$

(m) $(x + 12)^2$ (n) $(x - 6)^2$ (o) $(y - 1)(y + 1)$

B **4.** Expand and simplify

(a) $2(x + 5) + 3(x + 4)$ (b) $3(m - 4) + 5(m + 6)$

(c) $4(3x - 5) - 6(2x - 1)$ (d) $2(3y - 4) - 2(2y - 1)$

(e) $3(2x - 5) - (x - 4)$ (f) $2(m - 3) - 4 + 2(m - 5)$

(g) $5(x - 6) - 4(y + 3)$ (h) $3x - 2(x + 5) - (x - 4)$

(i) $3(x^2 - 5x + 2) - 4(x - 6)$ (j) $4(x^2 - x - 1) - 2(x^2 + 6x - 5)$

(k) $4(x^2 - 2xy - y^2) - 3(x^2 - y^2)$ (l) $2x(x - 3) - 3x(2x - 1)$

(m) $t(3t^2 - 2) + 2t(t^2 - 2t - 3)$ (n) $2x^2 - x(3x - 1) + 5(x^2 - x - 2)$
(o) $2m(2m^2 - 3m - 1) - m(m^2 - 4)$ (p) $-3w(w - w^2 - 4) - w(1 - 2w - 3w^2)$

5. Expand and simplify.
(a) $(2x + 3)(x + 5)$ (b) $(3x + 4)(2x + 7)$ (c) $(7y - 2)(2y + 5)$
(d) $(2m - 5)(3m - 1)$ (e) $(4m - 3)^2$ (f) $(3x + 5)^2$
(g) $(2x - 5)(2x + 5)$ (h) $(4t + 7)(2t + 3)$ (i) $(5t - 6)^2$
(j) $(7t + 4)^2$ (k) $(3x - 2y)(4x - 3y)$ (l) $(5m + 2n)(4m - n)$
(m) $(3x + 5y)^2$ (n) $(3x + 7y)(4y - x)$ (o) $(7 - 8t)(7 + 8t)$
(p) $(4x - 9y)(2y + 7x)$ (q) $(9x + 10y)(8x + 3y)$ (r) $(7m - 5n)(8m + 3n)$
(s) $(3x^2 - 2x)(4x^2 - x)$ (t) $(4xy - x^2)(x^2 - xy)$ (u) $(2t^2 - 7)^2$
(v) $(x^4 - 3)(5x^4 - 6)$ (w) $(-2x + 3y)(4x - 7y)$ (x) $(4abc - 3x)(6abc - x)$

6. Expand and simplify.
(a) $2(x + 3)(x + 4) + 3(2x + 3)$
(b) $3(x + 1)(x + 2) + 2(x + 4)(x + 5)$
(c) $3(m - 2)(m - 3) - 4(m + 1)(m - 1)$
(d) $5(t - 3)(t + 4) - 5(t - 6)(t - 5)$
(e) $2(m + 3)^2 + 3(m - 1)^2 - 2(m - 4)$
(f) $4(2x + 1)(x + 5) - 3(3x - 2)(2x - 3)$
(g) $5(2m + 3)(4m + 1) + 2(5m + 6)(3m - 4)$
(h) $2(2x - 3)^2 - (3x + 5)(3x + 7) - 4x^2$
(i) $2(1 - 3t) - (2t - 1)^2 - 3(3t - 5)(4t + 1)$
(j) $5x^2 - (4x + 7)(x + 6) - (2x + 5)^2 + 3x$
(k) $4 - 2(6w - 7)(6w + 7) - 3(2w + 1)^2$

7. Expand and simplify.
(a) $(x + 2)(x^2 + x + 1)$ (b) $(2x + 3)(x^2 - 2x - 4)$
(c) $(2x^2 - x - 5)(3x + 1)$ (d) $(3m - 4)(m^2 - 3m - 2)$
(e) $(x^2 + 2x - 1)(x^2 - x - 5)$ (f) $(2m^2 - 3m + 1)(3m^2 + 2m + 2)$
(g) $(x + 6)(x^3 + 3x^2 - 5x - 4)$ (h) $(2w - 3x + 4y)(w + 5x - 3y)$

8. Express the area of the rectangle
in terms of x.

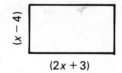

9. Express the area of the square in
terms of x.

C **10.** Expand and simplify.
(a) $(2x - 3)(x - 4)(2x + 5)$
(b) $(x^2 - 3x - 1)^2$
(c) $(x + \frac{1}{x})(x - \frac{1}{x})$
(d) $(1 + x - \frac{1}{x})(2 - x + \frac{2}{x})$
(e) $(w + x + y + z)^2$

1.2 COMMON FACTOR

Expressing a given polynomial as a product of two or more polynomials is called *factoring*. The distributive property, which is used to find products, is also used to find factors.

$$\xrightarrow{\text{EXPANDING}}$$
$$3x(2x - 1) = 6x^2 - 3x$$
$$\xleftarrow{\text{FACTORING}}$$

When a factor is contained in every term of an algebraic expression, it is called a *common factor*. We can determine common factors by inspection.

EXAMPLE 1. *Factor completely*

(a) $5xy + 10y$

(b) $6x^3 - 3x^2 + 9x$

Solution

(a)
$$5xy + 10y = 5y \cdot x + 5y \cdot 2$$
$$= 5y(x + 2)$$

(b)
$$6x^3 - 3x^2 + 9x = 3x \cdot 2x^2 - 3x \cdot x + 3x \cdot 3$$
$$= 3x(2x^2 - x + 3)$$

We shall agree that a polynomial is completely factored when no more variable factors can be removed and no more integer factors other than 1 or −1 can be removed.

EXAMPLE 2. *Factor completely*
$$2x(y + 3) + 5w(y + 3)$$

Solution   Think of $(y + 3)$ as one number.
$$2x(y + 3) + 5w(y + 3) = (y + 3) \cdot 2x + (y + 3) \cdot 5w$$
$$= (y + 3)(2x + 5w)$$

56	29	84
11	11	12
58	86	91
13	14	▓

Determine the pattern. Find the missing number.

EXERCISE 1-2

A **1.** Factor completely, where possible.

(a) $2x + 6$

(b) $5y - 10$

(c) $3x + 6y$

(d) $7w - 7$

(e) $3x + 11$

(f) $2x^2 - 82$

(g) $3 - 9y$

(h) $2x^2 + 6x$

(i) $3x - 5y$

(j) $6y^2 - 7y$

(k) $10w^2 - 5w$

(l) $8wx - 12x$

(m) $15x + 10y$

(n) $7mn - 9x$

(o) $2tw + 4tx - 6ty$

B **2.** Factor completely, where possible.

(a) $25x^3 + 10x^2 + 15x$

(b) $y^5 - y^4 + y^3 - y^2$

(c) $36x^5 - 9y^3$

(d) $12xy + 4wx - 8xz$

(e) $9m^3 - 6m^2t + 3mt^2$

(f) $7xyz - 14xy + 21txy$

(g) $7pqr - 5xy + 8t$

(h) $22xy - 11y^2 + 33wy$

(i) $36mn^2 - 24m^2n + 28mn$

(j) $7rst - 14r^2s^2t$

(k) $18r^2s^3 - 9rs^2 - 27r^3s^2$

(l) $20m^6n^4 - 30m^5n^5 + 40m^7n^3 - 10m^5n^3$

(m) $14rst + 17xy - 3w$

(n) $40x^5y^7 - 32x^7y^6 - 28x^8y^4 - 36x^7y^5$

3. Factor.

(a) $3m(x + y) + 2(x + y)$

(b) $3x(y - 1) + 2(y - 1)$

(c) $9x(m + 3) - 2(m + 3)$

(d) $5y(m + n) + t(m + n)$

(e) $5w(x - 2) - 3t(x - 2)$

(f) $2t(x + 5) + (x + 5)$

(g) $4mn(t - 4) - (t - 4)$

(h) $2m(x + y) + 4(x + y)$

(i) $3xy(m - n) - 6x(m - n)$

(j) $2(t + 5)^2 - 3(t + 5)$

(k) $5t(2x - 3) - 10m(2x - 3)$

(l) $4(w + 3)^3 + 5(w + 3)^2$

How many words can you find that contain the letter sequence SCU?

1.3 FACTORING $ax^2 + bx + c$, $a = 1$

Many polynomials, such as $x^2 + 7x + 12$, can be written as the product of two linear polynomials.

FACTORING

$$x^2 + 7x + 12 = (x + 3)(x + 4)$$

EXPANDING

An analysis of a general expansion of two linear polynomials will simplify factoring.

$$(x + r)(x + s) = x^2 + sx + rx + rs$$
$$= x^2 + (s + r)x + rs$$
$$= x^2 + bx + c$$

Here, $b = (s + r)$ and $c = rs$.

To write $x^2 + 8x + 15$ in the form $(x + r)(x + s)$,

$$b = r + s = 8$$
$$\text{and } c = rs = 15$$

Hence $r = 3$ and $s = 5$ and the factors of $x^2 + 8x + 15$ are $(x + 3)$, $(x + 5)$.

EXAMPLE 1. *Factor* $x^2 - 3x - 10$

Solution For $x^2 - 3x - 10$

$$r + s = -3 \text{ and } rs = -10$$

The two integers that add to give -3 and multiply to give -10 are -5 and 2.

$$x^2 - 3x - 10 = (x - 5)(x + 2)$$

EXERCISE 1-3

A **1.** Complete the factoring.

(a) $x^2 + 9x + 20 = (x + 5)()$

(b) $x^2 + 5x + 6 = (x + 3)()$

(c) $x^2 - 7x + 12 = (x - 4)()$

(d) $m^2 - 3m - 18 = ()(m - 6)$

(e) $y^2 + 5y - 14 = ()(y + 7)$ (f) $t^2 - 2t - 24 = (t - 6)()$

(g) $s^2 - 8s + 16 = ()(s - 4)$ (h) $w^2 + 10w + 25 = (w + 5)()$

(i) $n^2 + 3n - 40 = ()(n + 8)$ (j) $x^2 - x - 42 = (x + 6)()$

(k) $y^2 - y - 2 = (y + 1)()$ (l) $x^2 - 10x + 16 = (x - 2)()$

B   **2.** Factor, if possible.

(a) $x^2 + 7x + 10$ (b) $m^2 + 8m + 12$ (c) $n^2 + 6n + 8$

(d) $w^2 - 7w + 10$ (e) $x^2 - 9x + 20$ (f) $x^2 - 6x - 14$

(g) $r^2 - r - 30$ (h) $m^2 + m - 42$ (i) $n^2 + 11n + 18$

(j) $x^2 + 12x + 20$ (k) $w^2 + 2w - 18$ (l) $s^2 + 6x - 16$

(m) $y^2 - 2y - 35$ (n) $x^2 + 3x - 40$ (o) $t^2 + 17t + 72$

(p) $w^2 + 18w + 90$ (q) $r^2 - 18r + 80$ (r) $m^2 - 6m + 9$

(s) $y^2 + 10y + 25$ (t) $x^2 + 2x - 63$ (u) $w^2 + 3w + 5$

(v) $x^2 - 20x + 100$ (w) $m^2 - 8x - 20$ (x) $n^2 + 10n - 24$

3. Factor completely.

(a) $2x^2 + 4x + 2$ (b) $3w^2 + 12w + 9$ (c) $m^2 - 4m - 77$

(d) $5x^2 - 35x + 50$ (e) $n^2 + 16x + 55$ (f) $w^2 - 13w + 30$

(g) $3x^2 + 3x + 3$ (h) $2x^2 - 28x + 90$ (i) $2w^2 + 28w + 98$ ✔

(j) $35 - 12m + m^2$ (k) $16 + 6x - x^2$ (l) $2x^2 - 6x + 10$

(m) $4x^2 - 48x + 144$ (n) $m^2 + 11m - 42$ (o) $x^2 - 35x + 300$

(p) $m^2 - 9m - 112$ (q) $x^2 + 4x - 117$ (r) $x^2 - 28x + 195$

(s) $w^2 - 15w - 76$ (t) $t^2 + 15t - 126$ (u) $s^2 - 8s + 12$

1.4   FACTORING $ax^2 + bx + c$, $a \neq 1$

Factoring trinomials of this type, such as $6x^2 + 17x + 12$, is simplified if we break up the middle term into two parts.

$$6x^2 + 17x + 12 = 6x^2 + 9x + 8x + 12$$
$$= (6x^2 + 9x) + (8x + 12)$$
$$= 3x(2x + 3) + 4(2x + 3)$$
$$= (2x + 3)(3x + 4)$$

Use $+$, $-$, $\times$, $\div$, $(\ )$ to make a true statement.

$$6 \ 2 \ 2 = 5 \ 7 \ 4$$

In the previous example we replaced $17x$ by $9x + 8x$. We might have used other sums such as $10x + 17x$ or $-20x + 3x$. However, $9x + 8x$ is the required sum. The decision as to what two terms must be used will be clarified if we analyze the general expansion.

$$(px + r)(qx + s) = pqx^2 + psx + qrx + rs$$
$$= pqx^2 + (ps + qr)x + rs$$
$$= ax^2 + bx + c$$

If we break up the middle term bx into two terms, say mx and nx, then it is clear that

$$m + n = ps + qr = b$$
$$\text{and} \quad mn = pqrs = ac$$

EXAMPLE 1. *Factor* $6x^2 + 7x + 2$

Solution For $6x^2 + 7x + 2$, $a = 6$, $b = 7$ and $c = 2$.

In order to replace $7x$ by $mx + nx$, we must determine m and n.

$$m + n = b = 7$$
$$mn = ac = 12$$

Therefore m and n are 3 and 4.

$6x^2 + 7x + 2$

$$= 6x^2 + 3x + 4x + 2$$
$$= (6x^2 + 3x) + (4x + 2)$$
$$= 3x(2x + 1) + 2(2x + 1)$$
$$= (2x + 1)(3x + 2)$$

3 4 5
■■

■■■■ ■■ Find the
■■■■ ■   missing digits
in this multi-
■■ 7 6 ■ plication.

EXERCISE 1-4

A **1.** If possible, determine integer values for m and n.

(a) $m + n = 7$, $mn = 10$ (b) $m + n = 5$, $mn = 6$

(c) $m + n = -7$, $mn = 12$ (d) $m + n = -3$, $mn = -15$

(e) $m + n = -2$, $mn = 5$ (f) $m + n = 9$, $mn = 18$

(g) $m + n = 7$, $mn = -30$ (h) $m + n = -8$, $mn = 16$

(i) $m + n = -1$, $mn = -20$ (j) $m + n = 5$, $mn = -14$

(k) $m + n = 2$, $mn = 1$ (l) $m + n = 2$, $mn = -35$

(m) $m + n = 7$, $mn = 8$ (n) $m + n = -2$, $mn = -24$

(o) $m + n = 10$, $mn = 25$ (p) $m + n = -3$, $mn = -18$

B **2.** Factor.

(a) $6x^2 + 13x + 5$ (b) $2w^2 + 5w + 3$ (c) $6x^2 - 7x + 2$

(d) $4m^2 + 27m + 18$ (e) $3w^2 - 10w + 8$ (f) $15t^2 - t - 2$

(g) $2m^2 - m - 10$ (h) $4x^2 + 25x + 6$ (i) $6n^2 - 13n + 6$

3. (a) $4t^2 + 31t + 21$ (b) $6m^2 + 5m - 4$ (c) $2x^2 + 17x + 30$

(d) $9x^2 + 6x + 1$ (e) $4m^2 + 21m - 18$ (f) $6x^2 - 19x + 10$

(g) $10x^2 + 29x + 10$ (h) $6t^2 - 17t - 14$ (i) $9w^2 - 24w + 16$

1.5   FACTORING SPECIAL QUADRATICS

We can use the following identities to factor special quadratics.

$$a^2 + 2ab + b^2 = (a + b)(a + b) = (a + b)^2$$
$$a^2 - 2ab + b^2 = (a - b)(a - b) = (a - b)^2$$

Perfect
Squares

$$a^2 - b^2 = (a - b)(a + b)$$

Difference of
squares

EXAMPLE 1. *Factor* $9x^2 + 30x + 25$

Solution

$$9x^2 + 30x + 25 = (3x)^2 + 2(3x)(5) + (5)^2$$
$$= (3x + 5)(3x + 5)$$
$$= (3x + 5)^2$$

EXAMPLE 2. *Factor* $4x^2 - 12x + 9$

Solution

$$4x^2 - 12x + 9 = (2x)^2 - 2(2x)(3) + (3)^2$$
$$= (2x - 3)(2x - 3)$$
$$= (2x - 3)^2$$

EXAMPLE 3. *Factor* $16x^2 - 49$

Solution

$$16x^2 - 49 = (4x)^2 - (7)^2$$
$$= (4x - 7)(4x + 7)$$

EXERCISE 1-5

A **1.** Factor.

(a) $x^2 - 16$ (b) $m^2 + 6m + 9$ (c) $r^2 - 10r + 25$

(d) $m^2 - 49$ (e) $t^2 - 8t + 16$ (f) $x^2 - 36$

(g) $x^2 + 14x + 49$ (h) $m^2 - 4m + 4$ (i) $w^2 + 20w + 100$

(j) $y^2 - 2y + 1$ (k) $x^2 - 64$ (l) $n^2 + 18n + 81$

(m) $s^2 + 16s + 64$ (n) $r^2 - 6r + 9$ (o) $x^2 - 144$

B **2.** Factor, if possible.

(a) $4x^2 - 25$ (b) $4x^2 + 4x + 1$ (c) $9x^2 - 6x + 1$

(d) $9x^2 + 16$ (e) $16m^2 - 8m + 1$ (f) $100t^2 - 49$

(g) $4w^2 - 12w + 9$ (h) $25s^2 + 40s + 16$ (i) $9 - 49y^2$

(j) $4 - 20x + 25x^2$ (k) $49y^2 + 42y + 9$ (l) $1 - 14m + 49m^2$

(m) $1 + 4x^2$ (n) $4r^2 + 28r + 49$

3. Factor.

(a) $9x^2 - 36$ (b) $x^2 - 2x - 8$ (c) $6x^2 - 11x - 10$

(d) $3mnt - 6m^2t - 9nt$ (e) $16x^2 + 8x + 1$ (f) $2x^2 - 2x - 24$

(g) $5m(x - 2) - 4(x - 2)$ (h) $x^2 + 7x + 5x^3$ (i) $6x^2 + 9x + 12$

(j) $6m^2 - 17m - 14$ (k) $9x^2 - 30x + 25$

(l) $5x(m - n) - 10y(m - n)$

4. Factor

(a) $4m^2 + 8m - 60$ (b) $8 - 18x^2$

(c) $mn^2 + 9mn + 18m$ (d) $15y^2 - 22y + 8$

(e) $36x^2 + 60 + 25$ (f) $2(x + y)^2 - m(x + y)$

(g) $49m^2n^5 - 28m^3n^6 - 14m^6n^7$ (h) $8x^2 + 34x + 35$

(i) $27x(m + 3) - 3x^2(m + 3)$ (j) $48m^2 - 27$

(k) $24m^2 - 14m - 3$ (l) $21t^2 + 58t + 21$

1.6 MULTIPLICATION AND DIVISION OF RATIONAL EXPRESSIONS

We multiply rational expressions the same way we multiply rational numbers. Recall that

$$\frac{2}{3} \cdot \frac{5}{9} = \frac{2 \times 5}{3 \times 9} = \frac{10}{27}$$

> For rational expressions $\frac{P}{Q}$ and $\frac{R}{S}$,
>
> $$\frac{P}{Q} \cdot \frac{R}{S} = \frac{PR}{QS}, \quad Q, S \neq 0$$

When multiplying rational expressions, first factor the numerators and denominators and divide by any common factors. Then express the product as a rational expression.

EXAMPLE 1. *Multiply* $\dfrac{x^2 - x - 20}{x^2 - 9}$ by $\dfrac{x - 3}{x^2 + 6x + 8}$

WRITE YOUR STORY Each letter represents a different digit in this addition

Solution

$$\frac{x - x - 20}{x^2 - 9} \cdot \frac{x - 3}{x^2 + 6x + 8}$$

$$= \frac{(x - 5)(x + 4)}{(x - 3)(x + 3)} \cdot \frac{(x - 3)}{(x + 4)(x + 2)}$$

$$= \frac{x - 5}{(x + 3)(x + 2)}, \quad x \neq 3, -3, -4, -2$$

Note that we state the restrictions $x \neq 3$, $x \neq -4$ because division by zero is not allowed in the real numbers.

Rational expressions are divided the same way as we divide rational numbers. Recall that

$$\frac{3}{5} \div \frac{7}{2} = \frac{3}{5} \times \frac{2}{7} = \frac{6}{35}$$

> For rational expressions $\frac{P}{Q}$ and $\frac{R}{S}$,
>
> $$\frac{P}{Q} \div \frac{R}{S} = \frac{P}{Q} \times \frac{S}{R} = \frac{PS}{QR}, \quad Q, R, S \neq 0$$

EXAMPLE 2. *Divide* $\dfrac{3x - 3}{x^2 - x - 6}$ by $\dfrac{x^2 - 6x + 5}{x^2 - 3x - 10}$

Solution

$$\frac{3x - 3}{x^2 - x - 6} \div \frac{x^2 - 6x + 5}{x^2 - 3x - 10}$$

$$= \frac{3x - 3}{x^2 - x - 6} \cdot \frac{x^2 - 3x - 10}{x^2 - 6x + 5}$$

$$= \frac{3(x-1)}{(x+2)(x-3)} \cdot \frac{(x+2)(x-5)}{(x-1)(x-5)}$$

$$= \frac{3}{x-3}, \quad x \neq 1,3,5,-2$$

EXERCISE 1-6

Express each of the following as rational expressions in lowest terms. Assume that all variables are restricted so that no denominator or divisor is equal to zero.

A **1.** (a) $\dfrac{4}{x} \cdot \dfrac{x}{2}$ (b) $\dfrac{3}{m} \cdot \dfrac{m}{4}$ (c) $\dfrac{1}{3} \cdot \dfrac{5}{6}$

(d) $\dfrac{mn}{5} \cdot \dfrac{7}{mnt}$ (e) $2 \cdot \dfrac{x}{y}$ (f) $7 \div \dfrac{1}{4}$

(g) $\dfrac{x}{y} \div \dfrac{y}{x}$ (h) $\dfrac{x}{y} \div \dfrac{1}{5}$ (i) $\dfrac{5}{(x-1)} \cdot \dfrac{(x-1)}{7}$

(j) $\dfrac{1}{x-7} \div \dfrac{7}{x-7}$ (k) $y \div \dfrac{1}{y}$ (l) $\dfrac{x^3}{y^2} \cdot \dfrac{y^3}{x^4}$

(m) $\dfrac{(x-1)(x+3)}{(x+2)(x-1)} \cdot \dfrac{(x+2)}{(x-5)}$ (n) $\dfrac{m(x+y)}{n(x-y)} \div \dfrac{m}{n}$ (o) $\dfrac{x+y}{x-y}$

B **2.** (a) $\dfrac{6x^2y^2}{xy} \cdot \dfrac{5x^2y}{10xy^2}$ (b) $\dfrac{4x^5y^4}{9x^2y} \cdot \dfrac{3xy^2}{8x^2y}$

(c) $\dfrac{5mn}{6m^2n} \div \dfrac{10mn^2}{9m^3n^2}$ (d) $\dfrac{6r^2s}{5xy^3} \div \dfrac{9rs}{10xy^4}$

(e) $\dfrac{27x^6y^4}{8m^2n^2} \cdot \dfrac{16mn}{9x^5y^2}$ (f) $\dfrac{3x^2}{7x^3y} \div \dfrac{1}{14x}$

3. (a) $\dfrac{x-7}{5x} \cdot \dfrac{10x^2}{x-7}$ (b) $\dfrac{14x^2}{y-3} \cdot \dfrac{3y-9}{7x}$

(c) $\dfrac{x^2-9}{4t^2} \div \dfrac{2x+6}{16t^3}$ (d) $\dfrac{6x^2}{3x+3} \div \dfrac{5x}{x^2+3x+2}$

(e) $\dfrac{3mn}{mn+2m} \cdot \dfrac{n^2+2n}{6m}$ (f) $\dfrac{4x+4}{8x^2} \div (x+1)$

4. (a) $\dfrac{x^2+3x+2}{x^2+4x+3} \cdot \dfrac{x^2+x-6}{x^2-4}$ (b) $\dfrac{t^2-7t+12}{t^2+2t-15} \div \dfrac{t^2-3t-4}{t^2+5t}$

(c) $\dfrac{w^2+8w+15}{w^2-13w+42} \cdot \dfrac{w^2-3w-28}{w^2+7w+12}$ (d) $\dfrac{4x+12}{x^2+2x-3} \cdot \dfrac{x^2-8x+7}{x^2-14x+49}$

(e) $\dfrac{x^2-9}{x^2-2x-24} \cdot \dfrac{x^2+3x-4}{x^2+8x+15} \div \dfrac{x^2-4x+3}{10x+50}$

(f) $\dfrac{m^2+10m+21}{m^2+8m-9} \cdot \dfrac{m^2+10m+9}{m^2+3m-28} \cdot \dfrac{m^2-4m}{m^2+3m}$

(g) $\dfrac{x^2-2x}{x^2+6x-27} \cdot \dfrac{x^2+8x+16}{x^2+2x-8} \div \dfrac{x^2-16}{x^2+5x-24}$

(h) $\dfrac{w^2 - 16w + 63}{w^2 - 18w + 81} \cdot \dfrac{w^2 - 13w + 36}{w^2 - 3w - 18} \cdot \dfrac{w^2 - w - 30}{w^2 - 11w + 28}$

5. (a) $\dfrac{2x^2 - x - 3}{6x^2 + x - 15} \cdot \dfrac{9x^2 + 3x - 20}{3x^2 - x - 4}$

(b) $\dfrac{6w^2 + 19w + 10}{12w^2 + 25w + 7} \div \dfrac{4w^2 - 25}{6w^2 - 13w - 5}$

(c) $\dfrac{6x^2 + 8x}{3x^2 - 8x - 35} \cdot \dfrac{3x^2 + 25x + 42}{6x^2 - 7x - 20} \div \dfrac{2x^2 + 7x - 30}{4x^2 - 20x + 25}$

(d) $\dfrac{6t^2 + 11t + 4}{15t^2 - 11t + 2} \cdot \dfrac{6t^2 + t - 1}{6t^2 + 11t + 4} \cdot \dfrac{25t^2 + 5t - 6}{2t^2 - 13t - 7}$

(e) $\dfrac{3m^2 + 22m + 24}{2m^2 + 13m + 6} \cdot \dfrac{m^2 - 6m}{2m^2 - 11m - 6} \div \dfrac{3m^2 + 4m}{2m^2 + m}$

C **6.** (a) $\dfrac{\frac{x^2 - 9}{6x^2}}{\frac{x + 3}{3x}}$ (b) $\dfrac{\frac{x - 7}{x}}{x^2 - 49}$ (c) $\dfrac{\frac{x^2 + 6x + 9}{x + 3}}{x}$

(d) $\dfrac{8x^2 - 10xy - 3y^2}{6x^2 - 19xy + 15y^2} \cdot \dfrac{12x^2 - 17xy - 5y^2}{16x^2 + 8xy + y^2}$

1.7 LEAST COMMON MULTIPLE

How many grooves are there on a record?

In order to add or subtract rational expressions it is necessary to know how to determine the *least common multiple* (LCM) of two or more polynomials.

The LCM for 20 and 24 is the smallest number that has 20 and 24 as factors. To determine the LCM for 20 and 24 we first factor 20 and 24.

$$20 = 2 \times 2 \times 5$$
$$24 = 2 \times 2 \times 2 \times 3$$

The LCM for 20 and 24 must include all the separate factors that make up 20 and 24.

The LCM is $2 \times 2 \times 2 \times 3 \times 5 = 120$.

EXAMPLE 1. *Find the* LCM *for*
$$x^2 - 6x + 5 \ and \ x^2 + x - 30$$

Solution   Factor each polynomial
$$x^2 - 6x + 5 = (x - 1)(x - 5)$$
$$x^2 + x - 30 = (x - 5)(x + 6)$$

The LCM is $(x - 1)(x - 5)(x + 6)$.

EXERCISE 1-7

B Find the LCM for each of the following. Answers may be left in factored form.

1. (a) 8, 20
(c) 12, 18, 30
(e) 20, 30, 45
(b) 8, 10, 25
(d) 25, 30, 35
(f) 20, 28, 35

2. (a) $10x^3, 15x^4, 20x^2$
(c) $3m^2n, 6mn^2, 2mn$
(e) $3ab, 6bc, 9ac$
(b) $2x^2, 4xy, 6y^2$
(d) $10x^3, 25x^2y, 15xy^2$
(f) $6a^2b, 15ab^2, 24ab$

3. (a) $x - 1, x - 4$
(c) $x^2 + 7x + 12, x^2 + 9x + 20$
(e) $2x - 6, 6x - 18$
(g) $m^2 - m - 2, m^2 - 5m + 6, m^2 - 8m + 15$
(h) $3x + 12, x^2 + 11x + 28, x^2 - x - 56$
(i) $x^2 - 5x, x^2 - 25, x^2 + x - 20$
(b) $x + 1, x + 2, x - 3$
(d) $x^2 + x, x^2 - 1$
(f) $x^2 - 2x - 3, x^2 + 2x - 15$

1.8 ADDITION AND SUBTRACTION OF RATIONAL EXPRESSIONS

To add or subtract rational expressions with equal denominators we use the distributive property.

$$\frac{a}{b} + \frac{c}{b} = \frac{1}{b} \cdot a + \frac{1}{b} \cdot c = \frac{1}{b}(a + c) = \frac{a + c}{b}$$

Evaluate CXV + XII + VII + CCLXV.

EXAMPLE 1. *Simplify*

(a) $\dfrac{5}{7} + \dfrac{3}{7} - \dfrac{4}{7}$

(b) $\dfrac{3}{x + 1} - \dfrac{2}{x + 1} + \dfrac{5}{x + 1}$

Solution

(a)
$$\frac{5}{7} + \frac{3}{7} - \frac{4}{7} = \frac{5 + 3 - 4}{7}$$
$$= \frac{4}{7}$$

(b)
$$\frac{3}{x + 1} - \frac{2}{x + 1} + \frac{5}{x + 1} = \frac{3 - 2 + 5}{x + 1}$$
$$= \frac{6}{x + 1}, x \neq -1$$

To add or subtract rational expressions with different denominators, equivalent fractions with a common denominator are found. The lowest common denominator (LCD) is the LCM of the denominators.

EXAMPLE 2. *Simplify* $\dfrac{2x-3}{3}+\dfrac{x+2}{2}-\dfrac{x-1}{4}$

Solution   The LCD is 12.

$$\frac{2x-3}{3}+\frac{x+2}{2}-\frac{x-1}{4}=\frac{4(2x-3)}{4\cdot 3}+\frac{6(x+2)}{6\cdot 2}-\frac{3(x-1)}{3\cdot 4}$$

$$=\frac{4(2x-3)}{12}+\frac{6(x+2)}{12}-\frac{3(x-1)}{12}$$

$$=\frac{4(2x-3)+6(x+2)-3(x-1)}{12}$$

$$=\frac{8x-12+6x+12-3x+3}{12}$$

$$=\frac{11x+3}{12}$$

EXAMPLE 3.   *Simplify:* $\dfrac{3}{2x^2}-\dfrac{1}{3x}+\dfrac{7}{5x^3}$

Solution: The LCD is $30x^3$.

$$\frac{3}{2x^2}-\frac{1}{3x}+\frac{7}{5x^3}=\frac{15x\cdot 3}{15x\cdot 2x^2}-\frac{10x^2\cdot 1}{10x^2\cdot 3x}+\frac{6\cdot 7}{6\cdot 5x^3}$$

$$=\frac{45x}{30x^3}-\frac{10x^2}{30x^3}+\frac{42}{30x^3}$$

$$=\frac{-10x^2+45x+42}{30x^3}\,,\; x\neq 0$$

EXAMPLE 4.   *Simplify* $\dfrac{2}{x^2-7x+10}-\dfrac{3}{x^2+x-6}$

The LCD is
$(x+3)(x-2)(x-5)$

Solution

$$\frac{2}{x^2-7x+10}-\frac{3}{x^2+x-6}=\frac{2}{(x-2)(x-5)}-\frac{3}{(x+3)(x-2)}$$

$$=\frac{2\cdot(x+3)}{(x+3)(x-2)(x-5)}-\frac{3\cdot(x-5)}{(x-5)(x+3)(x-2)}$$

$$=\frac{2(x+3)-3(x-5)}{(x+3)(x-2)(x-5)}$$

$$=\frac{2x+6-3x+15}{(x+3)(x-2)(x-5)}$$

$$=\frac{-x+21}{(x+3)(x-2)(x-5)}\,,\; x\neq 2,5,-3$$

EXERCISE 1-8

Perform the indicated operations and simplify. Assume that all variables are restricted so that no denominator is equal to zero.

A **1.** (a) $\dfrac{5}{7} - \dfrac{1}{7} + \dfrac{3}{7}$ (b) $\dfrac{3}{11} + \dfrac{5}{11} - \dfrac{2}{11}$

(c) $\dfrac{6}{x} + \dfrac{5}{x}$ (d) $\dfrac{7}{m} - \dfrac{3}{m} + \dfrac{4}{m}$

(e) $\dfrac{x}{2} + \dfrac{y}{2}$ (f) $\dfrac{4x}{5} - \dfrac{1}{5}$

(g) $\dfrac{2}{x+1} + \dfrac{3}{x+1}$ (h) $\dfrac{m}{x-3} - \dfrac{n}{x-3}$

(i) $\dfrac{3}{(x+2)(x+1)} - \dfrac{2}{(x+2)(x+1)}$ (j) $\dfrac{3m^2}{(x-3)(x+4)} - \dfrac{m^2}{(x-3)(x+4)}$

B **2.** (a) $\dfrac{1}{2} + \dfrac{3}{5} - \dfrac{1}{4}$ (b) $\dfrac{7}{6} - \dfrac{3}{8} + 1\dfrac{1}{2}$

(c) $\dfrac{3x}{4} - \dfrac{x}{2} + \dfrac{x}{6}$ (d) $\dfrac{2x+y}{3} + \dfrac{4x+3y}{2}$

(e) $\dfrac{3m-7}{4} - \dfrac{2m-1}{3}$ (f) $\dfrac{x-2y}{6} + 1 - \dfrac{x+3y}{4}$

(g) $3x + \dfrac{x-4}{7} - \dfrac{x-1}{2}$ (h) $\dfrac{5t-1}{6} - \dfrac{4t+3}{8}$

3. (a) $\dfrac{3}{2x} + \dfrac{4}{3x} - \dfrac{1}{x}$ (b) $\dfrac{4}{5x} - \dfrac{3}{4x} - \dfrac{1}{10x}$

(c) $\dfrac{5}{2x} - \dfrac{3}{4x^2} - \dfrac{1}{3x}$ (d) $\dfrac{2}{s^2} - \dfrac{3}{st} + \dfrac{4}{t^2}$

(e) $\dfrac{2x+3}{xy} - \dfrac{1}{x} + \dfrac{4}{x}$ (f) $x - \dfrac{1}{x} + 4$

(g) $3 - \dfrac{2}{y} + y$ (h) $1 + \dfrac{1}{x} + y$

4. (a) $\dfrac{2}{x+1} + \dfrac{3}{x+2}$ (b) $\dfrac{3}{m-4} + \dfrac{2}{m+1}$

(c) $\dfrac{5}{x-3} - \dfrac{4}{x+2}$ (d) $\dfrac{1}{2} - \dfrac{3}{x+1}$

(e) $4 - \dfrac{1}{x+1} + \dfrac{3}{5}$ (f) $\dfrac{x+1}{x} + \dfrac{x-1}{x-2}$

(g) $3 - \dfrac{1}{x-2} + \dfrac{x+1}{x+3}$ (h) $4 + \dfrac{1}{x+1} - \dfrac{1}{x-1}$

5. (a) $\dfrac{2}{x^2+x-2} + \dfrac{3}{x^2+5x+6}$ (b) $\dfrac{3}{x^2-3x+2} + \dfrac{5}{x^2-5x+4}$

(c) $\dfrac{4}{x^2+4x-5} - \dfrac{2}{x^2+11x+30}$ (d) $\dfrac{7}{t^2-5t+4} - \dfrac{1}{t^2+3t-28}$

(e) $\dfrac{m}{m^2+6m+5} - \dfrac{2m}{m^2-3m-4}$ (f) $\dfrac{2x}{x^2+5x} + \dfrac{x}{x^2+8x+15}$

C 6. (a) $\dfrac{2}{2x^2 + 11x - 6} + \dfrac{5}{3x^2 + 16x - 12}$ (b) $\dfrac{4}{9m^2 - 1} - \dfrac{2}{6m^2 + 11m + 3}$

(c) $\dfrac{x + 1}{x^2 + 4x + 3} - \dfrac{4}{x - 5}$ (d) $\dfrac{x^2 + 2x - 3}{x^2 + 7x + 12} + \dfrac{x^2 - x - 6}{x^2 - 2x - 8}$

1.9 ADDITION AND SUBTRACTION OF MATRICES

The *matrix* (the plural is *matrices*) is a powerful tool of mathematics and the sciences. The technological and population explosions have resulted in an information explosion. It has become important to organize information in a logical manner in order to obtain quick and accurate access. Matrices help to perform this function.

A matrix is a rectangular array of numbers enclosed by parentheses.

Last season's football record for a football division is

	Won	Lost	Tied
Cougars	8	4	2
Panthers	7	6	1
Tigers	6	6	2
Lions	4	9	1

We can present this information as a matrix as follows.

$$\begin{pmatrix} 8 & 4 & 2 \\ 7 & 6 & 1 \\ 6 & 6 & 2 \\ 4 & 9 & 1 \end{pmatrix}$$

column

Row $\begin{pmatrix} 3 & 2 & 2 \\ 4 & 6 & 9 \\ -3 & 6 & 0 \end{pmatrix}$

The individual numbers are the *entries* of the matrix. The number of *rows* (horizontal) and *columns* (vertical) determine the dimensions of the matrix. The example above is a 4 × 3 (four by three) matrix. The number of rows is always given first.

A matrix having only one row, such as (3 5 9) is called a *row matrix*.

A matrix having only one column, such as $\begin{pmatrix} 5 \\ 2 \end{pmatrix}$ is called a *column matrix*.

C
ROW
L
U
M
N

Two matrices are equal if they have the same dimensions and the same corresponding entries.

$$\begin{pmatrix} 2 & 1 & 2 \\ 3 & 0 & 5 \end{pmatrix} = \begin{pmatrix} \dfrac{4}{2} & \dfrac{3}{3} & 2 \\ 3 & 0 & \dfrac{10}{2} \end{pmatrix}$$

It is only possible to add matrices if they have the same dimensions. For example, the results for July and August for a baseball division are given as follows.

JULY	WON	LOST
TIGERS	15	5
JAYS	13	7
SOX	8	12
REDS	4	16

or $J = \begin{pmatrix} 15 & 5 \\ 13 & 7 \\ 8 & 12 \\ 4 & 16 \end{pmatrix}$

AUGUST	WON	LOST
TIGERS	7	14
JAYS	15	6
SOX	8	12
REDS	10	10

or $A = \begin{pmatrix} 7 & 14 \\ 15 & 6 \\ 8 & 12 \\ 10 & 10 \end{pmatrix}$

The two month totals are found by adding the elements in the corresponding positions.

$$J + A = \begin{pmatrix} 15 & 5 \\ 13 & 7 \\ 8 & 12 \\ 4 & 16 \end{pmatrix} + \begin{pmatrix} 7 & 14 \\ 15 & 6 \\ 8 & 12 \\ 10 & 10 \end{pmatrix}$$

$$= \begin{pmatrix} 22 & 19 \\ 28 & 13 \\ 16 & 24 \\ 14 & 26 \end{pmatrix}$$

> The sum of two matrices of the same dimensions is the matrix whose entries are the sums of the corresponding entries of the matrices being added.
>
> $$\begin{pmatrix} a & b \\ c & d \end{pmatrix} + \begin{pmatrix} e & f \\ g & h \end{pmatrix} = \begin{pmatrix} a+e & b+f \\ c+g & d+h \end{pmatrix}$$

The matrices $\begin{pmatrix} 4 & 3 \\ -1 & 5 \end{pmatrix}$ and $\begin{pmatrix} -1 & 3 & 4 \\ 5 & -2 & 6 \end{pmatrix}$ cannot be added because they do not have the same dimensions.

The *negative* of a matrix A is the matrix $-A$, each of whose entries is the negative of the corresponding entry in A.

For example

if $A = \begin{pmatrix} 3 & 5 \\ -2 & -4 \end{pmatrix}$, then $-A = \begin{pmatrix} -3 & -5 \\ 2 & 4 \end{pmatrix}$

As with real numbers, we define subtraction of matrices in terms of addition.

$$\text{If } A = \begin{pmatrix} 2 & 4 \\ -1 & 3 \end{pmatrix} \text{ and } B = \begin{pmatrix} 5 & -3 \\ -6 & -2 \end{pmatrix}$$

$$\text{then} \quad A - B = A + (-B)$$

$$= \begin{pmatrix} 2 & 4 \\ -1 & 3 \end{pmatrix} + \begin{pmatrix} -5 & 3 \\ 6 & 2 \end{pmatrix}$$

$$= \begin{pmatrix} -3 & 7 \\ 5 & 5 \end{pmatrix}$$

Associated with each matrix, say B, is the *transpose* of B, written B^{T}. The transpose of a matrix B is obtained by interchanging the rows and columns of B. For example

$$\text{if } B = \begin{pmatrix} 2 & 0 \\ 3 & 4 \\ 1 & 5 \end{pmatrix} \text{ then } B^{\mathsf{T}} = \begin{pmatrix} 2 & 3 & 1 \\ 0 & 4 & 5 \end{pmatrix}$$

The transpose of a matrix may be used in computer solution of systems of equations, for example in economics, engineering, and many other fields.

EXERCISE 1-9

A **1.** State the dimensions of each matrix.

(a) $\begin{pmatrix} 2 & 3 & -5 \\ 7 & -1 & 6 \end{pmatrix}$

(b) $\begin{pmatrix} 5 & -4 \\ -3 & 2 \end{pmatrix}$

(c) $\begin{pmatrix} 3 & 7 \\ -2 & -1 \\ -4 & 3 \end{pmatrix}$

(d) $(8 \quad -9 \quad -10 \quad 2)$

(e) $\begin{pmatrix} 1 \\ -4 \\ 5 \end{pmatrix}$

(f) (6)

(g) $\begin{pmatrix} 3 & 5 & -7 \\ 4 & -2 & 6 \\ 9 & -3 & -5 \end{pmatrix}$

(h) $\begin{pmatrix} 6 \\ -2 \end{pmatrix}$

(i) $(5 \quad 7 \quad 9)$

2. State the negative of each matrix in **1.**

3. State the dimensions of the transpose of each of the matrices in **1.**

4. For the matrix $\begin{pmatrix} 5 & -2 & 3 \\ 1 & 0 & 6 \\ -3 & 4 & 1 \end{pmatrix}$ state

(a) the entries in the third row.
(b) the entries in the second column
(c) the entries in the second row.
(d) the entry in the first row and second column
(e) the entry in the second row and third column

(f) the negative of the matrix.
(g) the dimensions of the matrix.
(h) the transpose of the matrix.

5. State the values of x, y and z.

(a) $\begin{pmatrix} 3 & 0 \\ x & 4 \end{pmatrix} = \begin{pmatrix} 3 & y \\ 7 & 4 \end{pmatrix}$

(b) $\begin{pmatrix} -3 & 6 \\ -4 & 1 \end{pmatrix} = \begin{pmatrix} x & 6 \\ -4 & 1 \end{pmatrix}$

(c) $\begin{pmatrix} x & 2 \\ 3 & y \end{pmatrix} = \begin{pmatrix} -1 & 2 \\ 3 & -4 \end{pmatrix}$

(d) $\begin{pmatrix} 3 & x & 2 \\ 4 & -1 & z \end{pmatrix} = \begin{pmatrix} 3 & 7 & 2 \\ y & -1 & 3 \end{pmatrix}$

(e) $\begin{pmatrix} x+1 & 4 \\ 3 & 5 \end{pmatrix} = \begin{pmatrix} 5 & 4 \\ 3 & y-1 \end{pmatrix}$

(f) $\begin{pmatrix} 2 & x \\ -3 & y \\ 4 & 2 \end{pmatrix} = \begin{pmatrix} 2 & -4 \\ z & 3 \\ 4 & 2 \end{pmatrix}$

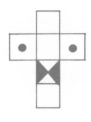

Which of the following figures can you make from the pattern above?

 B **6.** Perform the indicated operations (where possible).

(a) $\begin{pmatrix} 3 & 6 \\ 5 & 2 \end{pmatrix} + \begin{pmatrix} 4 & 5 \\ 3 & 7 \end{pmatrix}$

(b) $\begin{pmatrix} 2 & -3 \\ 4 & 0 \\ -1 & 2 \end{pmatrix} + \begin{pmatrix} -5 & 4 \\ -7 & 3 \\ 6 & 4 \end{pmatrix}$

(c) $\begin{pmatrix} 5 & 3 & 6 \\ 4 & -1 & 0 \end{pmatrix} + \begin{pmatrix} -3 & 5 \\ 6 & 4 \end{pmatrix}$

(d) $\begin{pmatrix} 2 & 7 \\ 3 & 6 \end{pmatrix} - \begin{pmatrix} -4 & -5 \\ 2 & 7 \end{pmatrix}$

(e) $\begin{pmatrix} 6 \\ 3 \\ -2 \end{pmatrix} - \begin{pmatrix} -1 \\ 4 \\ -7 \end{pmatrix}$

(f) $\begin{pmatrix} 5 & 6 \\ 8 & -3 \\ 1 & 0 \end{pmatrix} - \begin{pmatrix} -4 & 3 & 5 \\ 6 & -7 & 2 \end{pmatrix}$

(g) $(3 \quad -5) + (-7 \quad 8)$

(h) $\begin{pmatrix} 2 & -6 \\ 4 & 3 \end{pmatrix} + \begin{pmatrix} -8 & 2 \\ -5 & 3 \end{pmatrix} + \begin{pmatrix} 0 & 6 \\ -5 & 1 \end{pmatrix}$

7. Given $A = \begin{pmatrix} 1 & 2 \\ 3 & 4 \end{pmatrix}$, $B = \begin{pmatrix} -2 & 3 \\ 0 & 4 \end{pmatrix}$ and $C = \begin{pmatrix} -1 & 2 \\ -3 & -4 \end{pmatrix}$, find each of the following matrices.

(a) $A + B$
(b) $A + C$
(c) $A - C$
(d) $C - A$
(e) $(A + B) + C$
(f) $A + (B + C)$
(g) $(B - C) - (C + B)$
(h) $B^{\mathsf{T}} + C$
(i) $B - A^{\mathsf{T}}$

8. Solve each equation for the 2×2 matrix X.

(a) $X + \begin{pmatrix} 2 & 3 \\ 4 & 1 \end{pmatrix} = \begin{pmatrix} 5 & 6 \\ 3 & 0 \end{pmatrix}$

(b) $\begin{pmatrix} -3 & 4 \\ -5 & 2 \end{pmatrix} + X = \begin{pmatrix} -2 & -7 \\ 4 & 3 \end{pmatrix}$

(c) $X - \begin{pmatrix} 3 & 4 \\ -1 & 0 \end{pmatrix} = \begin{pmatrix} 7 & 5 \\ 3 & -4 \end{pmatrix}$

(d) $\begin{pmatrix} 5 & 3 \\ -1 & 2 \end{pmatrix} - X = \begin{pmatrix} 4 & 7 \\ -6 & 2 \end{pmatrix}$

1.10   SCALAR MULTIPLICATION

In matrix algebra, a real number is often called a *scalar*. Multiplying a matrix by a real number is called *scalar multiplication*.

If x is a real number, then $2x = x + x$. So if A is a matrix then we write $2A = A + A$.

$$\text{If} \quad A = \begin{pmatrix} 1 & 3 \\ 4 & 5 \end{pmatrix}$$

$$\text{then} \; 2A = A + A = \begin{pmatrix} 1 & 3 \\ 4 & 5 \end{pmatrix} + \begin{pmatrix} 1 & 3 \\ 4 & 5 \end{pmatrix}$$

$$= \begin{pmatrix} 2 & 6 \\ 8 & 10 \end{pmatrix}$$

$$= \begin{pmatrix} 2 \cdot 1 & 2 \cdot 3 \\ 2 \cdot 4 & 2 \cdot 5 \end{pmatrix}$$

$$\text{similarly} \; 3A = A + A + A = \begin{pmatrix} 1 & 3 \\ 4 & 5 \end{pmatrix} + \begin{pmatrix} 1 & 3 \\ 4 & 5 \end{pmatrix} + \begin{pmatrix} 1 & 3 \\ 4 & 5 \end{pmatrix}$$

$$= \begin{pmatrix} 3 & 9 \\ 12 & 15 \end{pmatrix}$$

$$= \begin{pmatrix} 3 \cdot 1 & 3 \cdot 3 \\ 3 \cdot 4 & 3 \cdot 5 \end{pmatrix}$$

$$k \begin{pmatrix} a & b \\ c & d \end{pmatrix} = \begin{pmatrix} ka & kb \\ kc & kd \end{pmatrix}$$

> If k is a real number and A is a matrix, then kA is the matrix obtained by multiplying each entry of A by k.

EXAMPLE 1. *If $A = \begin{pmatrix} 0 & 4 \\ 3 & 5 \end{pmatrix}$ and $B = \begin{pmatrix} -1 & 2 \\ -4 & 6 \end{pmatrix}$, find $2A + 3B$.*

Solution

$$2A + 3B = 2 \begin{pmatrix} 0 & 4 \\ 3 & 5 \end{pmatrix} + 3 \begin{pmatrix} -1 & 2 \\ -4 & 6 \end{pmatrix}$$

$$= \begin{pmatrix} 0 & 8 \\ 6 & 10 \end{pmatrix} + \begin{pmatrix} -3 & 6 \\ -12 & 18 \end{pmatrix}$$

$$= \begin{pmatrix} -3 & 14 \\ -6 & 28 \end{pmatrix}$$

EXERCISE 1-10

A **1.** Perform each scalar multiplication.

(a) $3 \begin{pmatrix} 4 & 0 \\ 1 & 5 \end{pmatrix}$

(b) $2 \begin{pmatrix} 0 \\ 1 \\ -6 \end{pmatrix}$

(c) $-4(5 \quad -2 \quad -3)$

(d) $\frac{1}{2} \begin{pmatrix} 8 & 6 \\ 4 & -10 \end{pmatrix}$

(e) $5 \begin{pmatrix} 3a & 2b \\ -5a & 3b \end{pmatrix}$

(f) $-2 \begin{pmatrix} 5 & -7 \\ -3 & -1 \end{pmatrix}$

B **2.** Perform the indicated operations.

(a) $2 \begin{pmatrix} 4 & 3 \\ 7 & 1 \end{pmatrix} + 3 \begin{pmatrix} 5 & 0 \\ -2 & -1 \end{pmatrix}$

(b) $3 \begin{pmatrix} -5 & -1 \\ 0 & 1 \end{pmatrix} + 4 \begin{pmatrix} 6 & 0 \\ -1 & 0 \end{pmatrix}$

(c) $3\begin{pmatrix} 2 & 1 \\ 0 & 5 \\ -3 & 6 \end{pmatrix} + 5\begin{pmatrix} -1 & -2 \\ 3 & 0 \\ 4 & -2 \end{pmatrix}$ (d) $2\begin{pmatrix} 3 & -1 \\ 4 & 2 \end{pmatrix} - 3\begin{pmatrix} -5 & 1 \\ -2 & 3 \end{pmatrix}$

(e) $2\begin{pmatrix} 3 & -1 & 0 \\ -2 & 1 & -2 \end{pmatrix} - 3\begin{pmatrix} -5 & 2 & 2 \\ -1 & 0 & 1 \end{pmatrix}$ (f) $2\begin{pmatrix} -5 & -3 \\ 4 & 1 \end{pmatrix} - \begin{pmatrix} -5 & 2 \\ 3 & -4 \end{pmatrix}$

3. If $A = \begin{pmatrix} 2 & -3 \\ 4 & 0 \end{pmatrix}$ and $B = \begin{pmatrix} -1 & 2 \\ -3 & 5 \end{pmatrix}$, find each of the following.

(a) $3A$ (b) $2B$ (c) $A - B$ (d) $3A + 2B$
(e) $2A - 3B$ (f) $2B - 4A$ (g) $2(A - B)$ (h) $3(B - A)$

4. Solve each equation for the 2×2 matrix X.

(a) $2X = \begin{pmatrix} 4 & -8 \\ 6 & -10 \end{pmatrix}$

(b) $3X = \begin{pmatrix} 9 \\ -6 \\ -12 \end{pmatrix}$

(c) $2X + \begin{pmatrix} 0 & 1 \\ 1 & 0 \end{pmatrix} = \begin{pmatrix} 4 & 5 \\ 3 & 8 \end{pmatrix}$

(d) $2X + \begin{pmatrix} 1 & 3 \\ -1 & 5 \end{pmatrix} = 3\begin{pmatrix} -3 & 5 \\ 1 & 1 \end{pmatrix}$

(e) $X - \begin{pmatrix} 0 & 3 \\ 5 & -2 \end{pmatrix} = 2\begin{pmatrix} 4 & -1 \\ 3 & -5 \end{pmatrix}$

(f) $2X - 2\begin{pmatrix} 3 & 4 \\ 1 & 0 \end{pmatrix} = 4\begin{pmatrix} -2 & 4 \\ 0 & 1 \end{pmatrix}$

1.11 MULTIPLICATION OF MATRICES

It would seem that multiplication of matrices should be done in a manner similar to addition of matrices. However, if multiplication is done in this way then the range of applications is extremely limited. Since we are interested in the applications of matrices we will multiply matrices in a way that turns out to be useful. At first the procedure may seem unnecessarily complicated. However, the applications will justify the method.

To multiply matrices it is not necessary that they have the same dimensions. What is necessary is that the number of columns of the first matrix be the same as the number of rows of the second matrix.

We will illustrate matrix multiplication by determining the revenue of a parking lot.

	Number of cars	Number of buses
Monday	72	15
Tuesday	83	7

Charge/vehicle in dollars	
Cars	4
Buses	12

	Revenue in dollars
Monday	m
Tuesday	t

Before applying matrix multiplication we will determine m and t by another procedure.

$$m = 72(4) + 15(12) = 468$$
$$t = 83(4) + 7(12) = 416$$

These calculations for m and t suggest a pattern for matrix multiplication.

$$\begin{pmatrix} 72 & 15 \\ 83 & 7 \end{pmatrix} \begin{pmatrix} 4 \\ 12 \end{pmatrix} = \begin{pmatrix} 468 \\ 416 \end{pmatrix}$$

The entry 468 is in row 1 and column 1 of the product matrix. It is obtained by multiplying, respectively, the entries in row 1 of $\begin{pmatrix} 72 & 15 \\ 83 & 7 \end{pmatrix}$ by those in column 1 of $\begin{pmatrix} 4 \\ 12 \end{pmatrix}$, and adding the results. That is, $72 \cdot 4 + 15 \cdot 12 = 468$.

Similarly, the entry 416 is in row 2 and column 1 of the product matrix. It is obtained by multiplying the entries in row 2 of $\begin{pmatrix} 72 & 15 \\ 83 & 7 \end{pmatrix}$ by those in column 1 of $\begin{pmatrix} 4 \\ 12 \end{pmatrix}$, and adding the results. That is, $83 \cdot 4 + 7 \cdot 12 = 416$.

You obtain the entries of the product matrix by adding the products of elements of a row of the first matrix with the corresponding elements of a column of the second matrix.

The product of an $m \times n$ matrix A and an $n \times p$ matrix B is the $m \times p$ matrix whose entry in row i and column j is the sum of the products of corresponding elements of row i in A and column j in B.

EXAMPLE 1. *Find the product:* $\begin{pmatrix} 3 & -4 \\ 2 & 1 \end{pmatrix} \begin{pmatrix} -2 & -1 & 0 \\ -3 & 2 & 1 \end{pmatrix}$

Note that matrix multiplication is possible in this example because the number of columns in the first matrix is the same as the number of rows in the second matrix.

Solution

$$\begin{pmatrix} 3 & -4 \\ 2 & 1 \end{pmatrix} \begin{pmatrix} 2 & -1 & 0 \\ -3 & 2 & 1 \end{pmatrix} = \begin{pmatrix} 18 & & \\ & & \end{pmatrix}$$

$$\begin{pmatrix} 3 & -4 \\ 2 & 1 \end{pmatrix} \begin{pmatrix} 2 & -1 & 0 \\ -3 & 2 & 1 \end{pmatrix} = \begin{pmatrix} 18 & -11 & \\ & & \end{pmatrix}$$

$$\begin{pmatrix} 3 & -4 \\ 2 & 1 \end{pmatrix} \begin{pmatrix} 2 & -1 & 0 \\ -3 & 2 & 1 \end{pmatrix} = \begin{pmatrix} 18 & -11 & -4 \\ & & \end{pmatrix}$$

$$\begin{pmatrix} 3 & -4 \\ 2 & 1 \end{pmatrix} \begin{pmatrix} 2 & -1 & 0 \\ -3 & 2 & 1 \end{pmatrix} = \begin{pmatrix} 18 & -11 & -4 \\ 1 & & \end{pmatrix}$$

$$\begin{pmatrix} 3 & -4 \\ 2 & 1 \end{pmatrix} \begin{pmatrix} 2 & -1 & 0 \\ -3 & 2 & 1 \end{pmatrix} = \begin{pmatrix} 18 & -11 & -4 \\ 1 & 0 & \end{pmatrix}$$

$$\begin{pmatrix} 3 & -4 \\ 2 & 1 \end{pmatrix} \begin{pmatrix} 2 & -1 & 0 \\ -3 & 2 & 1 \end{pmatrix} = \begin{pmatrix} 18 & -11 & -4 \\ 1 & 0 & 1 \end{pmatrix}$$

A square matrix whose main diagonal from upper left to lower right has entries 1, while all other entries are 0, is called an *identity matrix*. An identity matrix, when multiplied by another square matrix A, leaves the matrix A unchanged.

EXAMPLE 2.   *Find the product:* $\begin{pmatrix} 1 & 0 \\ 0 & 1 \end{pmatrix}\begin{pmatrix} 3 & -2 \\ 4 & -3 \end{pmatrix}$

Solution

$$\begin{pmatrix} 1 & 0 \\ 0 & 1 \end{pmatrix}\begin{pmatrix} 3 & -2 \\ 4 & -3 \end{pmatrix} = \begin{pmatrix} 3 & \\ & \end{pmatrix}$$

$$\begin{pmatrix} 1 & 0 \\ 0 & 1 \end{pmatrix}\begin{pmatrix} 3 & -2 \\ 4 & -3 \end{pmatrix} = \begin{pmatrix} 3 & -2 \\ & \end{pmatrix}$$

$$\begin{pmatrix} 1 & 0 \\ 0 & 1 \end{pmatrix}\begin{pmatrix} 3 & -2 \\ 4 & -3 \end{pmatrix} = \begin{pmatrix} 3 & -2 \\ 4 & \end{pmatrix}$$

$$\begin{pmatrix} 1 & 0 \\ 0 & 1 \end{pmatrix}\begin{pmatrix} 3 & -2 \\ 4 & -3 \end{pmatrix} = \begin{pmatrix} 3 & -2 \\ 4 & -3 \end{pmatrix}$$

EXERCISE 1-11

B   **1.** Perform the following multiplications, if possible.

(a) $\begin{pmatrix} 3 & 1 \\ 2 & 4 \end{pmatrix}\begin{pmatrix} 2 & 1 & 0 \\ 3 & 0 & 1 \end{pmatrix}$

(b) $\begin{pmatrix} 5 & -2 & 3 \\ 1 & 2 & -1 \end{pmatrix}\begin{pmatrix} 4 & 3 \\ 1 & -1 \\ 0 & 2 \end{pmatrix}$

(c) $\begin{pmatrix} 3 & 4 \\ -1 & 2 \end{pmatrix}\begin{pmatrix} 5 & 4 \\ 1 & -2 \\ 3 & 1 \end{pmatrix}$

(d) $(1 \quad -3 \quad 5) \begin{pmatrix} 3 \\ 0 \\ -3 \end{pmatrix}$

(e) $\begin{pmatrix} 2 & -1 & 2 \\ -3 & 4 & -1 \\ 5 & 0 & 3 \end{pmatrix}\begin{pmatrix} 5 & 2 & 5 \\ -1 & 2 & -1 \\ 4 & 3 & 4 \end{pmatrix}$

(f) $\begin{pmatrix} 4 & -2 & 3 \\ -1 & -3 & 5 \\ 3 & 1 & -2 \end{pmatrix}\begin{pmatrix} 3 \\ 0 \\ -1 \end{pmatrix}$

(g) $\begin{pmatrix} 5 \\ 2 \\ -1 \\ 3 \end{pmatrix}(4 \quad -2)$

(h) $\begin{pmatrix} 6 & 2 \\ -3 & 5 \\ 7 & -1 \end{pmatrix}\begin{pmatrix} 4 & -1 \\ 3 & 5 \\ 2 & -7 \end{pmatrix}$

(i) $\begin{pmatrix} 7 \\ 8 \end{pmatrix}\begin{pmatrix} -1 & -3 & 4 \\ 6 & 5 & -2 \end{pmatrix}$

(j) $\begin{pmatrix} 3 & -2 & 4 \\ 5 & 1 & 6 \\ 5 & 2 & -3 \end{pmatrix}\begin{pmatrix} 1 & 0 & 0 \\ 0 & 1 & 0 \\ 0 & 0 & 1 \end{pmatrix}$

(k) $\begin{pmatrix} 1 & 0 \\ 0 & 1 \end{pmatrix}\begin{pmatrix} -3 & 5 \\ 6 & 4 \end{pmatrix}$

(l) $\begin{pmatrix} -2 & -5 \\ -7 & 3 \end{pmatrix}\begin{pmatrix} 0 & 1 \\ 1 & 0 \end{pmatrix}$

(m) $\begin{pmatrix} 3 & -4 & 6 \\ 5 & -2 & 3 \\ 7 & 4 & 5 \\ 6 & 0 & -1 \end{pmatrix}\begin{pmatrix} -1 \\ 2 \\ -3 \end{pmatrix}$

(n) $\begin{pmatrix} 2 & 1 & -2 & 3 \\ 5 & 4 & 0 & -1 \\ 3 & -1 & -2 & 2 \end{pmatrix}\begin{pmatrix} 5 & 2 \\ -3 & 1 \\ 4 & -2 \\ -3 & 0 \end{pmatrix}$

C   2. If $A = \begin{pmatrix} 2 & 1 \\ 3 & 2 \end{pmatrix}$, $B = \begin{pmatrix} 0 & -1 \\ 2 & -3 \end{pmatrix}$ and $C = \begin{pmatrix} 1 & 2 \\ -1 & -2 \end{pmatrix}$, find

(a) AB and BA
(b) BC and CB
(c) $A(B + C)$ and $AB + AC$
(d) $A(B - C)$ and $AB - AC$
(e) $A(BC)$ and $(AB)C$
(f) $(A - B)(A + B)$ and $A^2 - B^2$
(g) $(A - B)^2$ and $A^2 - 2AB + B^2$
(h) $(A + B)^2$ and $A^2 + 2AB + B^2$

1.12   APPLICATIONS OF MATRICES

Matrices can be very useful in analyzing business problems. The following example illustrates how this can be done.

EXAMPLE 1.   *A fresh fruit distributor supplies three types of fruit: apples, peaches and pears. The following table indicates the number of cases ordered by four different stores.*

	apples	peaches	pears
Store 1	60	40	30
Store 2	70	30	25
Store 3	50	20	30
Store 4	80	40	20

Apples cost $15/case; peaches $14/case and pears $12/case. Determine the total income from each store.

Solution   Let A represent the amounts ordered by each store.

$$A = \begin{pmatrix} 60 & 40 & 30 \\ 70 & 30 & 25 \\ 50 & 20 & 30 \\ 80 & 40 & 20 \end{pmatrix}$$

Let C represent the costs of each case.

$$C = \begin{pmatrix} 15 \\ 14 \\ 12 \end{pmatrix}$$

$$\begin{pmatrix} 60 & 40 & 30 \\ 70 & 30 & 25 \\ 50 & 20 & 30 \\ 80 & 40 & 20 \end{pmatrix} \begin{pmatrix} 15 \\ 14 \\ 12 \end{pmatrix} = \begin{pmatrix} 1820 \\ 1770 \\ 1390 \\ 2000 \end{pmatrix}$$

The product matrix represents the total income from each store. Store 1 paid $1820 for all 3 products; store 2, $1770; store 3, $1390; store 4, $2000.

The total income from all four stores, $6980, is obtained by adding the entries in the product matrix.

The preceding example illustrates how matrices present a large amount of information in a concise form. Matrices are also very useful in the solving of systems of equations as we shall see in chapter 7.

EXERCISE 1-12

B **1.** The following table indicates the number of cases of canned peas, carrots and corn ordered by four different stores from a cannery.

	Peas	Carrots	Corn
Store 2	30	20	10
Store 2	20	15	5
Store 3	40	30	20
Store 4	50	25	30

Peas cost $18/case, carrots $16/case and corn $14/case.
(a) Write the total order as a matrix.
(b) Write the cost/case as a column matrix.
(c) Using matrix multiplication, find the amount owing to the cannery by each store.
(d) Find the total amount owing to the cannery.

2. The Ace Sports Company supplies baseballs, footballs and basketballs to five local high schools. The following table indicates the number of each type of ball ordered by each school.

	Baseballs	Footballs	Basketballs
Churchill H.S.	30	10	15
Vanier H.S.	20	15	20
Central H.S.	15	20	25
High Park H.S.	20	15	30
Parkside H.S.	25	15	30

Baseballs cost $4 each, footballs $40 each and basketballs $30 each.
(a) Write the total order as a matrix.
(b) Write the cost of each as a column matrix.
(c) Use matrix multiplication to find the amount owing to the company by each high school.
(d) Use matrix multiplication to find the company's income from footballs.
(e) Use matrix multiplication to find the company's income from baseballs and basketballs.
(f) Find the total amount owing to the company by the five schools.

3. The following table represents the number of tickets issued for various traffic violations in Satellite City for the months of January, February and March.

	no parking	no stopping	careless driving	illegal U-turn
January	157	84	24	12
February	236	75	15	9
March	173	72	10	13

The fines for these offences are $10, $20, $50 and $30 respectively.
(a) Write the violations as a matrix.
(b) Write the fines as a column matrix.
(c) Use matrix multiplication to determine the amount of money collected each month.
(d) What is the total amount collected over the three month period?

4. The Argus Instrument Company distributes four types of calculators— M51, M52, M61 and M62. The following table indicates the number of each type ordered by five stores.

	M51	M52	M61	M62
Store 1	10	20	10	30
Store 2	20	40	25	50
Store 3	30	30	40	20
Store 4	25	50	30	40
Store 5	20	30	50	40

Each M51, M52, M61 and M62 costs $20, $30, $50 and $80 respectively.
(a) Write the total order as a matrix.
(b) Write the cost of each as a column matrix.
(c) Use matrix multiplication to determine the amount owing by each store.
(d) Use matrix multiplication to determine the company's income from the M51 and M62 calculators.
(e) Find the total amount owing to the company from the five stores.

5. A pharmaceutical supply company receives the following orders from five different stores during the month of May.

Store I ordered 3 cases of toothpaste, 5 cases of deodorant and 2 cases of bath powder. Store II ordered 6 cases of deodorant, 3 cases of bath powder and 6 cases of toothpaste. Store III ordered 4 cases of bath powder, 5 cases of toothpaste and 6 cases of deodorant. Store IV ordered 3 cases of deodorant, 2 cases of bath powder and 6 cases of toothpaste. Store V ordered 4 cases of toothpaste, 5 cases of deodorant and 2 cases of bath powder.

Toothpaste costs $60/case, deodorant $84/case and bath powder $35/case.
(a) Write the order as a matrix.
(b) Write the cost/case as a matrix.
(c) Use matrix multiplication to determine the total income from each store.
(d) Find the total amount owing to the company for the month of May.

REVIEW EXERCISE

B **1.** Expand and simplify.
(a) $2(x - 3) + 3(x - 5) - 4(x + 2)$
(b) $(x - 4)(x - 7) - 2(x - 6)$
(c) $(m + 2)^2 + (m - 7)(m + 7) + (m - 3)^2$
(d) $2(w - 3)(w + 4) - (w - 7)(w - 6) - 16$
(e) $(2x - 3)(3x - 1) - (x - 4)(2x - 5)$
(f) $5(3x + 2)(x + 4) - (2x - 1)^2 + 3(3x - 5)$
(g) $(2x + 3)(x^2 - 6x - 4)$
(h) $(2x^2 - x - 5)(x - 2)$
(i) $5(2t - 1)(t + 3) - (t - 7)(2t + 7) - 6$
(j) $6 - (5x - 1)(4x - 3) - 2(3x - 5)^2$

2. Factor.
(a) $3mn - 9m^2n - 12mn^2$ (b) $x^2 - x - 30$
(c) $x^2 - 81$ (d) $x^2 + 8x + 16$
(e) $2x^2 + 15x + 28$ (f) $6m^2 - 23m + 20$
(g) $36t^2 - 49$ (h) $5x(m - 7) - 3(m - 7)$
(i) $2x^2 + 8x - 120$ (j) $x^2 - 14x + 49$
(k) $10m^2 - 23m - 5$ (l) $100m^2 - 121$
(m) $9x^2y - 3x + 12xy^2$ (n) $25x^2 - 20x + 4$
(o) $4m^2 + 28m + 49$ (p) $12x^2 + 31x + 7$
(q) $5x^2(m - n) - 2x(m - n)$ (r) $3x^2 - 48$

3. Express each of the following as rational expressions in lowest terms. Assume that all variables are restricted so that no denominator or divisor is equal to zero.

(a) $\dfrac{25m^3n^2}{16xy} \cdot \dfrac{32x^3y^2}{5m^2n}$ (b) $\dfrac{21t^4w^2}{8xy} \div \dfrac{14tw}{12x^2y^3}$

(c) $\dfrac{x^2 + 2x}{x + 3} \cdot \dfrac{x^2 - 9}{x^2 - x - 6}$ (d) $\dfrac{m^2 - 3m - 4}{3m + 6} \div \dfrac{m^2 - 9m + 20}{m^2 - 3m - 10}$

(e) $\dfrac{x^2 + 8x + 12}{x^2 + 3x - 28} \cdot \dfrac{x^2 - 3x - 4}{x^2 - 3x - 10} \div \dfrac{x^2 + 7x + 6}{x^2 + 2x - 35}$

(f) $\dfrac{t^2 - t - 6}{t^2 - 2t - 99} \cdot \dfrac{t^2 + 6t - 27}{t^2 - 9} \cdot \dfrac{t^2 - 22t + 121}{t^2 - 9t - 22}$

4. Perform the indicated operations and simplify. Assume that all variables are restricted so that no denominator is equal to zero.

(a) $\dfrac{2}{7} + \dfrac{1}{3} - \dfrac{4}{21}$ (b) $\dfrac{3x}{5} - \dfrac{x}{6} + \dfrac{7x}{10}$

(c) $\dfrac{3x+1}{2} - \dfrac{x+1}{3} + \dfrac{x}{4}$

(d) $\dfrac{m-3}{9} - \dfrac{m+4}{2} - \dfrac{m-7}{6}$

(e) $\dfrac{5}{2x^2} - \dfrac{1}{3x} + \dfrac{5}{6x^3}$

(f) $\dfrac{3}{x+1} + \dfrac{4}{x-1}$

(g) $\dfrac{3}{x^2-4x+3} + \dfrac{2}{x^2+x-12}$

(h) $\dfrac{4}{x^2-2x-15} - \dfrac{3}{x^2-25}$

(i) $\dfrac{1}{m^2-4m} - \dfrac{2}{m^2-10m+24}$

(j) $\dfrac{4}{x^2+8x+15} - \dfrac{3}{x^2+4x-5}$

5. Perform the indicated operation.

(a) $\begin{pmatrix} 3 & 4 \\ -2 & 7 \end{pmatrix} + \begin{pmatrix} -5 & 2 \\ -4 & 6 \end{pmatrix}$

(b) $\begin{pmatrix} 3 & 1 \\ 4 & -3 \\ -5 & 0 \end{pmatrix} + \begin{pmatrix} -2 & -3 \\ 5 & -6 \\ 7 & 4 \end{pmatrix}$

(c) $\begin{pmatrix} 5 & 7 \\ -2 & -1 \end{pmatrix} - \begin{pmatrix} -3 & 6 \\ 4 & 7 \end{pmatrix}$

(d) $\begin{pmatrix} 2 & 3 & -2 \\ -1 & 4 & 6 \end{pmatrix} - \begin{pmatrix} -3 & -6 & 0 \\ 4 & 5 & 2 \end{pmatrix}$

(e) $3\begin{pmatrix} 4 & 1 \\ 2 & -6 \end{pmatrix} + 2\begin{pmatrix} -1 & 3 \\ 4 & -2 \end{pmatrix}$

(f) $4\begin{pmatrix} -5 & 6 \\ 8 & 4 \\ -1 & 0 \end{pmatrix} - 2\begin{pmatrix} -9 & -1 \\ 0 & 1 \\ -2 & 2 \end{pmatrix}$

6. Multiply, if possible.

(a) $\begin{pmatrix} 2 & 4 \\ 1 & 3 \end{pmatrix}\begin{pmatrix} -5 & 4 \\ 3 & -1 \end{pmatrix}$

(b) $\begin{pmatrix} 6 & 1 \\ 4 & 0 \\ -1 & 2 \end{pmatrix}\begin{pmatrix} 8 & 0 \\ -5 & 2 \\ -1 & 4 \end{pmatrix}$

(c) $\begin{pmatrix} -3 & 7 \\ 4 & 6 \end{pmatrix}\begin{pmatrix} 1 & 0 \\ 0 & 1 \end{pmatrix}$

(d) $\begin{pmatrix} 2 & 4 & -6 \\ 3 & -1 & 2 \end{pmatrix}\begin{pmatrix} 5 & -2 \\ 4 & 3 \\ -1 & -1 \end{pmatrix}$

(e) $\begin{pmatrix} 3 & -5 & 6 \end{pmatrix}\begin{pmatrix} 5 \\ 0 \\ -1 \end{pmatrix}$

(f) $\begin{pmatrix} 1 & 0 & 0 \\ 0 & 1 & 0 \\ 0 & 0 & 1 \end{pmatrix}\begin{pmatrix} 3 & 4 & 1 \\ -2 & 4 & 2 \\ 3 & -1 & 5 \end{pmatrix}$

7. The Riley Sports Company supplies footballs, helmets and shoulder pads to four high schools. The following table indicates the number of each ordered by each school.

	Footballs	Helmets	Shoulder Pads
Westview H.S.	20	25	16
East H.S.	15	14	18
St. Mary's H.S.	22	30	10
Glendale H.S.	14	16	12

Footballs cost $50 each, helmets $60 each and shoulder pads $65 each.
(a) Write the total order as a matrix.
(b) Write the cost of each as a column matrix.
(c) Use matrix multiplication to determine the total amount owing by each school.
(d) Find the total amount owing to the company by the schools.

REVIEW AND PREVIEW TO CHAPTER 2
DECIMALS

EXERCISE 1

1. Express as decimals:

(a) $\frac{1}{2}$ (b) $\frac{1}{4}$ (c) $\frac{3}{4}$ (d) $\frac{1}{5}$ (e) $\frac{3}{5}$

(f) $\frac{3}{8}$ (g) $\frac{5}{8}$ (h) $2\frac{1}{8}$ (i) $3\frac{4}{5}$ (j) $4\frac{7}{8}$

2. Express as common fractions:

(a) 0.35   (b) 0.75   (c) 0.42   (d) 0.611   (e) 0.525

(f) 0.037   (g) 0.541   (h) 3.52   (i) 4.64   (j) 5.625

3. (a) Add 3.125, 42.53, 0.65, 5.2701

(b) Subtract 31.375 from 48.5

(c) Divide 35.45 by 45.5

(d) Multiply 0.3825 by 5.25

4. Round off to two decimal places:

(a) 3.125   (b) 5.144   (c) 63.25   (d) 5.155   (e) 10.034

5. Round off to two significant figures:

(a) 3.125   (b) 5.144   (c) 63.25   (d) 5.155   (e) 10.034

THE RULE OF THREE

EXERCISE 2

1. How far will a car travel on 25ℓ of gasoline if it goes 300 km on 40ℓ?

2. If you can earn $87.64 for seven hours' work, how much can you earn in a 40 h week?

3. The Norseman 1 satellite revolves about the moon 6 times in 4 h. How many times does it revolve in 22 h?

4. It takes about 1680 kJ to melt 5 g of ice. How much ice can be melted with 10 000 kJ?

5. It takes 2.478 MJ to vaporize 10 g of chloroform. How much energy is required to vaporize 5000 g of chloroform?

6. A pendulum completes 17 vibrations in 13 s. How many vibrations does it make in 25 s?

7. The price of copper pipe is $72.00 for 20 m. What is the cost of 9 m of pipe?

8. It takes a radio wave about 1.3 s to go from earth to the moon, a distance of 383 000 km. How far will the radio wave travel in 25 s?

9. In electroplating, 42 g of copper are deposited in 18 min. How much copper is deposited in 2 h 10 min?

10. Sound travels approximately 1360 m in 4.0 s. How far will sound travel in 9 s?

CHAPTER 2

Real Numbers

God made the integers, all the rest is the work of man.

L. Kronecker

2.1   DECIMAL NOTATION

We have studied

$$Q = \left\{ \frac{a}{b} \,\middle|\, a, b \in I, b \neq 0 \right\}$$

and found that rational numbers could also be expressed in decimal form. Decimal equivalents such as $\frac{1}{2} = 0.5$, $\frac{3}{4} = 0.75$, and $\frac{5}{8} = 0.625$, are called terminating decimals because the division process terminates, while decimal equivalents such as

$$\frac{1}{3} = 0.333\ldots = 0.\dot{3}$$

$$\frac{1}{6} = 0.166\,6\ldots = 0.16\dot{6}$$

$$\frac{1}{7} = 0.142\,857\,142\ldots = 0.\dot{1}42\,85\dot{7}$$

are called *periodic* decimals.

EXAMPLE 1.   *For each of the following, find the decimal equivalent, state the period and length of period in each case.*

(a) $\frac{5}{8}$ (b) $\frac{5}{11}$ (c) $\frac{10}{3}$ (d) $\frac{3}{13}$

Solution

For convenience we present the solution in a table.

Common Fraction	Decimal Equivalent	Period	Length of Period
$\frac{5}{8}$	0.625 000 . . .	0	1
$\frac{5}{11}$	0.454 545 . . .	45	2
$\frac{10}{3}$	3.333 3 . . .	3	1
$\frac{3}{13}$	0.230 769 230 7 . . .	230 769	6

Note that the terminating decimal 0.625 can be considered a periodic decimal with period 0.

EXAMPLE 2. *Express as common fractions (a)* $0.3\dot{6}$ *(b)* $2.1\dot{4}5\dot{3}$.

Solution

(a) Let $x = 0.363\,636\ldots$

             ⟨2⟩ ⟨1⟩

① $100x = 36.363\,6\ldots$

② $x = 0.363\,6\ldots$

subtract

①−② $99x = 36$

               $x = \dfrac{36}{99} = \dfrac{4}{11}.$

Relocate the decimal point after (⟨1⟩) and before (⟨2⟩) the first period.

(b) Let $x = 2.145\,345\,3\ldots$

              ⟨2⟩ ⟨1⟩

① $10\,000x = 21\,453.453\ldots$

② $10x = 21.453\ldots$

subtract

①−② $9\,990x = 21\,432$

           $x = \dfrac{21\,432}{9\,990} = 2\dfrac{242}{1665}.$

Every rational number can be expressed as a terminating decimal or as a periodic decimal. Every terminating or periodic decimal represents a rational number.

We can take a rational number such as

$$0.252\,525\,25\ldots\ldots$$

and manufacture numbers which are non-periodic:

$$0.251\,251\,125\,111\,251\,111\ldots\ldots$$
$$0.252\,252\,225\,222\,252\,222\ldots\ldots$$
$$0.251\,252\,253\,254\,255\ldots\ldots\ldots$$

These three numbers have patterns that are easily recognized, however they are not periodic and hence do not represent rational numbers. In the same manner we can continue to manufacture many other non-periodic decimals. These non-periodic decimals are called *irrational* numbers and we designate this set as $\bar{Q}$.

$\boxed{\bar{Q} \text{ is the set of non-periodic decimals}}$

EXERCISE 2-1

A **1.** Identify each of the following as rational or irrational:

(a) $0.225\,225\,225\ldots$ (b) $0.252\,255\,222\ldots$ (c) $3.125\,125\ldots$

(d) $4.317\,327\,337\ldots$ (e) $2.141\,516\ldots$ (f) $0.230\,530\,530\,5\ldots$

15	36	21
5	12	7
27	33	60
9	11	

Determine the pattern. Find the missing number.

2. State the period and length of the period for each of the following:
(a) $4.\dot{2}0\dot{5}$ (b) $6.0\dot{2}0\dot{4}$ (c) $3.15\dot{4}\dot{2}$ (d) $0.\dot{3}42\dot{7}$
(e) $4.01222\ldots$ (f) $0.72525\ldots$ (g) $0.3636\ldots$ (h) $122.122122\ldots$
(i) $4.012012\ldots$ (j) $4.01212\ldots$ (k) $6.543\,\dot{2}\dot{1}$ (l) $18.650\,\dot{2}47\,\dot{3}$

3. The decimal equivalent of a rational number $\dfrac{a}{b}$ is periodic and the maximum length of the period is $(b-1)$.

What is the maximum length of the period of the decimal equivalent of each of the following?
(a) $\frac{1}{5}$ (b) $\frac{5}{6}$ (c) $\frac{3}{7}$ (d) $\frac{2}{13}$
(e) $\frac{5}{17}$ (f) $\frac{11}{31}$ (g) $\frac{11}{43}$ (h) $\frac{19}{71}$

B   **4.** Express in decimal form.
(a) $\frac{3}{4}$ (b) $\frac{5}{8}$ (c) $\frac{9}{16}$ (d) $\frac{7}{4}$ (e) $\frac{11}{8}$
(f) $\frac{5}{32}$ (g) $\frac{41}{50}$ (h) $\frac{3}{11}$ (i) $\frac{15}{11}$ (j) $\frac{11}{15}$
(k) $\frac{53}{100}$ (l) $\frac{53}{99}$ (m) $\frac{1}{9}$ (n) $\frac{4}{9}$ (o) $\frac{12}{11}$

5. Express in the form $\dfrac{a}{b}$.

(a) 0.625 (b) 0.732 (c) 3.21 (d) 4.65
(e) $0.7\dot{2}$ (f) $0.\dot{7}$ (g) $0.\dot{2}1\dot{5}$ (h) $0.\dot{3}01\,\dot{4}$
(i) $0.3\dot{7}$ (j) $0.24\dot{5}$ (k) $0.30\dot{2}\,\dot{5}$ (l) $0.72\dot{1}$
(m) $3.2\dot{5}$ (n) $4.07\dot{5}$ (o) $7.037\,\dot{5}$ (p) $7.037\,\dot{5}$

6. Express in the form $\dfrac{a}{b}$.

(a) $0.\dot{1}42\,85\dot{7}$ (b) $0.\dot{4}28\,57\dot{1}$ (c) $0.\dot{2}85\,71\dot{4}$
(d) $0.\dot{8}57\,14\dot{2}$ (e) $0.\dot{5}71\,42\dot{8}$ (f) $0.\dot{7}14\,28\dot{5}$

C   **7.** Express your final answer in the form $\dfrac{a}{b}$.

(a) $(0.\dot{6})(0.5)$ (b) $(0.\dot{3})(0.25)$
(c) $(0.\dot{3})^2$ (d) $(0.\dot{1}\dot{8})(0.5)$
(e) $(0.\dot{5})(0.2)$ (f) $(0.\dot{6})(0.2)$

Find unequal rational numbers such that
$$x^y = y^x.$$

8. Express in the form $\dfrac{a}{b}$.

(a) $0.4\dot{9}$ (b) $0.2\dot{9}$ (c) $0.5\dot{9}$ (d) $0.\dot{9}$

9. Determine which of the following pairs of numbers are equal.
(a) $3.\dot{2}\dot{5},\ 3.2\dot{5}\dot{2}$ (b) $4.\dot{3}\dot{6},\ 4.3\dot{6}\dot{3}$

10. Express the following sums in the form $\dfrac{a}{b}$.

(a) $0.1 + 0.01 + 0.001 + \ldots$ (b) $0.2 + 0.02 + 0.002 + \ldots$
(c) $0.25 + 0.002\,5 + 0.000\,025 + \ldots$ (d) $0.18 + 0.001\,8 + 0.000\,018 + \ldots$

2.2 GRAPHING ON A REAL NUMBER LINE

The set of real numbers, R, is the set of all periodic and non-periodic decimals. We can also define R as the union of the set of rational numbers, Q, and the set of irrational numbers, $\bar{Q}$.

$$\boxed{R = Q \cup \bar{Q}}$$

Examples of real numbers are -2, $\sqrt{2}$, $\sqrt{5}$, and $\pi = 3.141\,59\ldots$, where $\sqrt{2}$, $\sqrt{5}$ and π are irrational.

It can be shown that $\sqrt{2}$ is irrational as follows: Suppose $\sqrt{2} = \dfrac{a}{b}$, where $\dfrac{a}{b}$ is in simplest form. Squaring both sides

$$2 = \frac{a^2}{b^2}$$

$$2b^2 = a^2$$

If a is odd, then $a = (2n+1)$ and $a^2 = 4n^2 + 4n + 1$ which is odd.

Because the value of $2b^2$ is even, then a^2 is even so that a is also even. If we now let $a = 2c$, then $a^2 = 4c^2$

$$2b^2 = 4c^2$$

$$b^2 = 2c^2$$

Continuing the same reasoning we have now shown that b is also even. If a and b are both even as shown, then the fraction $\dfrac{a}{b}$ is not in simplest form because both a and b have 2 as a factor. This contradicts the original assumption that $\dfrac{a}{b}$ was in simplest form. We then must conclude that the assumption that $\sqrt{2}$ is a rational number is false so that $\sqrt{2}$ must be irrational.

Although $\sqrt{2}$ is an irrational number and cannot be represented by a periodic decimal, it can be associated with a position on a number line. If we construct a square with sides one unit on a number line as in Figure 2-1, then the diagonal OA has a length $\sqrt{2}$ units.

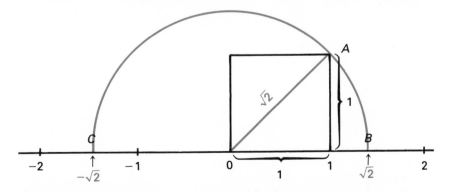

By the Pythagorean Theorem

$$OA^2 = 1^2 + 1^2$$
$$= 2$$
$$OA = \sqrt{2}$$

Figure 2-1

Using compasses with centre O and radius $OA = \sqrt{2}$, we see that the arc cuts the line at B and C making CO and OB equal to $\sqrt{2}$ units.

The irrational number π can be located on a number line by rolling a circle with diameter 1 unit along the line as in Figure 2-2.

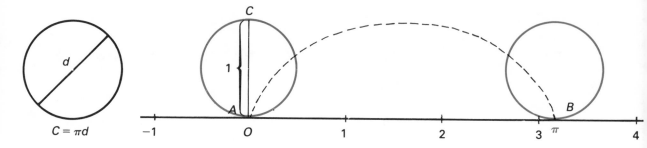

Figure 2-2

If $AC = 1$ unit, then the circumference of the circle is π units. If the circle is permitted to make one complete rotation along the line, then AB is equal in length to the circumference. The point B has the coordinate π.

In 1876 Richard Dedekind, a German mathematician, showed that there is a one-to-one correspondence between the real numbers and all the points on a number line. Because of this property, we note that there are no "holes" or "gaps" in the real number line and we say that the real number system is *complete*.

Henceforth, unless otherwise stated, we shall assume that all variables represent real numbers.

EXAMPLE 1. *Graph each set on a number line.*
(a) $\{x \in R \mid x < 2\}$
(b) $\{x \in R \mid x \geq -2\}$
(c) $\{x \in R \mid -3 \leq x \leq 2\}$

Solution

○ { open dot, point is not included

• { closed dot, point is included

(a) $\{x \in R \mid x < 2\}$

(b) $\{x \in R \mid x \geq -2\}$

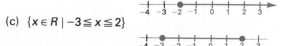

(c) $\{x \in R \mid -3 \leq x \leq 2\}$

EXAMPLE 2. *Given* $A = \{x \in R \mid x > -3\}$
$B = \{x \in R \mid x \leq 0\}$
$C = \{x \in R \mid x \geq 2\}$
graph each of the following on a number line.
(a) $A \cap B$ (b) $B \cup C$

Solution

A

B

C

(a) $A \cap B$

(b) $B \cup C$

In set-builder notation, $A \cap B$ can be written

$$\{x \in R \mid -3 < x \leqq 0\}$$

$\cap$
intersection

$\cup$
union

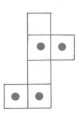

Which of the following figures can you make from the pattern above?

EXERCISE 2-2

A **1.** Identify as members of N, Q, or $\bar{Q}$.
(a) $\frac{3}{4}$ (b) $\sqrt{25}$ (c) $\sqrt{7}$ (d) -2 (e) 0.36
(f) $\sqrt{3}$ (g) $0.\dot{3}$ (h) $\frac{2}{3}$ (i) π (j) $\sqrt{16}$
(k) $1.2\dot{5}$ (l) 0.7 (m) $0.\dot{7}$ (n) $3\frac{1}{7}$ (o) $-\sqrt{3}$

2. Describe each of the following in set-builder notation.
(a) 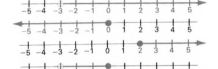   (b)

(c)   (d)

(e)   (f)

B **3.** Graph the following sets, $(x \in R)$:
(a) $\{x \mid x > 1\}$ (b) $\{x \mid x \geqq -2\}$
(c) $\{x \mid x \leqq 3\}$ (d) $\{x \mid x \neq 0\}$
(e) $\{x \mid x > -2\}$ (f) $\{x \mid x \leqq 0\}$

4. Graph the following on a number line, $(x \in R)$:
(a) $\{x \mid x > -1\} \cap \{x \mid x \leqq 3\}$
(b) $\{x \mid x \leqq 0\} \cup \{x \mid x \geqq 3\}$
(c) $\{x \mid x \leqq -2\} \cup \{x \mid x > 0\}$
(d) $\{x \mid x \leqq 0\} \cap \{x \mid x \geqq 0\}$

5. Graph on a number line, $(x \in R)$:
(a) $\{x \mid -2 \leqq x \leqq 1\} \cap \{x \mid 0 < x \leqq 3\}$
(b) $\{x \mid -3 \leqq x < 0\} \cup \{x \mid 0 \leqq x \leqq 2\}$
(c) $\{x \mid -2 \leqq x \leqq 3\} \cap \{x \mid x \neq 3\}$
(d) $\{x \mid -1 < x \leqq 2\} \cup \{x \mid x + 1 = 0\}$

C **6.** Use the methods described in this section to locate the following points on a number line.
(a) $\sqrt{3}$ (b) $\sqrt{5}$ (c) $-\sqrt{3}$ (d) $\sqrt{6}$
(e) $-\pi$ (f) 2π (g) $\sqrt{8}$ (h) $-\sqrt{5}$

7. Graph on a number line.
(a) $\{x \in R \mid x^2 > 4\}$ (b) $\{x \in R \mid x^2 < 4\}$
(c) $\{x \in R \mid x \leqq 2 \text{ and } x \geqq -3\}$ (d) $\{x \in R \mid x \leqq -2 \text{ or } x \geqq 1\}$

real numbers   37

8. Use a contradiction to prove that the following are not rational numbers.

(a) $\sqrt{3}$ (b) $\sqrt{5}$ (c) $\sqrt{7}$

2.3 ORDER AND DENSITY

Because there is a one-to-one correspondence between the set of real numbers and the points on the number line, we say that the set of real numbers is *complete*. This property helps us to determine whether one number is less than, equal to, or greater than another number according to their positions on a number line. When comparing two numbers, a and b, only one of

(i) $a < b$

(ii) $a = b$

(iii) $a > b$

is true. This is called the *trichotomy* property of order.

If $a - b > 0$, then $a > b$.

If $a - b = 0$, then $a = b$.

If $a - b < 0$, then $a < b$.

We will now state some properties of inequality in R.

> Transitive Property $a, b, c \in R$
> If $a < b$, and $b < c$, then $a < c$.
> If $a = b$, and $b = c$, then $a = c$.
> If $a > b$, and $b > c$, then $a > c$.

If $2 < 5$, then we can add the same positive or negative quantity to both sides and the sense of the inequality is unchanged:

$$2 + 3 < 5 + 3 \quad \text{also} \quad 2 - 6 < 5 - 6$$
$$5 < 8 \qquad\qquad\qquad -4 < -1$$

> For $a, b, c \in R$
> If $a < b$, then $a + c < b + c$

If $2 < 5$, then we can multiply both sides by the same positive quantity and the sense of the inequality is unchanged:

$$3 \times 2 < 3 \times 5$$
$$6 < 15$$

If both sides are multiplied by a negative quantity, then the sense of the inequality is reversed:

$$2 < 5$$
$$(-3)(2) \; ? \; (-3)(5)$$
$$-6 > -15$$

We generalize these results to:

> For $a, b, c \in R$
> If $a < b$, and $c > 0$ then $ac < bc$,
> If $a < b$, and $c < 0$ then $ac > bc$,

If we take two irrational numbers

$$b = 2.152\ 753\ 124 \ldots$$

$$a = 2.152\ 636\ 363 \ldots$$

then we can find a rational number and an irrational number between a and b:

Rational: $a < 2.1527 < b$
Irrational: $a < 2.152\ 731\ 234\ 5 \ldots < b$

This shows that both Q and $\bar{Q}$ are dense in the real numbers.

We can find a number between any two real numbers. For $a, b \in R$, $a < b$, $\dfrac{a+b}{2} \in R$ and

$$a < \frac{a+b}{2} < b$$

We can prove this result as follows:
Given: $a < b$

Proof: (i) $b - \dfrac{a+b}{2} = \dfrac{2b - a - b}{2}$

$$= \frac{b-a}{2}$$

$$> 0, \text{ because } a < b$$

$\therefore \quad \dfrac{a+b}{2} < b$

(ii) $\dfrac{a+b}{2} - a = \dfrac{a+b-2a}{2}$

$$= \frac{b-a}{2}$$

$$> 0, \quad \text{because} \quad a < b$$

$\therefore \quad a < \dfrac{a+b}{2}$

and $a < \dfrac{a+b}{2} < b$

This shows that between any two real numbers we can find another real number.

To determine which is the largest of three numbers.

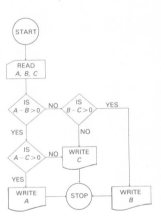

EXERCISE 2-3

A 1. Arrange the elements of each set in increasing order:
(a) $\{0.5, 0.45, 0.65\}$ (b) $\{-2, 4, -1, 3, 0\}$
(c) $\{\frac{1}{2}, -\frac{1}{2}, 1, \frac{2}{3}\}$ (d) $\{-5, 0, -2, -4, 1\}$

2. Arrange in decreasing order:
(a) $\{0.75, 0.33, 0.28, 0.2\}$ (b) $\{-3, 5, -2, 1, 0\}$
(c) $\{\frac{2}{3}, -\frac{1}{3}, -2, 3, 0\}$ (d) $\{-2, 0, 2, -3, 1\}$

3. Find simpler inequalities:
(a) $x + 3 > 7$ (b) $x - 2 < 3$ (c) $x + 4 < 4$
(d) $x + 3 < 0$ (e) $2x > 8$ (f) $3x < 9$
(g) $-x > 2$ (h) $-x < 2$ (i) $-2x > 6$

(j) $\frac{1}{2}x < 3$ (k) $-\frac{1}{3}x > 2$ (l) $-\frac{x}{4} < 1$

4. Find a real number between each of the following pairs of real numbers:
(a) $3, 4$ (b) $-2, 1$ (c) $-3, -5$ (d) $42, 43$
(e) $2.5, 2.6$ (f) $-2.6, -2.7$ (g) $-3.4, -3.5$ (h) $2.75, 2.83$
(i) $\frac{1}{2}, \frac{1}{3}$ (j) $-\frac{1}{3}, -\frac{1}{4}$ (k) $\frac{3}{4}, \frac{11}{16}$ (l) $-\frac{1}{5}, -\frac{3}{10}$

5. Find a rational number and irrational number between each of the following:
(a) $a = 7.217\,46\ldots$ (b) $c = -0.271\,55\ldots$ (c) $e = 4.275\ldots$
$b = 7.223\,45\ldots$ $d = -0.271\,45\ldots$ $f = 4.273\ldots$

2.4   EQUATIONS IN ONE VARIABLE I

Simple equations can be solved using the rules:

If $a = b$, then		
$a + c = b + c$	Rule I
$a - c = b - c$	Rule II
$a \times c = b \times c$	Rule III
$\dfrac{a}{c} = \dfrac{b}{c}, c \neq 0$	Rule IV

EXAMPLE 1.   Solve $3x - 4 = 2x + 6$, $x \in R$

Solution

$3x - 4 = 2x + 6$

$3x - 4 + 4 = 2x + 6 + 4$ (by Rule I)

$3x = 2x + 10$ (simplifying)

$3x - 2x = 2x + 10 - 2x$ (by Rule II)

$x = 10$

$\therefore$ the root is 10

EXAMPLE 2. $\quad 4a+7=5a-17-7a$

Solution

$$4a+7=5a-17-7a$$
$$4a+7=-2a-17 \qquad \text{(simplifying)}$$
$$4a+7-7=-2a-17-7 \qquad \text{(by Rule II)}$$
$$4a=-2a-24 \qquad \text{(simplifying)}$$
$$4a+2a=-2a-24+2a$$
$$6a=-24 \qquad \text{(by Rule IV)}$$
$$\frac{6a}{6}=-\frac{24}{6}$$
$$a=-4$$

Check:

L.S $= 4(-4)+7 \qquad$ R.S. $= 5(-4)-17-7(-4)$

$\qquad = -16+7 \qquad\qquad\quad = -20-17+28$

$\qquad = -9 \qquad\qquad\qquad\quad = -9$

∴ the solution set is $\{-4\}$

EXERCISE 2-4

Solve for the variable.

A **1.** $5x+2=4x+5$
3. $7x+2=4+6x$
5. $6a+6=18$
7. $4a+16=20$
9. $2(b-1)=4$
11. $5(b+2)=20$

B **13.** $3a+6-2a=4-8$
15. $5+6a+3a=12-2a+10a$
17. $-3+4(a-1)=3(a+5)$
19. $3b-8=5b-4$
21. $3b+6-7b=12-8b+2$
23. $2(b-6)+8=4(b+7)$
25. $4(x-5)-2(x+1)=3(1-x)$
27. $2(x-2)+3(x+1)=4x+1$
29. $2(x-5)=4(x-7)-(x-9)$

2. $6x-3=5x+2$
4. $4x+7=3x+3$
6. $3a+2=17$
8. $5a+24=-6$
10. $3(b+1)=6$
12. $4(b-3)=0$
14. $5a+2-2a=7a-5a+6$
16. $-3-2a+6a=11+a+2a$
18. $6(a-3)=5(a+2)-8$
20. $3-6b+6=2b-7$
22. $-4b+4+2b=3b-16$
24. $2(2a-1)+4=5(a+1)$
26. $(x+1)-2(x+3)-3(x-2)=13$
28. $4(x-2)-3(x+1)=1-3x$
30. $2(x-3)-4(1-2x)=3(2x-2)$

Put the numbers from 1 to 9 in the spaces to make the statements true.

$\square-\square\div\square=1$

$\square-\square\times\square=1$

$\square+\square-\square=1$

2.5 EQUATIONS IN ONE VARIABLE II

In this section we present equations involving common fractions and decimals.

EXAMPLE 1. *Solve* $\dfrac{2}{3}x - \dfrac{1}{2}(x-3) = \dfrac{2x-3}{4}$

Solution

To clear fractions we multiply both sides of the equation by the lowest common denominator. (LCD is 12)

$$12\left[\dfrac{2}{3}x - \dfrac{1}{2}(x-3)\right] = \left[\dfrac{2x-3}{4}\right]12$$

$$8x - 6(x-3) = (2x-3)3$$

$$8x - 6x + 18 = 6x - 9$$

$$-4x = -27$$

$$x = \dfrac{-27}{-4}$$

$$x = 8\dfrac{3}{4}$$

EXAMPLE 2. *Solve* $2.5(3.2x - 4.7) - 1.7(3.6x + 2.0) = 8.35$

Solution
We can proceed in two ways.
Method (i)

$$2.5(3.2x - 4.7) - 1.7(3.6x + 2.0) = 8.35$$

$$8.00x - 11.75 - 6.12x - 3.40 = 8.35$$

$$1.88x - 15.15 = 8.35$$

$$1.88x = 23.50$$

$$x = 12.5$$

Method (ii)
We clear decimal fractions by multiplying both sides by 100.

$$100[2.5(3.2x - 4.7) - 1.7(3.6x + 2.0)] = [8.35]100$$

$$800x - 1175 - 612x - 340 = 835$$

$$188x - 1515 = 835$$

$$188x = 2350$$

$$x = 12.5$$

EXERCISE 2-5

Solve for the variable:

A
1. $\frac{1}{3}x = 5$
2. $\frac{3}{4}x = 8$
3. $a - \frac{1}{2} = \frac{3}{2}$
4. $2b + \frac{3}{4} = 1$
5. $a - \frac{1}{3} = \frac{1}{2}$
6. $2(x - \frac{1}{4}) = \frac{1}{2}$
7. $0.5x = 3.2$
8. $2.5a = 12.5$
9. $10x = 42.4$
10. $b + 3.5 = 8.5$

is to

as

is to

11. $y - 2.3 = 3.1$

12. $2x + 4.3 = 8.3$

B **13.** $\dfrac{b-1}{3} = 6$

14. $\dfrac{b+2}{8} = \dfrac{1}{4}$

15. $\dfrac{c}{3} - \dfrac{1}{2} = \dfrac{1}{4}$

16. $\dfrac{2c}{3} + 2 = \dfrac{1}{2}$

17. $\dfrac{2c+1}{3} = 6$

18. $\dfrac{c-7}{2} = \dfrac{1}{4}$

19. $\dfrac{2-3c}{4} = \dfrac{6-2c}{5}$

20. $\dfrac{3c+7}{4} - \dfrac{c}{3} = -\dfrac{1}{3}$

21. $\frac{1}{2}x - \frac{1}{3}(x+2) = \frac{5}{6}$

22. $\dfrac{3x}{2} - \dfrac{5x}{4} = \dfrac{3x+1}{2}$

23. $9.8x - 3.7 = 6.1$

24. $3.0(x - 2.5) = 7.5$

25. $4.2 - 3.5x = 2.1$

26. $3.5 = 5.2 - 6.3(x + 1.4)$

27. $5.5x - 2.3 = 3.2(2.5x - 4.6)$

28. $3.5x - 2.4(x + 3.5) = 0$

29. $3.1(2.5x - 4.3) - 3.8x = 4.3(1.4 - 2.3x)$

30. $6.2(1.1x - 2.5) + 3.7(2.4x - 3.7) = 8.4x - 5.2$

2.6 PROBLEM SOLVING

We can solve problems using algebraic methods. In this section we will solve problems using a single equation with one variable.

EXAMPLE 1. *Sam is twice Jennie's age. Three years ago, the sum of their ages was 45. How old is Jennie today?*

Solution

Let Jennie's age in years be x.
Then Sam's age in years is $2x$.

$$(x - 3) + (2x - 3) = 45$$
$$x - 3 + 2x - 3 = 45$$
$$3x - 6 = 45$$
$$3x = 51$$
$$x = 17$$

$\therefore$ Jennie's age is 17 a.
Sam's age is 34 a.

Check:

Three years ago Jennie: 14
Sam: 31
Sum of their ages: 45

EXAMPLE 2. *The cash box for the school play contains $233 in $2 bills and $5 bills. How many bills of each denomination are there if the total number of bills is 61.*

Solution

Let the number of $2 bills be x.
Then the number of $5 bills is $(61 - x)$.

$$2x + 5(61 - x) = 233$$
$$2x + 305 - 5x = 233$$
$$-3x + 305 = 233$$
$$-3x = -72$$
$$x = 24$$
$$61 - x = 37$$

∴ there are 24 $2 bills and 37 $5 bills.

Check

The total number of bills is $24 + 37 = 61$
The value of the bills is

$$\$2(24) + \$5(37) = \$48 + \$185$$
$$= \$233$$

EXAMPLE 3. *How many millilitres of 50% acid solution must be mixed with 30% solution to produce 100 ml of 45% solution?*

Solution

Let the amount of 50% solution be x ml.
Then the amount of 30% solution is $(100 - x)$ ml.

$$0.5x + 0.3(100 - x) = 0.45(100)$$
$$0.5x + 30 - 0.3x = 45$$
$$0.2x + 30 = 45$$
$$0.2x = 15$$
$$x = 75$$

∴ 75 ml of 50% solution are required.

Check:

50% of 75 ml contains 37.5 ml of acid.
30% of 25 ml contains   7.5 ml of acid.
Total acid: 45.0 ml

EXAMPLE 4. *A woman travels a certain distance by motor scooter at 50 km/h and returns at 60 km/h. Find the distance between the two places if the total travelling time was 11 h.*

Solution

Let the distance between the two places be x km.

D (km)	R (km/h)	T (h)
x	50	$\dfrac{x}{50}$
x	60	$\dfrac{x}{60}$

$$\frac{x}{50} + \frac{x}{60} = 11$$

$$300\left(\frac{x}{50} + \frac{x}{60}\right) = (11)300$$

$$6x + 5x = 3300$$

$$11x = 3300$$

$$x = 300$$

∴ the distance between the two places is 300 km.

Check:

$$\begin{array}{lr}
300 \text{ km @ } 50 \text{ km/h takes} & 6 \text{ h} \\
300 \text{ km @ } 60 \text{ km/h takes} & \underline{5 \text{ h}} \\
\text{Total Time is} & 11 \text{ h}
\end{array}$$

EXERCISE 2-6

Can you find three consecutive even numbers whose sum is 55?

A **1.** Express each of the following as an algebraic expression.
(a) a number increased by three.
(b) twice Mary's age.
(c) 5 less than x.
(d) the length is three times the width.
(e) twice a number increased by three.
(f) three consecutive numbers.
(g) three consecutive even numbers.
(h) Mary's age in five years.

B Solve the following problems using one variable.

2. The sum of three consecutive numbers is 66. Find the numbers.

3. The sum of three consecutive even numbers is 48. Find the numbers.

4. The sum of three consecutive odd numbers is 75. Find the numbers.

5. A department store employs 119 people. The full-time staff outnumbers the part-time staff by 13. How many people work part-time?

6. A boutique sold 3 more sweaters than skirts. Three times the number of skirts sold plus four times the number of sweaters is 96. How many sweaters were sold?

7. Mary is twice as old as Sally. In four years, the sum of their ages will be 32. How old are they today?

8. A box contains 35 small penlights, some worth $1.00 each and the remainder $2.00 each. How many of each are there if the total value of the flashlights is $35.00?

9. Sam pays a library fine of $1.60 using nickles, dimes and quarters. The number of nickles is two more than the number of dimes and the number of quarters is two fewer than the number of dimes. How many nickles, dimes and quarters are there?

10. How many millilitres of 50% acid solution must be mixed with 10% solution to produce 200 ml of 25% solution?

11. Kasmir travels 3 h by car and 4 h by bus. The speed of the car was 10 km/h faster than the bus. Find the speed of the bus if the total distance travelled was 660 km.

12. Shirley walks a certain distance, then returns along the same route. She walked 10 km/h going and returned at 8 km/h. How far did she walk if the round trip took 9 h?

13. A plane flies from Toronto to Ottawa at an average speed of 700 km/h. If the plane flies at an average speed of 500 km/h, then the trip takes 0.2 h longer. How far is it from Toronto to Ottawa?

14. A car travels a certain distance in 3 h. If the driver increases the speed by 10 km/h, the trip takes 2.5 h. How fast should the driver go to cover the distance in 2.5 h?

15. A family leaves for vacation by car. On the first day, they averaged 70 km/h. On the second day they averaged 90 km/h and drove for 1 h longer than the first day. How long did they travel on the first day if the total distance for two days was 890 km?

2.7   INEQUALITIES IN ONE VARIABLE I

The inequalities which follow can be solved using the rules:

	$a + c > b + c$	Rule I
If $a > b$, then	$a - c > b - c$	Rule II
	$ac > bc$ $\Big\}$	Rule III
	$\dfrac{a}{c} > \dfrac{b}{c}$ $\Big\}$ for $c > 0$	Rule IV
	$ac < bc$ $\Big\}$	Rule III*
	$\dfrac{a}{c} < \dfrac{b}{c}$ $\Big\}$ for $c < 0$	Rule IV*

EXAMPLE 1. *Solve*: $3+5x>4x+6$

Solution

$$3+5x>4x+6$$
$$3-3+5x>4x+6-3 \qquad \text{(by Rule II)}$$
$$5x>4x+3 \qquad \text{(simplifying)}$$
$$5x-4x>4x-4x+3 \qquad \text{(by Rule II)}$$
$$x>3$$

The solution set is $\{x \in R \mid x>3\}$

EXAMPLE 2. *Solve*: $3(x-5)+2x \leq 5-2(x+3)$

Solution:

$$3(x-5)+2x \leq 5-2(x+3)$$
$$3x-15+2x \leq 5-2x-6$$
$$5x-15 \leq -2x-1$$
$$5x+2x-15+15 \leq -2x+2x-1+15 \qquad \text{(by Rule I)}$$
$$7x \leq 14 \qquad \text{(simplifying)}$$
$$x \leq 2 \qquad \text{(by Rule IV)}$$

The solution set is $\{x \in R \mid x \leq 2\}$

EXERCISE 2-7

A Solve the following inequalities:
  1. $x+5>7$ **2.** $a-4<7$
  3. $3x<2x+4$ **4.** $5x-3 \geq 4x+2$ $-x<3$
  5. $3x \leq 12$ **6.** $5x+1 \leq 21$ $x>-3$
  7. $-3x>6$ **8.** $2x \leq 3x+2$

B Graph the solution set of each of the following. All variables have
  domain R.
  9. $6x+8<5x+5$ **10.** $4x-2 \geq 3x+5$
  11. $3+5m+1 \leq 1+4m$ **12.** $3x+1+2x>4x-6$
  13. $3a-2a+5 \leq -6$ **14.** $8x+4-6 \leq 7x$
  15. $7x-5 \geq 2x+20$ **16.** $5x \leq 3x-6$ $-2x \geq 8$
  17. $3m-6>6m+12$ **18.** $\frac{1}{2}x+3 \geq \frac{3}{4}x-1$ $x \leq -4$
  19. $3(c-5) \leq 4-(c-5)$ **20.** $2(x+3)<3x+5$
C **21.** $3a-7 \geq 2(a+2)+1$ **22.** $3b-2+2(b+1) \geq 2(2b+3)$
  23. $3(2x-1)-4 \leq 5(1+x)-1$ **24.** $-3+4(3+a)<5+3a$
  25. $3(2x-3)>2(1-3x)+4$ **26.** $2x+3(x-7) \leq 9(x-1)$
  27. $5(2x-1)-3(x+2) \leq 4$ **28.** $x-2(x-5)>3(x+1)-1$
  29. $5-2(x+4) \leq x-2(4-x)$ **30.** $3x-2(x+2)>2x+4(x-1)$

2.8 INEQUALITIES IN ONE VARIABLE II

EXAMPLE 1. *Graph the solution set of* $\dfrac{x}{3}+\dfrac{1}{2}<\dfrac{2x}{3}-\dfrac{5}{2}$, $x \in R$.

Solution

$$\frac{x}{3}+\frac{1}{2}<\frac{2x}{3}-\frac{5}{2}$$

$$6\left[\frac{x}{3}+\frac{1}{2}\right]<\left[\frac{2x}{3}-\frac{5}{2}\right]6 \qquad \text{(by Rule III)}$$

$$2x+3<4x-15 \qquad \text{(simplifying)}$$

$$2x+3-3<4x-15-3 \qquad \text{(by Rule II)}$$

$$2x<4x-18 \qquad \text{(simplifying)}$$

$$2x-4x<4x-18-4x \qquad \text{(by Rule II)}$$

$$-2x<-18$$

$$\frac{-2x}{-2}>\frac{-18}{-2} \qquad \text{(by Rule III*)}$$

$$x>9$$

EXAMPLE 2. *Graph the solution set of* $3.2x-5.7 \leqq 4.8x+1.5$

Solution

Method (i)

$$3.2x-5.7 \leqq 4.8x+1.5$$

$$3.2x-4.8x-5.7 \leqq 4.8x-4.8x+1.5 \qquad \text{(by Rule II)}$$

$$-1.6x-5.7 \leqq 1.5$$

$$-1.6x-5.7+5.7 \leqq 1.5+5.7 \qquad \text{(by Rule I)}$$

$$-1.6x \leqq 7.2$$

$$\frac{-1.6x}{-1.6} \geqq \frac{7.2}{-1.6} \qquad \text{(by Rule III*)}$$

$$x \geqq -4.5$$

Method (ii)

$$3.2x-5.7 \leqq 4.8x+1.5$$

$$10[3.2x-5.7] \leqq [4.8x+1.5]10$$

$$32x-57 \leqq 48x+15$$

$$32x - 48x - 57 + 57 \leqq 48x - 48x + 15 + 57$$

$$-16x \leqq 72$$

$$\frac{-16x}{-16} \geqq \frac{72}{-16}$$

$$x \geqq -4.5$$

EXERCISE 2-8

A Solve the following inequalities:

1. $\frac{1}{2}x < 3$ **2.** $\frac{2}{3}x \leqq 6$

3. $-\frac{1}{3}x \geqq 2$ **4.** $-\frac{3}{4}x < -6$

5. $0.5a > 3.5$ **6.** $0.25m \geqq 10$

7. $-2.5b \leqq 10$ **8.** $x + 2.4 \leqq 3.5$

B Solve:

9. $\frac{3}{5}x - \frac{1}{4} > 1 + \frac{1}{10}x$ **10.** $0 \geqq \frac{2}{3}a - \frac{1}{6}$

11. $\frac{3}{5}m - \frac{1}{4} \leqq 2$ **12.** $\frac{3}{4}b < \frac{1}{2}b - 2$

13. $\frac{1}{3}m - 2 \leqq \frac{1}{2}m + 3$ **14.** $\frac{2}{3}x - 1 \geqq 3 + \frac{1}{2}x$

15. $a - 3.1 \leqq 3.15 - 1.5a$ **16.** $0.8(x+4) > 0.2 - 0.7x$

17. $x - 0.75 \leqq 0.5(x+1)$ **18.** $2(x-1) > 5(1-0.3x)$

19. $7(0.5x - 0.3) \leqq 2.5x + 2.4$ **20.** $1.5(x-3) \geqq 0.5(x-9) - 2.5$

Solve and graph:

21. $\dfrac{a+1}{3} > \dfrac{a-2}{4}$ **22.** $\dfrac{b-3}{5} + 1 \leqq \dfrac{b+4}{3}$

23. $\dfrac{2x-3}{6} + \dfrac{1}{8} > \dfrac{3x+1}{4}$ **24.** $3 + \dfrac{x-3}{6} \geqq x$

25. $\dfrac{x-1}{2} > \dfrac{2-x}{6} + \dfrac{1}{2}$ **26.** $5x - 2 > 1.5(x-1) + 3$

27. $1.5(3x - 5) \leqq 3.5(x-1) - 1.5$ **28.** $8(0.4x+1) \geqq 5(x+1) - 2.8x$

29. $1.3(5x+2) - 3.1 \leqq 5.5(x+1) - 2$

30. $8(1.1 - 0.8x) > 7.4(1.4 - x) + 1$

2.9 EQUATIONS AND INEQUALITIES INVOLVING ABSOLUTE VALUE

If we wish to consider only the magnitude of a signed number, we can take its absolute value so that

$$|-3| = 3, \qquad |+5| = 5, \qquad |3-7| = |-4| = 4, \quad \text{and so on.}$$

This leads to the following definition:

State the output of the
following flow chart.

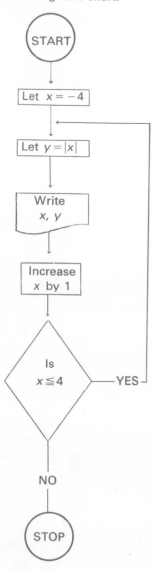

ABSOLUTE VALUE
The absolute value of a real number x, (written $|x|$) is

$$|x| = x, \quad \text{if} \quad x > 0$$
$$|x| = x, \quad \text{if} \quad x = 0$$
$$|x| = -x, \quad \text{if} \quad x < 0$$

EXAMPLE 1. *Use the definition of absolute value to evaluate (a)* $|-4|$,
(b) $|-2-(-5)|$, *(c)* $|7|-|-10|$

Solution

(a) $|-4| = -(-4) = 4$ because $-4 < 0$

(b) $|-2-(-5)| = |-2+5| = |+3| = 3$ $+3 > 0$

(c) $|7|-|-10| = 7-(10) = -3$ $-10 < 0$

    The next step is to apply the definition of absolute value to situa-
tions that involve variables.

EXAMPLE 2. *Solve* $|x| = 5, x \in R$.

Solution
There are two possibilities.

$$|x| = 5$$

If $x < 0$, $|x| = -x$.   or   If $x \geq 0$, $|x| = x$

           $-x = 5$ $x = 5$

            $x = -5$

Verify that both roots (5 and −5) satisfy the equation $|x| = 5$. It follows
that if $|x| = 5$, then the distance from the origin to a point with
coordinate x is 5.

We generalize this result in the following statement.

If $|x| = a$, then $x = a$ or $x = -a$
where a is a positive real number.

EXAMPLE 3. *Solve:* *(a)* $|x+3| = 5$ *(b)* $|5-2x| = 9$

Solution

(a) $|x+3| = 5$

$x+3 = 5$ or $x+3 = -5$ From example 2

    $x = 2$ $x = -8$

Since both 2 and −8 satisfy the equation, the solution set is $\{2, -8\}$

(b) $|5-2x|=9$

$5-2x=9$ or $5-2x=-9$

   $-2x=4$ $-2x=-14$

      $x=-2$ $x=7$

Since both -2 and 7 satisfy the equation, the solution set is $\{-2, 7\}$

From example 2

$|5-2(-2)|=?$

$|5-2(7)|=?$

EXAMPLE 4. *Solve and graph (a) $|x|<4$, (b) $|x|>4$, $x \in R$*

Solution

(a) Applying the definition of absolute value to $|x|<4$, we have two possibilities.

(i) $x<0, |x|=-x$ or   (ii) $x \geq 0, |x|=x$

       $\therefore \; -x<4, x<0$ $0 \leq x, x<4$

          $-4<x<0$ $0 \leq x<4$

We combine these results to give

         $-4<x<0$ or $0 \leq x<4$

                 $-4<x<4$

The solution set is $\{x \in R \mid -4<x<4\}$

(b) $|x|>4$

(i) $x<0, |x|=-x$ or   (ii) $x \geq 0, |x|=x$

    $-x>4$ $x>4$

$x<0, x<-4$ $x \geq 0, \quad x>4$

 $\therefore \; x<-4$ $\therefore \; x>4$

We combine these results to give

           $x<-4$ or $x>4$

The solution set is

         $\{x \in R \mid x<-4 \quad$ or $\quad x>4\}$

If 2 hens lay 2 eggs in 2 d, how many eggs will 30 hens lay in 80 d?

We generalize the results of example 4 in the following statement.

If $|x|<a$, then $-a<x<a$.
If $|x|>a$, then $x>a$ or $x<-a$.
where a is a positive real number.

EXAMPLE 5. *Solve and graph (a) $|2x+1|>5$*
*   (b) $|3-2x| \leq 5$*

(a) $|2x+1|>5$

             $2x+1>5$ or $2x+1<-5$

                $2x>4$ $2x<-6$

                 $x>2$ $x<-3$

The solution set is

$$\{x \in R \mid x < -3 \quad \text{or} \quad x > 2\}$$

(b) $\qquad |3-2x| \leqq 5$

$$-5 \leqq 3-2x \leqq 5$$

$$-5 \leqq 3-2x \quad \text{and} \quad 3-2x \leqq 5$$

$$2x \leqq 8 \qquad\qquad -2x \leqq 2$$

$$x \leqq 4 \qquad\qquad x \geqq -1$$

The solution set is

$$\{x \in R \mid -1 \leqq x \leqq 4\}$$

EXERCISE 2-9

A State the solution sets for $x \in R$.

1. $|x| = 2$ **2.** $|x| = 5$ **3.** $|x| = 3$

4. $|x| + 2 = 5$ **5.** $|x| - 3 = 0$ **6.** $|x| + |x| = 2 + |x|$

7. $|x| < 1$ **8.** $|x| \geqq 6$ **9.** $|x| + 2 \leqq 5$

B **10.** Write without using absolute values:

(a) $|x| < 2$ (b) $|x| - 1 < 3$ (c) $|2x| < 6$

(d) $|x| \geqq 2$ (e) $|x| - 2 > 0$ (f) $\left|\dfrac{x}{3}\right| \geqq 2$

11. Solve for $x \in R$.

(a) $|2x - 1| = 7$ (b) $|2x + 3| = 7$ (c) $|1 + 3x| = 5$

(d) $|1 - 2x| = 3$ (e) $|3 - 2x| = 5$ (f) $|2 - 3x| = 8$

12. Graph the solution set for each of the following where $x \in R$.

(a) $|x| = 6$ (b) $|x| \leqq 5$ (c) $|x| < 3$

(d) $|x + 2| < 5$ (e) $|x| > 1$ (f) $|x + 3| \geqq 2$

13. Graph the solution set of each of the following for $x \in R$.

(a) $|3 + 2x| < 7$ (b) $|4x + 2| \leqq 14$ (c) $|3 - 2x| < 5$

(d) $|4x - 2| > 6$ (e) $|3x + 2| \geqq 5$ (f) $|2x - 3| > 5$

C **14.** Solve the following for $x \in R$.

(a) $|x| + |-3| = 5$ (b) $|x| - |+3| = 5$ (c) $3 - |x| = 1$

(d) $\left|\dfrac{2}{3}x + \dfrac{3}{4}\right| = \dfrac{5}{8}$ (e) $\left|\dfrac{1}{2}x - \dfrac{2}{3}\right| = \dfrac{5}{6}$ (f) $|x + 3| = 4, \, x < 0$

15. State, with reasons, which of the following do not have real solutions.

(a) $|1 - x| < 0$ (b) $|2 + x| \leqq 0$ (c) $|x| + 1 = 0$

(d) $|5 - 2x| < -1$ (e) $|3 - 9x| > 0$ (f) $|2x - 5| \leqq 0$

16. Identify as (i) true, (ii) sometimes true, (iii) false:
(a) If $a < b$, then $|a| < |b|$.
(b) If $a > b$, then $|a| > |b|$.
(c) $a + b < |a + b|$
(d) $a + b \leq |a| + |b|$
(e) $|a + b| \leq |a| + |b|$
(f) $|a + b| = |a| + |b|$
(g) $|a - b| = |a| - |b|$
(h) $|a - b| \leq |a| - |b|$

Find the missing digits in this multiplication.

MF
FM
■ ■ 1
■ 1 ■
■ ■ ■ ■

REVIEW EXERCISE

B **1.** Find the decimal equivalents of:
(a) $\frac{7}{8}$ (b) $\frac{5}{13}$ (c) $\frac{2}{9}$ (d) $\frac{8}{11}$ (e) $\frac{3}{13}$

2. Express in the form $\dfrac{a}{b}$:
(a) $0.8\dot{1}$ (b) $0.1\dot{3}$ (c) $1.\dot{0}76\,92\dot{3}$ (d) $0.2\dot{3}\dot{5}$ (e) $0.13\dot{5}$

3. Draw the graph of:
(a) $\{x \in R \mid x \geq -2\}$ (b) $\{x \in R \mid -2 \leq x < 3\}$ (c) $\{x \in R \mid x \neq 2\}$

4. Graph the following:
(a) $\{x \in R \mid x \leq 3\} \cap \{x \in R \mid x > -1\}$
(b) $\{x \in R \mid -2 \leq x \leq 3\} \cup \{x \in R \mid 0 \leq x < 4\}$
(c) $\{x \in R \mid -3 < x \leq 0\} \cap \{x \in R \mid x = 2\}$

5. Arrange the elements of $\{0.3, -0.25, 0, 1.3. 0.54\}$ in
(a) increasing order   (b) decreasing order.

6. Find a rational and an irrational number between each of the following:
(a) $3, 4$ (b) $2.\dot{5}, 2.\dot{6}$ (c) $3.125\,125\ldots, 3.121\,2\ldots$

7. Solve for the variables:
(a) $3x - 5(x + 2) = 4$ (b) $3(a + 2) - 2(a + 1) = 5$
(c) $x(x + 1) - x^2 = 5$ (d) $3(a - 1) + 2a + 3 = 25$
(e) $\frac{1}{2}x + 2 = 3$ (f) $\frac{2}{3}x + \frac{3}{4} = \frac{1}{2}$
(g) $3.5(x - 1) = 1.5x - 1$ (h) $7(1 - 0.6x) = 1 - 5.2x$

8. Solve for the variables:
(a) $3 + x < 5$ (b) $2x + 3 \geq x + 2$
(c) $2(x + 3) \leq x + 2$ (d) $3x + 4 \geq 2(x + 1) + 3$
(e) $\dfrac{x + 2}{3} \leq 1$ (f) $\dfrac{x + 1}{5} > \dfrac{2x + 1}{3}$
(g) $2.5(3x + 1) > 5(1.3x + 1)$ (h) $6(x + 1) - 7.5 \leq 1.5(x + 2)$

9. Solve for the variables.
(a) $|x| = 7$ (b) $|x + 1| = 3$ (c) $|2x| = 8$
(d) $|2x + 1| = 5$ (e) $|x - 3| = 0$ (f) $|1 - 2x| = 3$

10. Graph the solution sets of each of the following:
(a) $|x| \leq 5$ (b) $|x| > 3$ (c) $|x + 2| < 4$
(d) $|x - 3| \geq 2$ (e) $|2x + 1| < 5$ (f) $|\frac{1}{2}x - \frac{2}{3}| > \frac{1}{3}$

To find a square root by Newton's method

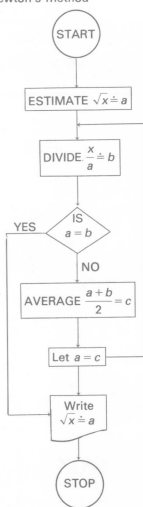

START

ESTIMATE $\sqrt{x} \doteq a$

DIVIDE $\dfrac{x}{a} \doteq b$

IS $a = b$ YES

NO

AVERAGE $\dfrac{a + b}{2} = c$

Let $a = c$

Write $\sqrt{x} \doteq a$

STOP

REVIEW AND PREVIEW TO CHAPTER 3

EXERCISE 1

Simplify:

1. $3x - 2x^2 + 5x + 7x^2$

2. $5ab - 3b + 7ab + 5b$

3. $6a^2b + 2ab - 5a^2b - 3ab$

4. $2ab^2 - 5ab + 3ab + 4ab^2$

5. $3xy + 7x^2 - 2xy + y^2$

6. $5a^2 + 2a - 3a^2 - 5a$

7. $3(a-2) + 5(a+1)$

8. $4(x-3) - 2(x-5)$

9. $3a(a-2) - a(a+2)$

10. $2(a^2 - 2a) - 3a(2 - 3a)$

EXERCISE 2

Expand:

1. $(3a+2)(2a-5)$

2. $(x-3)(x+3)$

3. $(a+5)^2$

4. $(x-7)(x+7)$

5. $(3x-5)(2x+5)$

6. $(2x+3)(x-2)$

7. $(a-3)^2$

8. $(x-7)(x+6)$

9. $(x-6)(x+7)$

10. $(a-10)(a+10)$

11. $(a-6)^2$

12. $(3a-5)(a+2)$

13. $(2x+3)^2$

14. $(3a-2)(3a+2)$

15. $(3a+7)(2-5a)$

EXERCISE 3

Evaluate:

1. $\sqrt{81}$

2. $\sqrt{144}$

3. $\sqrt{169}$

4. $\sqrt{196}$

5. $\sqrt{576}$

6. $\sqrt{625}$

7. $\sqrt{361}$

8. $\sqrt{289}$

9. $\sqrt{961}$

10. $\sqrt{729}$

11. $\sqrt{1024}$

12. $\sqrt{2025}$

13. $\sqrt{0.01}$

14. $\sqrt{121}$

15. $\sqrt{0.0049}$

16. $\sqrt{20.25}$

EXERCISE 4

Multiply:

1. $(3x^2 - 5x + 2)(x+2)$

2. $(2x^2 - 5x + 7)(x-3)$

3. $(x^2 - 7x + 4)(2x^2 - 5x + 3)$

4. $(-x^2 + 3x - 2)(x+4)$

5. $(3x^2 + 2x - 5)(2x^2 + 1)$

6. $(x^2 - 2)(2x - 5)$

EXERCISE 5

Calculate the value of the variable:

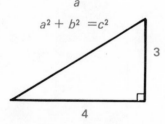

$a^2 + b^2 = c^2$

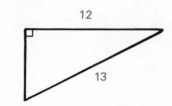

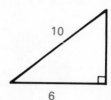

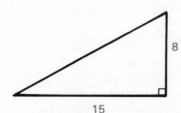

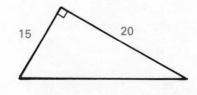

y

54   fmt : introduction

Radicals

What science can there be more noble, more excellent, more useful for men, more admirably high and demonstrative, than this of the mathematics?

Benjamin Franklin

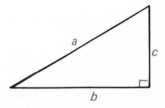

Pythagorean Theorem

Numbers such as $\sqrt{2}$, $\sqrt{3}$, $\sqrt{5}$, and $\sqrt{8}$ are called radicals. An approximation of the value of each of these radicals can be found using tables, slide rule, calculator, or a formal method. The existence of these numbers is illustrated in Figure 3-1. In this chapter, we will deal with operations with radicals.

and

$$a^2 = b^2 + c^2$$
$$a = \sqrt{b^2 + c^2}$$

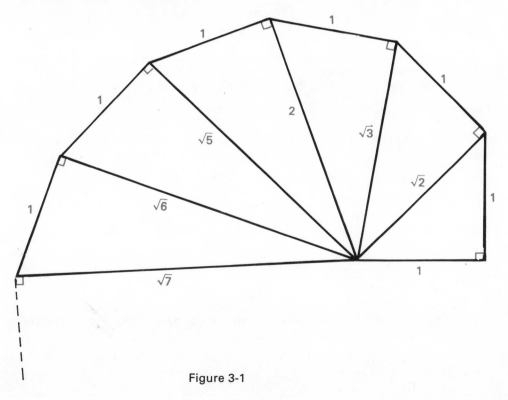

Figure 3-1

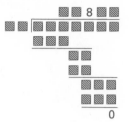

Find the missing digits in this division.

3.1 MIXED AND ENTIRE RADICALS

Although 9 has two square roots, +3 and −3, when we write $\sqrt{9}$ we mean the principal (positive) square root, +3.

Since $\qquad \sqrt{25} = 5$ and $\sqrt{4} = 2$,

then $\qquad \sqrt{25} \times \sqrt{4} = 5 \times 2$

$\qquad\qquad\qquad\qquad = 10$

But $\qquad 10 = \sqrt{100} = \sqrt{25 \times 4}$

This suggests that $\qquad \sqrt{25} \times \sqrt{4} = \sqrt{25 \times 4}.$

We generalize this result to the rule

$$\sqrt{a} \times \sqrt{b} = \sqrt{ab}, \quad \text{where} \quad a, b \geq 0$$

EXAMPLE 1. *Determine* $\sqrt{2} \times \sqrt{3}$ *to 3 significant digits.*

Solution

Method 1. $\qquad\qquad\qquad$ Method 2.

$\sqrt{2} \times \sqrt{3} \doteq 1.414 \times 1.732 \qquad \sqrt{2} \times \sqrt{3} = \sqrt{6}$

$\qquad \doteq 2.449 \qquad\qquad\qquad\qquad \doteq 2.449$

$\qquad\qquad \therefore \sqrt{2} \times \sqrt{3} \doteq 2.45$ to three significant digits.

Note that the first method required multiplying 1.414×1.732, while the second method required multiplying 2 by 3 which is much easier.

Radicals such as $3\sqrt{2}$, $2\sqrt{3}$ and $5\sqrt{3}$ are called *mixed radicals*, while radicals such as $\sqrt{12}$, $\sqrt{18}$, and $\sqrt{45}$ are called *entire radicals*.

EXAMPLE 2. *Express (a)* $5\sqrt{2}$ *(b)* $4\sqrt{5}$ *as entire radicals.*

Solution

(a) $5\sqrt{2} = \sqrt{25} \times \sqrt{2} \qquad\qquad$ (b) $4\sqrt{5} = \sqrt{16} \times \sqrt{5}$

$\qquad\quad = \sqrt{25 \times 2} \qquad\qquad\qquad\qquad = \sqrt{16 \times 5}$

$\qquad\quad = \sqrt{50} \qquad\qquad\qquad\qquad\qquad = \sqrt{80}$

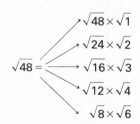

EXAMPLE 3. *Express (a)* $\sqrt{27}$, *(b)* $\sqrt{48}$ *as mixed radicals in simplest form.*

Solution

A radical is in *simplest* form when it has the smallest possible number under the radical sign.

(a) $\sqrt{27} = \sqrt{9} \times \sqrt{3} \qquad\qquad$ (b) $\sqrt{48} = \sqrt{16} \times \sqrt{3}$

$\qquad\quad = 3\sqrt{3} \qquad\qquad\qquad\qquad\qquad = 4\sqrt{3}$

EXAMPLE 4. *Simplify* (a) $3\sqrt{2} \times 2\sqrt{7}$
(b) $2\sqrt{5} \times 3\sqrt{15}$

Solution

(a) $3\sqrt{2} \times 2\sqrt{7} = \boxed{3 \times 2 \times \sqrt{2} \times \sqrt{7}}$
$= 6\sqrt{14}$

these steps may be done mentally.

(b) $2\sqrt{5} \times 3\sqrt{15} = 6\sqrt{75}$
$= \boxed{6 \times \sqrt{25} \times \sqrt{3}}$
$= 6 \times 5 \times \sqrt{3}$
$= 30\sqrt{3}$

EXAMPLE 5. *Simplify* (a) $\sqrt{9x^2y^4}$ (b) $\sqrt{25x^5y^3}$

Solution

(a) $\sqrt{9x^2y^4} = 3\,|x|\,y^2$ (b) $\sqrt{25x^5y^3} = 5x^2\,|y|\,\sqrt{xy}$

Note that absolute value bars, | |, are included to ensure that the simplified radical remains positive.

EXERCISE 3-1

A **1.** Evaluate:
(a) $\sqrt{16}$ (b) $\sqrt{49}$ (c) $\sqrt{81}$ (d) $\sqrt{100}$ (e) $\sqrt{121}$
(f) $\sqrt{\dfrac{4}{9}}$ (g) $\sqrt{\dfrac{36}{25}}$ (h) $\sqrt{\dfrac{64}{81}}$ (i) $\sqrt{\dfrac{36}{49}}$ (j) $\sqrt{\dfrac{1}{16}}$
(k) $\sqrt{196}$ (l) $\sqrt{289}$ (m) $\sqrt{0.04}$ (n) $\sqrt{441}$ (o) $\sqrt{0.0009}$

2. Simplify:
(a) $\sqrt{3} \times \sqrt{2}$ (b) $\sqrt{6} \times \sqrt{11}$ (c) $\sqrt{3} \times \sqrt{5}$ (d) $\sqrt{5} \times \sqrt{7}$
(e) $\sqrt{11} \times \sqrt{7}$ (f) $\sqrt{5} \times \sqrt{6}$ (g) $\sqrt{6} \times \sqrt{7}$ (h) $\sqrt{2} \times \sqrt{11}$
(i) $\sqrt{11} \times \sqrt{13}$ (j) $\sqrt{5} \times \sqrt{17}$ (k) $\sqrt{13} \times \sqrt{3}$ (l) $\sqrt{6} \times \sqrt{6}$

3. Simplify:
(a) $3\sqrt{2} \times 2\sqrt{5}$ (b) $5\sqrt{7} \times \sqrt{3}$ (c) $2\sqrt{5} \times 2\sqrt{3}$
(d) $6\sqrt{5} \times 7\sqrt{2}$ (e) $2\sqrt{5} \times 3\sqrt{6}$ (f) $4\sqrt{7} \times 2\sqrt{5}$
(g) $6\sqrt{2} \times 2\sqrt{5}$ (h) $2\sqrt{2} \times 3\sqrt{3}$ (i) $3\sqrt{2} \times 5\sqrt{3}$
(j) $4\sqrt{3} \times 2\sqrt{7}$ (k) $6\sqrt{5} \times 5\sqrt{2}$ (l) $2\sqrt{3} \times 4\sqrt{3}$

B **4.** Change to mixed radicals in simplest form:
(a) $\sqrt{12}$ (b) $\sqrt{18}$ (c) $\sqrt{20}$ (d) $\sqrt{32}$
(e) $\sqrt{45}$ (f) $\sqrt{75}$ (g) $\sqrt{50}$ (h) $\sqrt{1024}$
(i) $\sqrt{72}$ (j) $\sqrt{68}$ (k) $\sqrt{200}$ (l) $\sqrt{24}$
(m) $\sqrt{98}$ (n) $\sqrt{28}$ (o) $\sqrt{300}$ (p) $\sqrt{8}$

5. Change to entire radicals:
(a) $2\sqrt{3}$ (b) $5\sqrt{2}$ (c) $3\sqrt{5}$ (d) $5\sqrt{3}$
(e) $3\sqrt{11}$ (f) $5\sqrt{10}$ (g) $10\sqrt{3}$ (h) $2\sqrt{7}$
(i) $5\sqrt{8}$ (j) $3\sqrt{14}$ (k) $6\sqrt{7}$ (l) $11\sqrt{2}$
(m) $25\sqrt{3}$ (n) $20\sqrt{2}$ (o) $4\sqrt{10}$ (p) $5\sqrt{7}$

51	4	63	3
97	2	84	
87	1	72	5

Determine the pattern. Find the missing number.

6. Simplify:

(a) $\sqrt{2}\times\sqrt{6}$ (b) $\sqrt{10}\times\sqrt{6}$ (c) $\sqrt{7}\times\sqrt{14}$

(d) $\sqrt{3}\times\sqrt{6}$ (e) $\sqrt{15}\times\sqrt{5}$ (f) $\sqrt{5}\times\sqrt{50}$

(g) $\sqrt{5}\times2\sqrt{3}$ (h) $5\sqrt{2}\times3\sqrt{3}$ (i) $2\sqrt{10}\times5\sqrt{3}$

(j) $5\sqrt{7}\times2\sqrt{14}$ (k) $5\sqrt{3}\times2\sqrt{15}$ (l) $3\sqrt{3}\times2\sqrt{12}$

(m) $\sqrt{6}\times\sqrt{3}\times\sqrt{2}$ (n) $\sqrt{5}\times\sqrt{2}\times\sqrt{15}$

(o) $\sqrt{10}\times\sqrt{15}\times\sqrt{6}$ (p) $3\sqrt{2}\times2\sqrt{6}\times\sqrt{3}$

(q) $3\sqrt{5}\times2\sqrt{3}\times3\sqrt{5}$ (r) $3\sqrt{6}\times2\sqrt{3}\times4\sqrt{2}$

C   **7.** Simplify: ($x\in R$)

(a) $\sqrt{25x^4}$ (b) $\sqrt{49x^2}$ (c) $\sqrt{x^3x^5}$ (d) $5\sqrt{x^4}$

(e) $3x\sqrt{25x^2}$ (f) $\sqrt{5x}\sqrt{6x^2}$ (g) $\sqrt{5x^3}\sqrt{15x^2}$

(h) $\sqrt{(6x)(3x^3)}$ (i) $\sqrt{45x^3}$ (j) $\sqrt{18x^4}$

(k) $\sqrt{20x}$ (l) $3x\sqrt{3x^4}$ (m) $3x\sqrt{3x^3}$ (n) $\sqrt{2x}\sqrt{3x}$

(o) $\sqrt{8x^3}$ (p) $\sqrt{27x^6}$ (q) $\sqrt{125x^4}$ (r) $\sqrt{64x^5}$

(s) $\sqrt{99x^3}$ (t) $\sqrt{120x^7}$

Any natural number can be written as the sum at most 4 perfect squares.

$46 = 5^2 + 4 + 2^2 + 1^2$

$182 = 10^2 + 9^2 + 1^2$

Write 128, 213, and 318 as the sum of at most 4 perfect squares.

3.2 ADDITION AND SUBTRACTION OF RADICALS

Like terms such as $2a$ and $5a$ can be added using the distributive law

$$2a + 5a = \boxed{(2+5)a} = 7a$$

Radicals such as $5\sqrt{2}$ and $3\sqrt{2}$ are called *like radicals* and can be added in the same way.

$$5\sqrt{2} + 3\sqrt{2} = \boxed{(5+3)\sqrt{2}} = 8\sqrt{2}$$

EXAMPLE 1. *Simplify* (a) $5\sqrt{7} + 4\sqrt{7} - 3\sqrt{7}$

(b) $4\sqrt{5} + 7\sqrt{13} + 3\sqrt{5} - 2\sqrt{13}$

Solution

(a) $5\sqrt{7} + 4\sqrt{7} - 3\sqrt{7} = \boxed{(5+4-3)\sqrt{7}} = 6\sqrt{7}$

(b) $4\sqrt{5} + 7\sqrt{13} + 3\sqrt{5} - 2\sqrt{13} = \boxed{4\sqrt{5} + 3\sqrt{5} + 7\sqrt{13} - 2\sqrt{13}}$

$$= 7\sqrt{5} + 5\sqrt{13}$$

Note that $\sqrt{5}$ and $\sqrt{13}$ are not added because they are not like radicals.

EXAMPLE 2. *Simplify* $\sqrt{5} + \sqrt{45} - \sqrt{20}$

Solution

$$\sqrt{5} + \sqrt{45} - \sqrt{20} = \sqrt{5} + 3\sqrt{5} - 2\sqrt{5}$$
$$= 2\sqrt{5}$$

It is necessary to change all radicals to mixed radicals in simplest form before adding and subtracting, since unlike radicals cannot be added or subtracted.

EXERCISE 3-2

A **1.** Simplify:
(a) $3\sqrt{2}+5\sqrt{2}$ (b) $7\sqrt{3}-4\sqrt{3}$ (c) $6\sqrt{11}+7\sqrt{11}$
(d) $3\sqrt{5}+4\sqrt{5}$ (e) $2\sqrt{13}+7\sqrt{13}$ (f) $12\sqrt{5}-7\sqrt{5}$
(g) $5\sqrt{2}+\sqrt{2}$ (h) $\sqrt{3}+6\sqrt{3}$ (i) $7\sqrt{2}-\sqrt{2}$
(j) $8\sqrt{3}+10\sqrt{3}$ (k) $\sqrt{7}+\sqrt{7}$ (l) $2\sqrt{2}-\sqrt{2}$
(m) $\sqrt{2}+7\sqrt{2}+3\sqrt{2}$ (n) $5\sqrt{3}+7\sqrt{3}-4\sqrt{3}$

2. Simplify:
(a) $5\sqrt{2}-3\sqrt{2}+7\sqrt{11}+2\sqrt{11}$ (b) $3\sqrt{13}+2\sqrt{7}+11\sqrt{13}-5\sqrt{7}$
(c) $6\sqrt{3}+4\sqrt{3}-5\sqrt{2}+7\sqrt{2}$ (d) $5\sqrt{7}+2\sqrt{11}-3\sqrt{11}-\sqrt{7}$
(e) $4\sqrt{5}-2\sqrt{7}+3\sqrt{7}-\sqrt{5}$ (f) $5\sqrt{6}+2\sqrt{3}-5\sqrt{6}+4\sqrt{3}$
(g) $3\sqrt{10}+5\sqrt{10}-7$ (h) $12-6\sqrt{11}-5\sqrt{11}+4$

B **3.** Simplify:
(a) $\sqrt{3}+5+3\sqrt{3}-2$ (b) $6\sqrt{3}-2+4\sqrt{3}+7$
(c) $7+3\sqrt{5}-2\sqrt{5}+4$ (d) $3\sqrt{5}+2\sqrt{3}+3\sqrt{3}+4\sqrt{5}$
(e) $3\sqrt{7}+3-2\sqrt{7}-3$ (f) $5\sqrt{2}-4-7-3\sqrt{2}$

4. Simplify:
(a) $\sqrt{12}+\sqrt{27}$ (b) $\sqrt{18}-\sqrt{8}$
(c) $\sqrt{32}+\sqrt{50}$ (d) $\sqrt{50}-\sqrt{18}$
(e) $\sqrt{98}-\sqrt{8}$ (f) $\sqrt{75}-\sqrt{48}$
(g) $2\sqrt{8}+\sqrt{18}+4\sqrt{2}$ (h) $5\sqrt{12}-3\sqrt{12}-2\sqrt{3}$
(i) $\sqrt{8}-6\sqrt{2}+\sqrt{24}$ (j) $\sqrt{50}+3\sqrt{18}-10\sqrt{2}$
(k) $2\sqrt{48}+5\sqrt{27}$ (l) $\sqrt{98}-5\sqrt{2}$
(m) $6\sqrt{8}+7\sqrt{32}-5\sqrt{72}$ (n) $3\sqrt{8}+2\sqrt{2}$
(o) $3\sqrt{8}-2\sqrt{98}+\sqrt{50}$ (p) $3\sqrt{72}+2\sqrt{75}-3\sqrt{27}$

C **5.** Simplify:
(a) $5\sqrt{x}+2\sqrt{x}-4\sqrt{x}$ (b) $7\sqrt{a}+3\sqrt{a}-6\sqrt{a}$ $5\sqrt{x}+3\sqrt{x}=(5+3)\sqrt{x}=8\sqrt{x}$
(c) $5\sqrt{9x}+3\sqrt{4x}$ (d) $2\sqrt{36a}-5\sqrt{4a}$
(e) $4\sqrt{2x}-\sqrt{8x}$ (f) $2\sqrt{3a}-\sqrt{12a}$
(g) $3\sqrt{x^3}+5\sqrt{x^3}$ (h) $3\sqrt{8x^3}-2\,|x|\,\sqrt{2x}$

3.3 MULTIPLICATION OF BINOMIAL RADICAL EXPRESSIONS

Binomial radicals can be multiplied by applying the distributive property.

EXAMPLE 1. *Simplify* (a) $\sqrt{3}(\sqrt{2}-4)$
             (b) $3\sqrt{5}(\sqrt{2}+3\sqrt{10})$

Solution
(a) $\sqrt{3}(\sqrt{2}-4)$ (b) $3\sqrt{5}(\sqrt{2}+3\sqrt{10})$ $a(b+c)=ab+ac$

$=\sqrt{3}(\sqrt{2}-4)$ $=3\sqrt{10}+9\sqrt{50}$
$=\sqrt{6}-4\sqrt{3}$ $=3\sqrt{10}+45\sqrt{2}$

radicals   59

EXAMPLE 2. *Simplify* $(5\sqrt{2}-4\sqrt{3})(3\sqrt{2}+2\sqrt{3})$

Solution

$(a+b)^2 = a^2 + 2ab + b^2$

$$\begin{aligned}(5\sqrt{2}-4\sqrt{3})(3\sqrt{2}+2\sqrt{3}) &= 15(2)+10\sqrt{6}-12\sqrt{6}-8(3)\\ &= 30-2\sqrt{6}-24\\ &= 6-2\sqrt{6}\end{aligned}$$

EXAMPLE 3. *Simplify* $(3\sqrt{6}-2\sqrt{3})^2$

Solution

$$\begin{aligned}(3\sqrt{6}-2\sqrt{3})^2 &= (3\sqrt{6}-2\sqrt{3})(3\sqrt{6}-2\sqrt{3})\\ &= 9(6)-6\sqrt{18}-6\sqrt{18}+4(3)\\ &= 54-12\sqrt{18}+12\\ &= 66-12(3\sqrt{2})\\ &= 66-36\sqrt{2}\end{aligned}$$

EXAMPLE 4. *Simplify* $(2\sqrt{5}+\sqrt{7})(2\sqrt{5}-\sqrt{7})$

Solution

$(a+b)(a-b) = a^2 - b^2$

$$\begin{aligned}(2\sqrt{5}+\sqrt{7})(2\sqrt{5}-\sqrt{7}) &= 4(5)-2\sqrt{35}+2\sqrt{35}-7\\ &= 20-7\\ &= 13\end{aligned}$$

Radical expressions such as $(2\sqrt{5}+\sqrt{7})$ and $(2\sqrt{5}-\sqrt{7})$ give a product which is a rational number and are called conjugate expressions.

EXERCISE 3-3

A **1.** Simplify
(a) $\sqrt{3}(\sqrt{5}+\sqrt{2})$ (b) $\sqrt{7}(2+\sqrt{3})$
(c) $4(3\sqrt{2}-2\sqrt{5})$ (d) $2\sqrt{2}(1-\sqrt{2})$
(e) $\sqrt{3}(\sqrt{2}+\sqrt{6})$ (f) $3\sqrt{2}(\sqrt{2}+\sqrt{3})$
(g) $2\sqrt{3}(\sqrt{6}-1)$ (h) $\sqrt{3}(2+3\sqrt{2})$

2. State the conjugate of
(a) $3+\sqrt{2}$ (b) $\sqrt{5}-\sqrt{3}$ (c) $2\sqrt{3}+2\sqrt{5}$
(d) $3\sqrt{7}-\sqrt{6}$ (e) $2\sqrt{5}+3$ (f) $3\sqrt{5}-1$
(g) $2\sqrt{5}+\sqrt{3}$ (h) $3\sqrt{2}-\sqrt{5}$ (i) $2\sqrt{7}+\sqrt{5}$

Use $+, -, \times, \div, (\ )$ to make a true statement.

$4\ 2\ 7\ 3 = 4\ 1\ 6\ 6$

B **3.** Multiply the following binomial radicals.
(a) $(\sqrt{3}+2)(\sqrt{3}+4)$ (b) $(2\sqrt{3}+\sqrt{5})(\sqrt{3}+\sqrt{5})$
(c) $(\sqrt{3}+\sqrt{2})(2\sqrt{3}-\sqrt{2})$ (d) $(3\sqrt{5}+2)(2\sqrt{5}-3)$
(e) $(5\sqrt{7}-\sqrt{2})(\sqrt{7}-\sqrt{2})$ (f) $(3\sqrt{2}+\sqrt{5})(\sqrt{2}-3\sqrt{5})$
(g) $(5\sqrt{3}+\sqrt{7})(2\sqrt{3}-2\sqrt{7})$ (h) $(3\sqrt{5}+4)(2\sqrt{5}-3)$

4. Square the following binomial radicals.
(a) $(\sqrt{3}+\sqrt{2})^2$ (b) $(\sqrt{5}-\sqrt{2})^2$
(c) $(\sqrt{6}-\sqrt{3})^2$ (d) $(\sqrt{7}-\sqrt{6})^2$
(e) $(3\sqrt{2}+2)^2$ (f) $(8\sqrt{2}-5\sqrt{6})^2$

(g) $(4\sqrt{3}-\sqrt{2})^2$ (h) $(6\sqrt{10}+2\sqrt{3})^2$
(i) $3(2\sqrt{2}+3)^2$ (j) $4(2\sqrt{5}-3)^2$

5. Multiply the following binomial radicals.
(a) $(\sqrt{3}-\sqrt{2})(\sqrt{3}+\sqrt{2})$ (b) $(\sqrt{3}-2)(\sqrt{3}+2)$
(c) $(2\sqrt{5}+\sqrt{2})(2\sqrt{5}-\sqrt{2})$ (d) $(2\sqrt{3}+2)(2\sqrt{3}-2)$
(e) $(\sqrt{7}+2\sqrt{3})(\sqrt{7}-2\sqrt{3})$ (f) $(4\sqrt{5}-\sqrt{2})(4\sqrt{5}+\sqrt{2})$
(g) $(3\sqrt{6}+2)(3\sqrt{6}-2)$ (h) $(4\sqrt{7}-3\sqrt{2})(4\sqrt{7}+3\sqrt{2})$

C **6.** Simplify the following:
(a) $(2\sqrt{3}+2)(3\sqrt{3}-1)+(2\sqrt{3}+1)^2$
(b) $(3+\sqrt{2})(2-2\sqrt{2})-(5\sqrt{2}+1)(5\sqrt{2}-3)$
(c) $(\sqrt{5}+\sqrt{3})(\sqrt{5}-\sqrt{3})-(\sqrt{10}+2)(\sqrt{10}-2)$

7. Simplify the following $(x \geqq 0)$:
(a) $2\sqrt{x}(3\sqrt{x}+5)$ (b) $(\sqrt{x}+5)(\sqrt{x}-5)$
(c) $3\sqrt{x}(x+\sqrt{x})$ (d) $(\sqrt{x}-3)^2$
(e) $\sqrt{3x}(\sqrt{2x}+\sqrt{x})$ (f) $(3\sqrt{x}+1)(3\sqrt{x}-1)$
(g) $(4\sqrt{x}-2)^2$ (h) $(x-\sqrt{x})(x+\sqrt{x})$

3.4 DIVISION OF RADICAL EXPRESSIONS

Division is the inverse operation of multiplication, so that if

$$\sqrt{3}\times\sqrt{5}=\sqrt{15} \quad \text{then} \quad \frac{\sqrt{15}}{\sqrt{5}}=\sqrt{3}$$

The result $\dfrac{\sqrt{15}}{\sqrt{5}}=\sqrt{3}=\sqrt{\dfrac{15}{3}}$ can be generalized to

$$\boxed{\frac{\sqrt{ab}}{\sqrt{b}}=\sqrt{\frac{ab}{b}}=\sqrt{a}, \quad b\neq 0}$$

$$\frac{\sqrt{ab}}{\sqrt{b}}=\frac{\sqrt{a}\sqrt{b}}{\sqrt{b}}$$
$$=\sqrt{a}$$

EXAMPLE 1. *Simplify* (a) $\dfrac{\sqrt{14}}{\sqrt{2}}$ (b) $\dfrac{24\sqrt{21}}{6\sqrt{3}}$

Solution

(a) $\dfrac{\sqrt{14}}{\sqrt{2}}=\boxed{\sqrt{\dfrac{14}{2}}}=\sqrt{7}$

(b) $\dfrac{24\sqrt{21}}{6\sqrt{3}}=\boxed{\dfrac{24}{6}\sqrt{\dfrac{21}{3}}}=4\sqrt{7}$

EXAMPLE 2. Find $\dfrac{\sqrt{5}}{\sqrt{2}}$ correct to three figures:

Solution

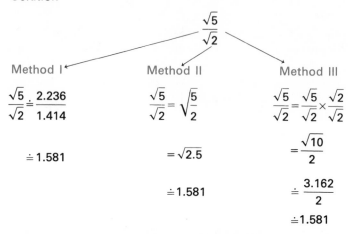

$$\frac{\sqrt{5}}{\sqrt{2}}$$

Method I

$$\frac{\sqrt{5}}{\sqrt{2}} \doteq \frac{2.236}{1.414}$$

$$\doteq 1.581$$

Method II

$$\frac{\sqrt{5}}{\sqrt{2}} = \sqrt{\frac{5}{2}}$$

$$= \sqrt{2.5}$$

$$\doteq 1.581$$

Method III

$$\frac{\sqrt{5}}{\sqrt{2}} = \frac{\sqrt{5}}{\sqrt{2}} \times \frac{\sqrt{2}}{\sqrt{2}}$$

$$= \frac{\sqrt{10}}{2}$$

$$\doteq \frac{3.162}{2}$$

$$\doteq 1.581$$

In method III, it was possible to change $\sqrt{2}$ to 2 by multiplying numerator and denominator by $\sqrt{2}$. This process is called *rationalizing the denominator*.

EXAMPLE 3. *Find the value of* $\dfrac{15\sqrt{7}}{2\sqrt{3}}$ *correct to two decimal places by first rationalizing the denominator.*

Solution

$$\frac{a}{b} = \frac{ax}{bx}$$

$$\frac{15\sqrt{7}}{2\sqrt{3}} = \frac{15\sqrt{7}}{2\sqrt{3}} \times \frac{\sqrt{3}}{\sqrt{3}}$$

$$= \frac{15\sqrt{21}}{2(3)}$$

$$= \frac{5\sqrt{21}}{2}$$

$$\doteq \frac{5 \times 4.583}{2} \doteq \frac{22.91}{2} \doteq 11.46$$

EXAMPLE 4. *Rationalize the denominator of* $\dfrac{4}{\sqrt{11}-\sqrt{3}}$

Solution

$$\frac{4}{\sqrt{11}-\sqrt{3}} = \frac{4}{\sqrt{11}-\sqrt{3}} \times \frac{\sqrt{11}+\sqrt{3}}{\sqrt{11}+\sqrt{3}}$$

$$= \frac{4(\sqrt{11}+\sqrt{3})}{11-3}$$

$$= \frac{4(\sqrt{11}+\sqrt{3})}{8}$$

$$= \frac{\sqrt{11}+\sqrt{3}}{2}$$

We multiply numerator and denominator by the conjugate radical.

$$(\sqrt{a}+\sqrt{b})(\sqrt{a}-\sqrt{b}) = a - b$$

EXERCISE 3-4

A **1.** Simplify.

(a) $\dfrac{\sqrt{14}}{\sqrt{7}}$ (b) $\dfrac{\sqrt{18}}{\sqrt{3}}$ (c) $\dfrac{27\sqrt{15}}{3\sqrt{5}}$ (d) $\dfrac{\sqrt{28}}{\sqrt{7}}$

(e) $\dfrac{\sqrt{72}}{\sqrt{24}}$ (f) $\dfrac{3\sqrt{8}}{\sqrt{2}}$ (g) $\dfrac{\sqrt{50}}{\sqrt{2}}$ (h) $\dfrac{3\sqrt{75}}{\sqrt{3}}$

B **2.** Find the following to three figure accuracy.

(a) $\dfrac{\sqrt{42}}{\sqrt{6}}$ (b) $\dfrac{\sqrt{12}}{\sqrt{6}}$ (c) $\dfrac{\sqrt{42}}{\sqrt{7}}$

(d) $\dfrac{15\sqrt{20}}{\sqrt{2}}$ (e) $\dfrac{20\sqrt{15}}{\sqrt{3}}$ (f) $\dfrac{\sqrt{36}}{\sqrt{3}}$

(g) $\dfrac{\sqrt{26}}{\sqrt{2}}$ (h) $\dfrac{3\sqrt{50}}{\sqrt{10}}$ (i) $\dfrac{2\sqrt{75}}{\sqrt{15}}$

(j) $\dfrac{\sqrt{18}+\sqrt{12}}{\sqrt{3}}$ (k) $\dfrac{15-\sqrt{75}}{5}$ (l) $\dfrac{9-\sqrt{45}}{3}$

3. Rationalize the denominator:

(a) $\dfrac{\sqrt{5}}{\sqrt{3}}$ (b) $\dfrac{2}{\sqrt{2}}$ (c) $\dfrac{3\sqrt{5}}{2\sqrt{6}}$ (d) $\dfrac{4\sqrt{7}}{5\sqrt{2}}$

(e) $\dfrac{3\sqrt{7}}{2\sqrt{3}}$ (f) $\dfrac{\sqrt{3}}{\sqrt{5}}$ (g) $\dfrac{3\sqrt{7}}{4\sqrt{2}}$ (h) $\dfrac{2\sqrt{3}}{\sqrt{6}}$

(i) $\dfrac{\sqrt{2}+\sqrt{3}}{\sqrt{5}}$ (j) $\dfrac{\sqrt{7}-4}{2\sqrt{3}}$ (k) $\dfrac{2\sqrt{5}-\sqrt{3}}{2\sqrt{3}}$ (l) $\dfrac{\sqrt{5}+\sqrt{7}-\sqrt{2}}{2\sqrt{2}}$

4. Find the value of each of the following to three figure accuracy by first rationalizing the denominator.

(a) $\dfrac{2}{\sqrt{3}}$ (b) $\dfrac{5}{\sqrt{7}}$ (c) $\dfrac{\sqrt{6}}{\sqrt{5}}$

(d) $\dfrac{2\sqrt{3}}{\sqrt{7}}$ (e) $\dfrac{\sqrt{3}}{2\sqrt{5}}$ (f) $\dfrac{3\sqrt{5}}{4\sqrt{2}}$

(g) $\dfrac{3\sqrt{6}}{2\sqrt{7}}$ (h) $\dfrac{5\sqrt{3}}{3\sqrt{7}}$ (i) $\dfrac{3\sqrt{21}}{\sqrt{5}}$

(j) $\dfrac{7\sqrt{2}}{2\sqrt{11}}$ (k) $\dfrac{5\sqrt{3}}{4\sqrt{7}}$ (l) $\dfrac{7\sqrt{7}}{2\sqrt{2}}$

5. Simplify by first rationalizing the denominator.

(a) $\dfrac{1}{\sqrt{5}-\sqrt{3}}$ (b) $\dfrac{1}{\sqrt{3}+\sqrt{2}}$ (c) $\dfrac{\sqrt{3}}{\sqrt{5}+\sqrt{2}}$

(d) $\dfrac{3}{\sqrt{2}-1}$ (e) $\dfrac{4}{\sqrt{6}-\sqrt{2}}$ (f) $\dfrac{7}{2\sqrt{5}+\sqrt{2}}$

(g) $\dfrac{5}{4-\sqrt{3}}$ (h) $\dfrac{3+\sqrt{2}}{3-\sqrt{2}}$ (i) $\dfrac{5+3\sqrt{3}}{5-2\sqrt{3}}$

(j) $\dfrac{3\sqrt{2}}{2\sqrt{2}-3}$ (k) $\dfrac{\sqrt{7}+\sqrt{5}}{\sqrt{7}-\sqrt{5}}$ (l) $\dfrac{3\sqrt{5}-2\sqrt{3}}{3\sqrt{5}+2\sqrt{3}}$

C   **6.** Rationalize the denominator in each of the following. (All variables are positive real numbers.)

(a) $\dfrac{1}{\sqrt{a}-\sqrt{b}}$ (b) $\dfrac{2}{\sqrt{x}+2}$ (c) $\dfrac{\sqrt{a}-\sqrt{b}}{\sqrt{a}+\sqrt{b}}$

(d) $\dfrac{3\sqrt{x}}{2\sqrt{x}-3}$ (e) $\dfrac{\sqrt{x}}{\sqrt{x+1}+2}$ (f) $\dfrac{\sqrt{a}+\sqrt{a+b}}{\sqrt{a}-\sqrt{a-b}}$

7. Rationalize the denominator in each of the following and simplify.

(a) $\dfrac{3}{(\sqrt{2}+\sqrt{3})-\sqrt{5}}$ (b) $\dfrac{3\sqrt{2}-\sqrt{8}+\sqrt{18}}{(\sqrt{6}+\sqrt{3})-\sqrt{2}}$

8. Solve the following equations, giving final answers with rational denominators.

(a) $3x=\sqrt{2}$ (b) $x\sqrt{3}=\sqrt{2}$ (c) $3x\sqrt{5}=\sqrt{10}$

(d) $x(\sqrt{2}-1)=3$ (e) $x(\sqrt{5}-\sqrt{2})=3$ (f) $2x\sqrt{3}-\sqrt{2}=x+2$

Simplify.

$$\dfrac{1}{1+\dfrac{1}{1+\dfrac{1}{1+1}}}$$

3.5 APPROXIMATIONS OF RADICALS (SQUARE ROOT)

When radicals appear in practical problems it is often necessary to convert them to decimal approximations so that they can be used. While $\sqrt{2}$ will not appear on a scale, an approximation to two figures, 1.4, can be located ($\sqrt{2}=1.4142\ldots$). Square roots of numbers can be found by a variety of methods such as a square root table, Newton's method, a formal method, slide rule, or calculator.

EXAMPLE 1. *Evaluate (a) $\sqrt{26.01}$ by Newton's method*
(b) $\sqrt{2.197}$ by a formal method

TWO
SEVEN
ELEVEN
TWENTY

Each letter represents a different digit in this addition

Solutions

(a)
Step 1 Estimate	Step 2 Divide	Step 3 Average	Step 4 Divide
$\sqrt{26.01} \doteq 5$	$\dfrac{26.01}{5}$ $\doteq 5.202$	$\dfrac{5+5.202}{2}$ $\doteq \dfrac{10.202}{2}$ $\doteq 5.101$	$\dfrac{26.01}{5.101}$ $\doteq 5.099$

When rounded off to three figures

$$5.101 \doteq 5.10 \quad \text{and} \quad 5.099 \doteq 5.10$$

$$\therefore \sqrt{26.01} \doteq 5.10 \text{ to three significant figures.}$$

(b) Step 1

```
    1.
1 | 2.19 70 00
    1
2 | 1
```

Step 2

```
      1.4
1 | 2.19 70 00
    1
 24 | 119
      96
 28 _| 23
```

Step 3

```
       1.4  8
1 | 2.19 70 00
    1
 24 | 119
      96
288 | 2370
     2304
       66
```

Step 4

```
        1.4  8  2
1 | 2.19 70 00
    1
 24 | 119
      96
288 | 2370
     2304
2962 | 6600
      5924
       676
```

$$\therefore \sqrt{2.197} \doteq 1.48 \text{ to three significant figures.}$$

EXAMPLE 2. *A ladder 20 m long leans against a wall with the foot of the ladder 20 m from the wall. How high up the wall will the ladder reach?*

Solution
Applying the Pythagorean relation,

$$h^2 + 2^2 = 6^2$$
$$h^2 + 4 = 36$$
$$h^2 = 32$$
$$h = \sqrt{32}$$
$$\doteq 5.657$$

the ladder will reach 5.657 m up the wall.

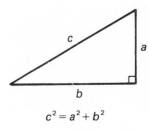

$$c^2 = a^2 + b^2$$

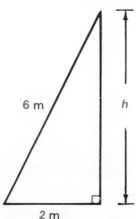

6 m   h

2 m

radicals   65

EXERCISE 3-5

Unless otherwise stated, give all answers to 3 significant figures.

B **1.** Evaluate by any method:

(a) $\sqrt{45}$ (b) $\sqrt{128}$ (c) $\sqrt{29}$ (d) $\sqrt{140}$

(e) $\sqrt{345}$ (f) $\sqrt{61.25}$ (g) $\sqrt{0.0345}$ (h) $\sqrt{0.002\,745}$

2. Determine the value of x in each of the following using the Pythagorean relationship.

(a)

(b)

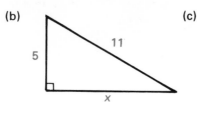

(c)

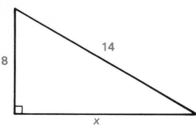

3. A 5 m ladder leans against a wall and the foot of the ladder is 2 m from the wall. Find the distance the ladder reaches up the wall.

4. Find the dimensions of a square whose area is 60 cm².

5. Find the length of the sides of a square having the same area as a rectangle with dimensions 4 cm by 7 cm.

6. The perimeter of a square can be found using the formula $P = 4\sqrt{A}$, where A is the area, and P the perimeter. Find the perimeter of a square having an area of 136 cm².

7. The period of a pendulum is given by the formula

$$T = 2\pi\sqrt{\frac{l}{9.8}}$$

where T is the period in seconds and l is the length of the pendulum in metres. Calculate the period when $\pi \doteq 3.14$ and the length is

(a) 19.6 m   (b) 0.98 m

8. The area of a triangle can be found using Heron's formula

$$A = \sqrt{s(s-a)(s-b)(s-c)}$$

where a, b, c are the lengths of the sides of the triangle and

$$s = \tfrac{1}{2}(a + b + c).$$

Calculate the area of the following triangles.

(a)

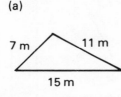

(b)

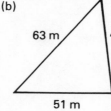

(c)

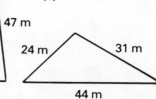

n	$\sqrt{n}$
1	1.000
2	1.414
3	1.732
4	2.000
5	2.236
6	2.449
7	2.645
8	2.828
9	3.000
10	3.162
11	3.316
12	3.464
13	3.605
14	3.741
15	3.872
16	4.000
17	4.123
18	4.242
19	4.358
20	4.472
21	4.582
22	4.690
23	4.795
24	4.898
25	5.000
26	5.099
27	5.196
28	5.291
29	5.385
30	5.477
31	5.567
32	5.656
33	5.744
34	5.830
35	5.916
36	6.000
37	6.082
38	6.164
39	6.244
40	6.324
41	6.403
42	6.480
43	6.557
44	6.633

9. A square has sides 7 cm long. Use the Pythagorean relation to find the length of a diagonal.

10. A rectangle is 5 cm by 7 cm. Find the length of a diagonal.

11. Find the diameter of a circle that will circumscribe a square with sides 3 cm.

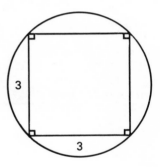

3

3

12. Find the length of a guy wire required to secure a 20 m tower 14 m from the base if you must add 4 m for fastening.

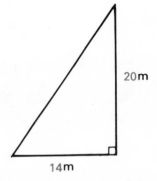

20 m

14 m

13. Three towns *A*, *B*, and *C* are situated so that *A* is 10 km east of *B* and *C* is 7 km north of *B*. Find the distance from *A* to *C*.

14. The greatest distance from which an object of height *h* can be seen from the same level is given by the formula

$$d = \sqrt{0.8\,h}$$

where *d* is in kilometres and *h* is in metres. From what distance can you see the light at the 300 m mark of the *CN* tower in Toronto?

15. A ladder 3.2 m from the foot of a wall reaches 8.4 m up the wall. How long is the ladder?

C   **16.** Find the altitude of an equilateral triangle with sides 8 cm.

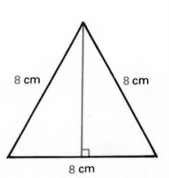

8 cm   8 cm

8 cm

17. Find the altitude to the shortest side of an isosceles triangle with sides 10 cm, 10 cm, and 6 cm.

REVIEW EXERCISE

B **1.** Express as entire radicals:

(a) $3\sqrt{2}$ (b) $5\sqrt{7}$ (c) $2\sqrt{11}$ ✓ (d) $7\sqrt{2}$ (e) $5\sqrt{5}$ ✓

2. Express as mixed radicals:

(a) $\sqrt{32}$ (b) $\sqrt{75}$ (c) $\sqrt{288}$ ✓ (d) $\sqrt{242}$ (e) $\sqrt{147}$ ✓

3. Simplify:

(a) $3\sqrt{5}\times 2\sqrt{10}$ (b) $6\sqrt{3}\times 2\sqrt{6}$ (c) $5\sqrt{2}\times 4\sqrt{6}$

(d) $2\sqrt{7}\times 3\sqrt{14}$ (e) $4\sqrt{6}\times 2\sqrt{12}$ (f) $3\sqrt{15}\times 2\sqrt{6}$

(g) $\dfrac{1}{2}\sqrt{\dfrac{2}{3}}\times\dfrac{1}{3}\sqrt{\dfrac{3}{4}}$ (h) $2\sqrt{\dfrac{14}{3}}\times 3\sqrt{\dfrac{3}{2}}$ (i) $3\sqrt{\dfrac{3}{8}}\times 2\sqrt{\dfrac{4}{9}}$

4. Expand:

(a) $\sqrt{3}(\sqrt{2}-5)$ (b) $2\sqrt{2}(3\sqrt{3}-5)$ (c) $\sqrt{5}(2\sqrt{3}-\sqrt{2})$

(d) $2\sqrt{2}(\sqrt{2}+1)$ (e) $5\sqrt{3}(\sqrt{6}-\sqrt{2})$ (f) $2\sqrt{3}(\sqrt{3}+\sqrt{6})$

5. Expand:

(a) $(\sqrt{3}+\sqrt{2})(\sqrt{3}-\sqrt{2})$ (b) $(\sqrt{5}+\sqrt{7})(\sqrt{5}+2\sqrt{7})$

(c) $(3\sqrt{3}+2)^2$ (d) $(5\sqrt{2}-3)^2$

(e) $(3\sqrt{3}-2)(3\sqrt{3}+2)$ (f) $(\sqrt{7}+\sqrt{5})(\sqrt{7}-\sqrt{5})$

6. Simplify:

(a) $\dfrac{\sqrt{18}}{\sqrt{3}}$ (b) $\dfrac{\sqrt{40}}{\sqrt{8}}$ (c) $\dfrac{3\sqrt{20}}{6\sqrt{5}}$ (d) $\dfrac{\sqrt{21}}{\sqrt{3}}$ (e) $\dfrac{\sqrt{200}}{\sqrt{2}}$

7. Simplify:

(a) $\sqrt{18}+\sqrt{32}-\sqrt{50}$

(b) $\sqrt{12}+\sqrt{27}+\sqrt{48}-\sqrt{75}$

(c) $3\sqrt{8}+2\sqrt{18}-\sqrt{32}$

(d) $3\sqrt{40}+2\sqrt{90}-\sqrt{1000}$

(e) $3\sqrt{150}+2\sqrt{24}-\sqrt{96}$

(f) $2\sqrt{20}-3\sqrt{125}+3\sqrt{80}$ ✓

(g) $3\sqrt{28}-2\sqrt{112}+4\sqrt{63}$ ✓

8. Simplify:

(a) $2\sqrt{12}+5\sqrt{2}+\sqrt{18}$

(b) $6\sqrt{27}-3\sqrt{12}+\sqrt{72}$

(c) $3\sqrt{8}+2\sqrt{27}-5\sqrt{12}+2\sqrt{32}$

(d) $3\sqrt{500}-10\sqrt{20}+4\sqrt{125}$

(e) $2\sqrt{2}+4\sqrt{4}+8\sqrt{8}$

9. Rationalize the denominator:

(a) $\dfrac{3}{\sqrt{2}}$ (b) $\dfrac{2\sqrt{5}}{\sqrt{2}}$ (c) $\dfrac{3\sqrt{7}}{\sqrt{3}}$ (d) $\dfrac{4}{\sqrt{6}}$

(e) $\dfrac{3\sqrt{5}}{\sqrt{10}}$ (f) $\dfrac{2\sqrt{7}}{\sqrt{14}}$ (g) $\dfrac{2\sqrt{3}}{\sqrt{5}}$ (h) $\dfrac{4\sqrt{3}}{\sqrt{8}}$

(i) $\dfrac{3}{\sqrt{5}+\sqrt{2}}$ (j) $\dfrac{4\sqrt{2}}{\sqrt{6}-\sqrt{5}}$ ✓ (k) $\dfrac{3\sqrt{2}}{3\sqrt{3}-1}$ ✓

(l) $\dfrac{5\sqrt{5}-\sqrt{2}}{\sqrt{3}}$ (m) $\dfrac{3\sqrt{7}-5\sqrt{2}}{2\sqrt{6}}$ ✓ (n) $\dfrac{3\sqrt{5}+6\sqrt{2}}{2\sqrt{3}}$

(o) $\dfrac{2\sqrt{5}+1}{2\sqrt{5}-1}$ (p) $\dfrac{3\sqrt{3}+\sqrt{2}}{\sqrt{3}+\sqrt{2}}$ ✓   (q) $\dfrac{5\sqrt{2}+\sqrt{7}}{3\sqrt{2}+\sqrt{7}}$

10. Evaluate correct to 2 digits using the square root table, by first rationalizing the denominator.

(a) $\dfrac{3}{\sqrt{5}}$ (b) $\dfrac{2\sqrt{7}}{\sqrt{3}}$ (c) $\dfrac{3\sqrt{5}}{\sqrt{15}}$ (d) $\dfrac{2\sqrt{7}}{\sqrt{2}}$ (e) $\dfrac{5}{\sqrt{10}}$

(f) $\dfrac{\sqrt{3}}{\sqrt{7}-2}$ (g) $\dfrac{2\sqrt{3}+\sqrt{5}}{2\sqrt{3}-\sqrt{5}}$ (h) $\dfrac{5\sqrt{2}-\sqrt{3}}{3\sqrt{2}+2\sqrt{3}}$

(i) $\dfrac{\sqrt{5}-\sqrt{2}}{\sqrt{7}}$ (j) $\dfrac{3\sqrt{2}-2}{\sqrt{2}}$ (k) $\dfrac{5\sqrt{3}+2\sqrt{3}-5\sqrt{2}}{\sqrt{6}}$

11. A 12 m ladder leans against a wall and reaches 10 m up the wall. How far is the foot of the ladder from the wall?

12. A boat sails 30 km north then 21 km east. How far is the boat from the starting point?

13. Find the diameter of the circle that will circumscribe a square 2 cm by 2 cm.

C   **14.** Express as mixed radicals.
(a) $\sqrt{36x}$ (b) $\sqrt{a^2 b}$ (c) $\sqrt{a^4 b^3}$ (d) $\sqrt{a^3 b^5}$

15. Simplify:
(a) $\sqrt{9x}+\sqrt{16x}-\sqrt{49x}$, $x>0$
(b) $2\sqrt{xy^2}-3y\sqrt{x}+2\sqrt{xy^2}$, $x,\ y>0$
(c) $3\sqrt{a^2 b}+2\sqrt{a^2 b}-5\sqrt{ab^2}$, $a,\ b>0$

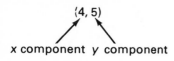

ordered pair
(4, 5)

x component y component

EXERCISE 1

State the co-ordinates of the points A to N.

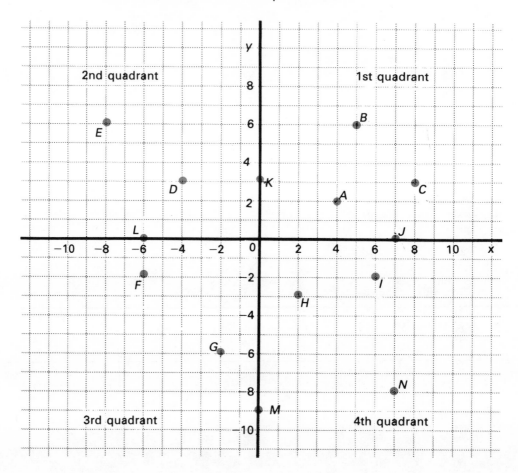

EXERCISE 2

BATTLESHIP

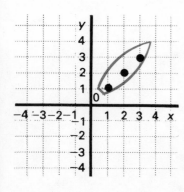

1. The game is played between two people.

2. Each player has two grids as shown in the diagram—one grid is used to record a player's shots. The other is used to record the positions of his own ships.

3. Ships may be entered in the grid horizontally, vertically or diagonally, but always in a straight line.

4. Each player enters
   1 battleship (5 points)
   1 aircraft carrier (4 points)
   1 cruiser (3 points)
   1 destroyer (2 points)

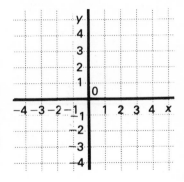

5. Players call shots alternately as ordered pairs. e.g. (2, −3). The opponent says "hit" or "miss" according to the result of the shot.

6. The opponent need not say what has been hit after a "hit" is called.

7. To sink a ship you must hit all dots of the ship. Once a ship has been sunk, the opponent must say what ship has been sunk.

8. The winner is the first player to sink all of the opponent's ships.

CHAPTER 4

Relations and Functions

Anyone who understands algebraic notation, reads at a glance in an equation results reached arithmetically only with great labour and pains.

A. Cournot

Rene Descartes (1596–1650)

Descartes was a French philosopher, scientist, and mathematician who spent much of his time travelling throughout Europe, sometimes as a soldier. He thought of many of his best ideas while lying in bed late in the morning. His most brilliant idea was probably inspired by a dream. The idea was to combine algebra and geometry—any algebraic equation represents a geometric curve and any curve is represented by an equation. This basic idea of analytic geometry (or coordinate geometry) was published in his book *La Geometrie* in 1637. Queen Christina of Sweden invited Descartes to join the Swedish court and, after she sent a battleship for him to make the journey, he finally accepted. However, the queen insisted on lessons from Descartes at 05:00. Getting up early, together with the cold Swedish winter, was too much for Descartes and he died after only a few weeks there.

4.1 BINARY RELATIONS

The study of how numbers relate to each other is the basis of mathematics. The following table shows the relationship between your distance from a storm and the time between the flash of lightning and the thunderclap.

$\frac{1}{2}$ is $\frac{1}{3}$ of it. What is it?

Time between Flash and Thunder (seconds)	Distance from Storm (metres)
1	330
2	660
3	990
4	1320
5	1650
6	1980

The above information could be displayed as a set of *ordered pairs*. This set of ordered pairs {(1, 330), (2, 660), (3, 990), (4, 1320), (5, 1650), (6, 1980)} is called a *binary relation*. The first component represents the time between flash and thunder and the second component the distance from the storm.

The pairs of numbers are called *ordered* pairs since the order of the components is important. We have decided to write the time in seconds first and the distance in metres second.

Using our definitions, what does (10, 3330) mean?

Does (15, 2) have any meaning in this example?

The set of first components of a relation is called the domain of the relation and the set of second components the range of the relation.

In our example the domain is the set {1, 2, 3, 4, 5, 6} and the range the set {330, 660, 990, 1320, 1650, 1980}

A relation is a set of ordered pairs.

EXAMPLE 1. *State the domain and the range of each of the following:*
(a) {(2, 3), (4, 4), (7, 6), (8, 9)}
(b) {(−7, 3), (2, 3), (5, 3)}
(c) {(−1, −12), (−1, 6), (−1, 9)}
(d) {(a, b), (d, q), (m, x)}

Bicycle

2

Binary

Solution
(a) Domain: {2, 4, 7, 8}
    Range: {3, 4, 6, 9}
(b) Domain: {−7, 2, 5}
    Range: {3}
(c) Domain: {−1}
    Range: {−12, 6, 9}
(d) Domain: {a, d, m}
    Range: {b, q, x}

EXERCISE 4-1

A **1.** A hockey team needs a minimum of 6 players.
(a) Complete the following table:

NUMBER OF HOCKEY TEAMS	MINIMUM NUMBER OF PLAYERS NEEDED
1	
2	
3	
4	
.	
.	
.	
50	

(b) State the domain of the relation.
(c) State the range of the relation.
(d) What does (25, 150) mean?

(e) What meaning, if any, do the following have: $(0, 0)$, $(3, 19\frac{1}{2})$, $(12, 4)$?

(f) Complete the following for the given relation: $(20, \blacksquare)$, $(31, \blacksquare)$, $(\blacksquare, 240)$.

2. State the domain and range of each of the following:

(a) $\{(5, 6), (7, 12), (8, 41)\}$

(b) $\{(-3, -7), (0, 6), (3, 11), (5, 20)\}$

(c) $\{(2, 7), (5, 7)\}$

(d) $\{(-6, 3), (-6, 8), (-6, 14)\}$

(e) $\{(a, b), (c, d), (e, f), (g, h)\}$

(f) $\{(3, 11), (4, 11), (7, 11), (15, 11)\}$

B　**3.** When Achilles had his famous race with a tortoise, he ran 400 m every minute.

(a) Complete the following table in your notebook:

Time (minutes)	Distance (metres)
1	
2	
	3600
	5400
20	

(b) What does $(6, 2400)$ mean?

(c) Complete the following for the given relation: $(\blacksquare, 3200)$, $(7, \blacksquare)$, $(11, \blacksquare)$.

(d) What meaning, if any, do the following have: $(5, 2000)$, $(2\frac{1}{2}, 1000)$, $(7, 100)$.

4. A mathematician has hired you to work for 14 d. The first day he will pay you \$1, the second day \$2, the third day \$4, and so on, always doubling the pay of the previous day.

(a) Complete the following table in your notebook.

DAY	PAY
1	1
2	2
3	4
4	8
.	
.	
.	
.	
14	

$1^3 + 5^3 + \blacksquare^3 + \blacksquare^3 = 13^3$

Find the missing digits.

Arrange 16 coins in 10 rows of 4 coins each.

(b) List the relation as a set of ordered pairs in the form (day, pay).
(c) List the elements of the domain.
(d) List the elements of the range.

5. As the number of sides of a polygon increases, so does the number of diagonals you are able to draw.
(a) Complete the following table.

NUMBER OF SIDES	NUMBER OF DIAGONALS
3	0
4	2
5	
6	
7	
8	

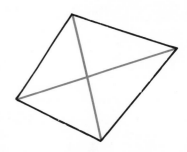

4 sides

2 diagonals

(b) List the relation as a set of ordered pairs: (number of sides, number of diagonals)
(c) List the elements of the domain.
(d) List the elements of the range.
(e) Why does $(4\frac{1}{2}, 3)$ have no meaning?
(f) What is the formula for determining the number of diagonals when you are given the number of sides the polygon has?

6. Bingo is a popular game where ordered pairs are used. For example the "caller" may call $(B, 7)$, which means "under the B, 7". All the possible ordered pairs the "caller" can call form a relation. What is the domain and range of this relation?

7. Baseball umpires use ordered pairs to umpire a game. "Three and two" may be written as $(3, 2)$ and means "3 balls, 2 strikes". What is the domain and range of the umpire's calls?

C **8.** A circle may be cut into a maximum of 2 pieces with one straight cut. Two straight cuts will produce 4 pieces (cuts do not have to pass through the centre).
(a) Complete the following table.

NUMBER OF CUTS	MAXIMUM NUMBER OF PIECES
0	1
1	2
2	4
3	
4	
5	

If it takes 10 min to fill a tub and 15 min to empty it, how long will it take to fill the tub when the plug is pulled?

(b) List the relation as a set of ordered pairs, (number of cuts, number of pieces).
(c) List the elements of the domain.

relations and functions 75

(d) List the elements of the range.

(e) Why will $(3\frac{1}{2}, \blacksquare)$ have no meaning?

(f) What is the maximum number of pieces you will get with 6 cuts?

(g) The formula for determining the maximum number of pieces when you are given the number of cuts is $\frac{1}{2}(n^2 + n + 2)$.

4.2 CARTESIAN PRODUCT

In the previous section, ordered pairs were generated from practical situations. Sets of ordered pairs may also be derived from 2 sets.

If $A = \{1, 2, 3\}$ and $B = \{6, 7\}$ then $A \times B$ (read "A cross B") is defined as $\{(1, 6), (1, 7), (2, 6), (2, 7), (3, 6), (3, 7)\}$. The first component of the ordered pair is selected from A and the second from B. This set is known as the *Cartesian Product* of A and B.

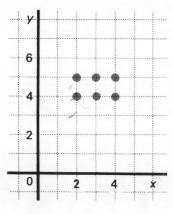

$$A \times B = \{(x, y) \mid x \in A, y \in B\}$$

EXAMPLE 1. *Given $S = \{4, 5\}$ and $T = \{2, 3, 4\}$, list and graph the elements of*

(a) $T \times S$

(b) $T \times T$

(c) $S \times T$

Solution

(a) $T \times S = \{(2, 4), (2, 5), (3, 4), (3, 5), (4, 4), (4, 5)\}$

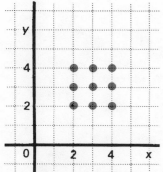

(b) $T \times T = \{(2, 2), (2, 3), (2, 4), (3, 2), (3, 3), (3, 4), (4, 2), (4, 3), (4, 4)\}$

(c) $S \times T = \{(4, 2), (4, 3), (4, 4), (5, 2), (5, 3), (5, 4)\}$

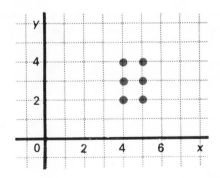

Note that $S \times T \neq T \times S.$

EXERCISE 4-2

A **1.** If $A = \{2, 3, 4, 5\}$ and $B = \{5, 6\}$, which of the following belong to $A \times B$?
(a) $(2, 6)$　　　(b) $(6, 3)$　　　(c) $(4, 4)$　　　(d) $(5, 5)$
2. If $M = \{0, 1\}$ and $P = \{1, 2\}$, which of the following belong to $P \times M$?
(a) $(1, 0)$　　　(b) $(2, 0)$　　　(c) $(0, 2)$　　　(d) $(0, 1)$
3. Describe the graph of $N \times N.$
4. Describe the graph of $I \times I.$
5. Describe the graph of $R \times R.$
6. Describe the graph of $N \times I.$
7. Describe the graph of $I \times N.$

B **8.** If $A = \{1, 2, 3\}$ and $B = \{2, 3\}$, list and graph the elements of
(a) $A \times B$　　　　　(b) $B \times B$　　　　　(c) $A \times A.$
9. (a) In question 8, how many ordered pairs are in
(i) $A \times B$　　　　(ii) $B \times B$　　　　(iii) $A \times A$?
(b) What is the rule for determining the number of ordered pairs in a Cartesian Product, without listing the pairs?
10. If $D = \{4, 5\}$, $E = \{6, 7\}$ and $F = \{8, 9\}$, list the elements of
(a) $E \times D$
(b) $D \times F$
(c) $F \times E$
(d) $D \times D$
11. If $G = \{-3, -2, -1\}$, $H = \{0, 1\}$ and $K = \{3, 4\}$,
(a) list the elements of (i) $G \times H$ (ii) $H \times K$ (iii) $G \times K$ (iv) $K \times K.$
(b) Which cross products in (a) belong to $N \times N$?
(c) Which cross products in (a) belong to $N \times I$?
(d) Which cross products in (a) belong to $I \times N$?
(e) Which cross products in (a) belong to $I \times I$?

12. If $M = \{0\}$, $S = \{-1, 1\}$ and $P = \{2, 3\}$,

(a) Does $S \times M = M \times S$? Why?

(b) How many ordered pairs are in the set $M \times P$?

(c) What other Cartesian Products, using the sets M, S and P, have the same number of ordered pairs as $M \times P$?

13. What must be true if $A \times B = B \times A$?

4.3 GRAPHING RELATIONS IN $N \times N$ AND $I \times I$

In this section we shall graph relations defined by algebraic equations.

EXAMPLE 1. *Given:* $A = \{1, 2, 3, 4, 5\}$,

(a) *Graph the relation $A \times A$.*

(b) *List and graph the relation*

$$\{(x, y) \mid y = x, x, y \in A\}$$

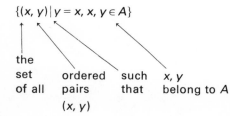

the set of all ordered pairs (x, y) such that x, y belong to A

(c) *List and graph the relation*

$$\{(x, y) \mid x + y = 7, x, y \in A\}$$

(d) *State the domain and range of the relations in (b) and (c)*

Solution

(a)   (b) $\{(1, 1), (2, 2), (3, 3), (4, 4), (5, 5)\}$

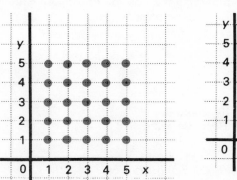

(c) {(2, 5), (3, 4), (4, 3), (5, 2)}

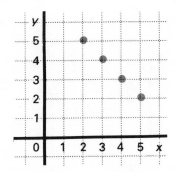

(d) In (b), domain: {1, 2, 3, 4, 5}
        range   : {1, 2, 3, 4, 5}
   In (c), domain: {2, 3, 4, 5}
        range   : {2, 3, 4, 5}

How can you find the one coin of seven that is of greater mass than the other coins while using only two determinations of mass?

EXAMPLE 2. *List and graph the following relations.*
(*a*) $\{(x, y) \mid y = x, x, y \in N\}$
(*b*) $\{(x, y) \mid y > x, x, y \in N\}$
(*c*) $\{(x, y) \mid y < x, x, y \in N\}$

Solution

(a) The set N is infinite so all members of the relation $y = x$ cannot be listed or graphed.

$$\{(1, 1), (2, 2), (3, 3), \ldots\}$$

A partial graph is shown below.

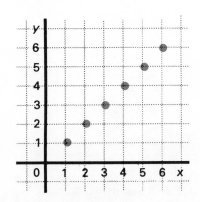

The set N is infinite and only a partial solution is shown.

(b) $\{(1, 2), (1, 3), (2, 3), (1, 4), (2, 4), (3, 4), \ldots\}$

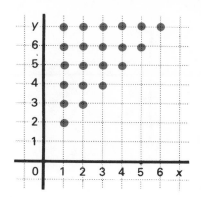

(c) $\{(2, 1), (3, 1), (3, 2), (4, 1), (4, 2), (4, 3), \ldots\}$

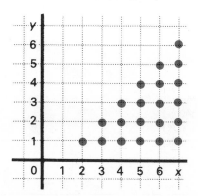

EXAMPLE 3.   *Graph $\{(x, y) \mid y = 2x - 1, x, y \in I\}$*

Solution
Set up a table of values.

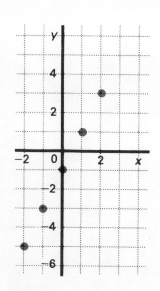

x	$2x - 1$	y
2	$2(2) - 1$	3
1	$2(1) - 1$	1
0	$2(0) - 1$	-1
-1	$2(-1) - 1$	-3
-2	$2(-2) - 1$	-5

The graph is only a partial graph of the relation since x can have values greater than 2 and less than -2.

EXAMPLE 4. *List and graph*

$$\{(x, y) \mid y = 3, \ x, y \in I\}$$

Solution
The set *I* is infinite so all members of the set cannot be listed or graphed.

$$\{\ldots (-3, 3), (-2, 3), (-1, 3), (0, 3), (1, 3), (2, 3), (3, 3), \ldots\}$$

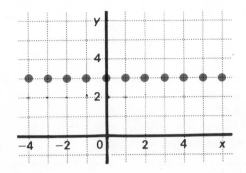

EXERCISE 4-3

A **1.** If $A = \{2, 3, 4, 5\}$, state the elements of

$$\{(x, y) \mid y = x, \ x, y \in A\}$$

2. If $B = \{0, 1, 2, 3, 4\}$, state the elements of

$$\{(x, y) \mid x + y = 4, \ x, y \in B\}$$

3. If $C = \{0, 1, 2, 3, 4, 5\}$, state the elements of

$$\{(x, y) \mid x - y = 1, \ x, y \in C\}$$

4. If $D = \{0, 1, 2\}$, state the elements of
(a) $\{(x, y) \mid x < y, \ x, y \in D\}$
(b) $\{(x, y) \mid y < x, \ x, y \in D\}$
(c) State the domain of (a).
(d) State the domain of (b).

5. If $E = \{6, 7, 8, 9\}$, state the elements of
(a) $\{(x, y) \mid x = 7, \ x, y \in E\}$
(b) $\{(x, y) \mid y = 9, \ x, y \in E\}$
(c) State the domain and range of (a).
(d) State the domain and range of (b).

B **6.** If $A = \{1, 2, 3, 4\}$
(a) List and graph the relation $A \times A$.
(b) List and graph the following relations.
(i) $\{(x, y) \mid y = x, x, y \in A\}$
(ii) $\{(x, y) \mid y > x, x, y \in A\}$
(iii) $\{(x, y) \mid y < x, x, y \in A\}$
(iv) $\{(x, y) \mid y = 2, \ x, y \in A\}$

State the output of the following flow chart.

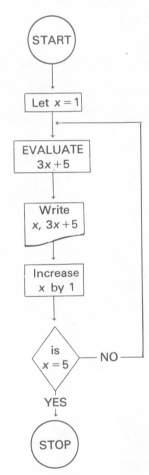

7. If $B = \{-2, -1, 0, 1, 2\}$, list and graph the following relations.

(a) $\{(x,y) \mid y = x, x, y \in B\}$

(b) $\{(x,y) \mid x > y, x, y \in B\}$

(c) $\{(x,y) \mid x + y = 0, x, y \in B\}$

(d) $\{(x,y) \mid x = -1, x, y \in B\}$

8. If $C = \{-4, -3, -2, -1, 0, 1\}$, list and graph the following relations.

(a) $\{(x,y) \mid y = x, x, y \in C\}$

(b) $\{(x,y) \mid x < y, x, y \in C\}$

(c) $\{(x,y) \mid x + y = -4, x, y \in C\}$

(d) $\{(x,y) \mid x > -1, x, y \in C\}$

(e) $\{(x,y) \mid y < -2, x, y \in C\}$

9. List and graph the following relations (only partial solutions need be shown—see example 2)

(a) $\{(x,y) \mid y = x, x, y \in I\}$

(b) $\{(x,y) \mid y > x, x, y \in I\}$

(c) $\{(x,y) \mid y < x, x, y \in I\}$

10. List four ordered pairs for each of the following.

(a) $\{(x, y) \mid y = x + 2, x, y \in N\}$

(b) $\{(x, y) \mid y = x - 4, x, y \in I\}$

(c) $\{(x, y) \mid y = 3x, x, y \in I\}$

(d) $\{(x, y) \mid x + y = 6, x, y \in N\}$

(e) $\{(x, y) \mid x - y = 4, x, y \in I\}$

(f) $\{(x, y) \mid y = 5, x, y \in N\}$

(g) $\{(x, y) \mid x = -3, x, y \in I\}$

(h) $\{(x, y) \mid y = 2x + 3, x, y \in I\}$

(i) $\{(x, y) \mid y = 5 - 2x, x, y \in I\}$

(j) $\{(x, y) \mid y = 4x + 1, x, y \in I\}$

(k) $\{(x, y) \mid y = -2x + 7, x, y \in I\}$

(l) $\{(x, y) \mid y = \dfrac{x+1}{2}, x, y \in I\}$

(m) $\{(x, y) \mid y = \tfrac{1}{3}x + 2, x, y \in I\}$

11. Graph the following relations, using four ordered pairs in each case.

(a) $\{(x, y) \mid y = x + 3, x, y \in I\}$

(b) $\{(x, y) \mid y = 2x + 4, x, y \in I\}$

(c) $\{(x, y) \mid y = 3x - 7, x, y \in I\}$

(d) $\{(x, y) \mid x + y = 8, x, y \in I\}$

(e) $\{(x, y) \mid y = \tfrac{1}{2}x - 3, x, y \in I\}$

(f) $\{(x, y) \mid y = \dfrac{x-1}{2}, x, y \in I\}$

(g) $\{(x, y) \mid y = 3 - 4x, x, y \in I\}$

(h) $\{(x, y) \mid x - y = 6, x, y \in I\}$

(i) $\{(x, y) \mid x + y = -4, x, y \in I\}$

(j) $\{(x, y) \mid x - y = -1, x, y \in I\}$

C **12.** Graph the following relations on the same set of axes.

(a) $y = x^2$, $x \in \{-2, -1, 0, 1, 2\}$

(b) $y = x^2 + 4$, $x \in \{-2, -1, 0, 1, 2\}$

(c) $y = x^2 - 3$, $x \in \{-2, -1, 0, 1, 2\}$

13. Graph the following relations on the same set of axes.
(a) $y = -x^2, x \in \{-2, -1, 0, 1, 2\}$
(b) $y = -x^2 + 3, x \in \{-2, -1, 0, 1, 2\}$
(c) $y = -x^2 - 4, x \in \{-2, -1, 0, 1, 2\}$

14. Graph the following relations on the same set of axes.
(a) $x = y^2, y \in \{-2, -1, 0, 1, 2\}$
(b) $x = y^2 + 2, y \in \{-2, -1, 0, 1, 2\}$
(c) $x = y^2 - 1, y \in \{-2, -1, 0, 1, 2\}$

15. Graph the relation

$$x^2 + y^2 = 25, x \in \{-5, -4, -3, 0, 3, 4, 5\}$$

16. Graph the relation

$$y = |x|, x \in \{-3, -2, -1, 0, 1, 2, 3\}$$

What mathematical symbol can you place between 2 and 3 to make a number greater than 2 but less than 3?

4.4 GRAPHING RELATIONS IN $R \times R$

In this section we will graph relations and expand the domain and range to include the Real Numbers.

EXAMPLE 1. *Graph the relation*

$$\{(x, y) \mid y = 2x - 3, x, y \in R\}$$

Solution

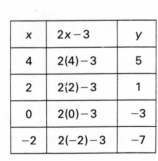

x	2x − 3	y
4	2(4) − 3	5
2	2(2) − 3	1
0	2(0) − 3	−3
−2	2(−2) − 3	−7

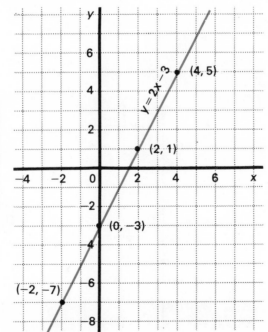

Why do we use a solid line instead of an isolated set of points as in the previous section?

EXAMPLE 2. *Graph the relation*

$$y = \frac{x+1}{3}, \ x, y \in R$$

Solution

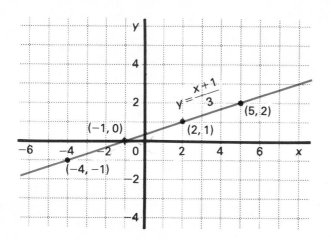

x	$\dfrac{x+1}{3}$	y
5	$\dfrac{5+1}{3}$	2
2	$\dfrac{2+1}{3}$	1
-1	$\dfrac{-1+1}{3}$	0
-4	$\dfrac{-4+1}{3}$	-1

EXAMPLE 3. *Graph the relation*

$$\{(x, y) \mid x = -2, \ x, y \in R\}$$

Solution

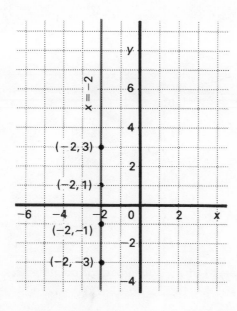

x	y
-2	3
-2	1
-2	-1
-2	-3

EXERCISE 4-4

B **1.** Graph the following relations. Use 4 ordered pairs in each case.
(a) $\{(x, y) \mid y = 2x - 1, x, y \in R\}$
(b) $\{(x, y) \mid y = x + 4, x, y \in R\}$
(c) $\{(x, y) \mid y = 3x - 2, x, y \in R\}$
(d) $\{(x, y) \mid y = 4x, x, y \in R\}$
(e) $\{(x, y) \mid y = 2x + 3, x, y \in R\}$
(f) $\{(x, y) \mid y = 5x - 6, x, y \in R\}$
(g) $\{(x, y) \mid y = 4, x, y \in R\}$
(h) $\{(x, y) \mid x = -2, x, y \in R\}$
(i) $\{(x, y) \mid x = 5, x, y \in R\}$
(j) $\{(x, y) \mid y = 0, x, y \in R\}$
(k) $\{(x, y) \mid x = 0, x, y \in R\}$

2. Graph the following relations. Use 4 ordered pairs in each case.
(a) $y = -2x + 4, x, y \in R$
(b) $y = \frac{1}{2}x + 1, x, y \in R$
(c) $y = \dfrac{x - 2}{3}, x, y \in R$
(d) $y = -\frac{1}{3}x - 2, x, y \in R$
(e) $y = \dfrac{x + 1}{2}, x, y \in R$
(f) $y = 4 - 3x, x, y \in R$
(g) $y = \frac{2}{3}x - 1, x, y \in R$
(h) $y = 5 - x, x, y \in R$
(i) $y = -3x - 2, x, y \in R$
(j) $y = \dfrac{2x + 3}{2}, x, y \in R$

C **3.** Graph the following relations, $x, y \in R$.
(a) $y = x^2$,   [Hint: let $x = 0, 1, -1, \ldots$]
(b) $y = x^2 + 3$
(c) $y = -2x^2$
(d) $y = -x^2 + 3$
(e) $y = x^2 + 4x + 4$ [Hint: let $x = -4, -3, -2, -1, 0$]

Use $+, -, \times, \div, (\ )$ to make a true statement.
$$8 \ 2 \ 3 = 9 \ 5 \ 5$$

4.5 GRAPHING GENERAL RELATIONS

In this section we will graph relations without using a defining equation.

EXAMPLE 1. *When you turn on a hot water faucet the temperature of the water depends on how many seconds the water has been running. Sketch a graph of this relation.*

Solution
The initial temperature of the water will be close to room temperature since this is the water that was in the pipes. The temperature of the

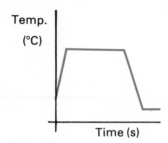

Temp. (°C)

Time (s)

water will quickly rise once the water from the hot water tank starts coming out. The next phase will be a decrease in temperature once you have drained the tank and the temperature will level off to the temperature of the water supplied by the city.

EXERCISE 4-5

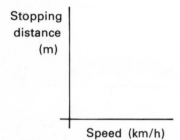

Temp.

Time

B **1.** You put some ice cubes in a glass, fill the glass with cold water and then let the glass sit on a table. Sketch a graph of the temperature of the water versus time sitting on the table. State the approximate domain and range of this relation.

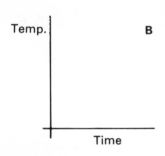

Stopping distance (m)

Speed (km/h)

2. The distance required to stop a car depends on how fast the car is moving. Sketch a graph of stopping distance versus speed of the car. State a reasonable domain and range for this relation.

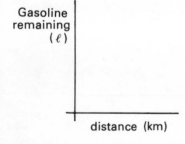

Gasoline remaining (ℓ)

distance (km)

3. If you start driving at a constant speed with a full tank of gasoline, the number of litres of gasoline remaining in the tank depends on how far you have driven. Sketch a graph of litres of gasoline remaining versus distance travelled. State a reasonable domain and range for this relation.

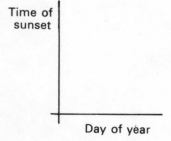

Time of sunset

Day of year

4. The time of sunset depends on the time of year. Sketch a graph of time of sunset versus day of the year. State a reasonable domain and range for this relation.

5. Your height depends on your age. Sketch a graph of height (in centimetres) versus age (in years). State a reasonable domain and range for this relation.

Height (cm) | Age (a)

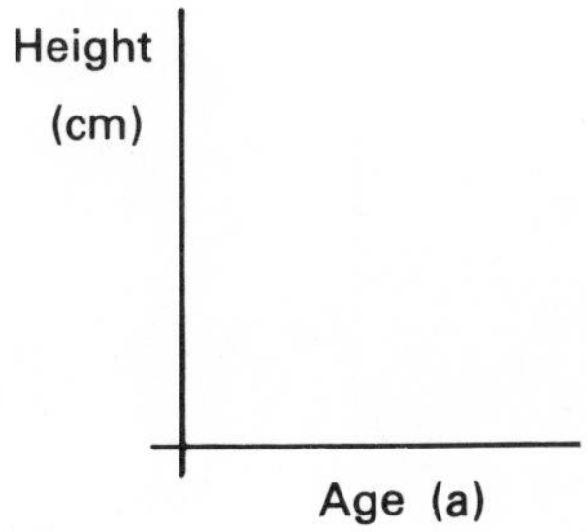

6. You fill an electric kettle with cold water and plug in the kettle. Sketch a graph of the water temperature versus the length of time the kettle is plugged in. State a reasonable domain and range for this relation.

Temp. (°C) | Time (s)

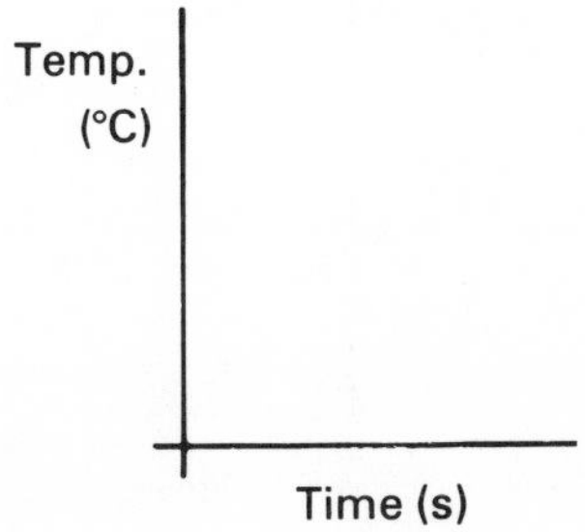

7. The number of people that attend a rock concert is determined by the popularity of the band. Sketch a graph of attendance versus popularity. Does this relation have a domain and range?

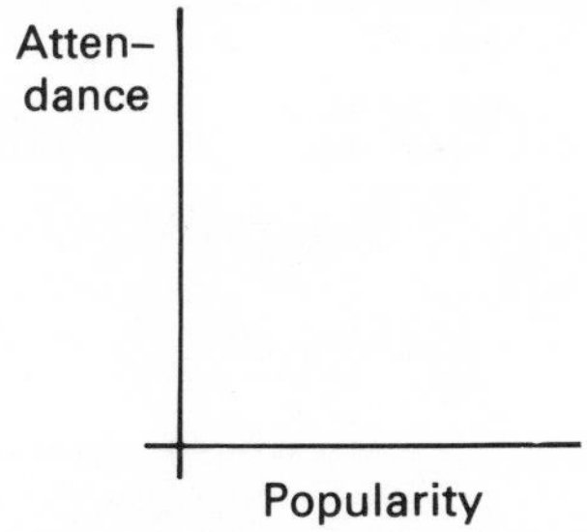

Atten-dance | Popularity

8. On a sunny day, the length of the shadow of a telephone pole depends on the time of day. Sketch a graph of length of shadow versus time of day. State a reasonable domain and range for this relation.

Length of shadow | Time of day

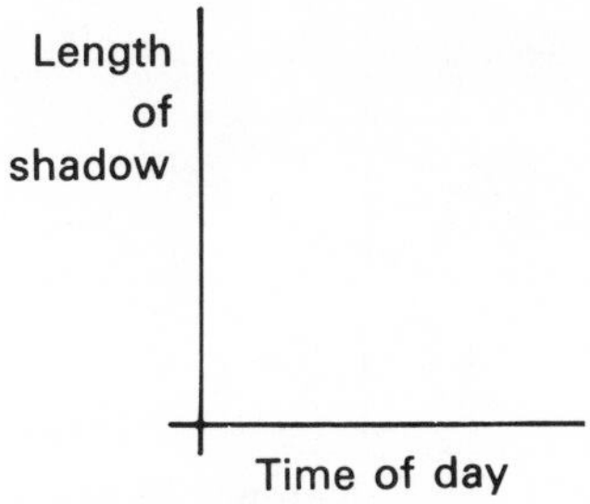

9. The number of Christmas cards a greeting card store sells depends on the time of year. Sketch a graph of number of cards sold versus the month of the year.

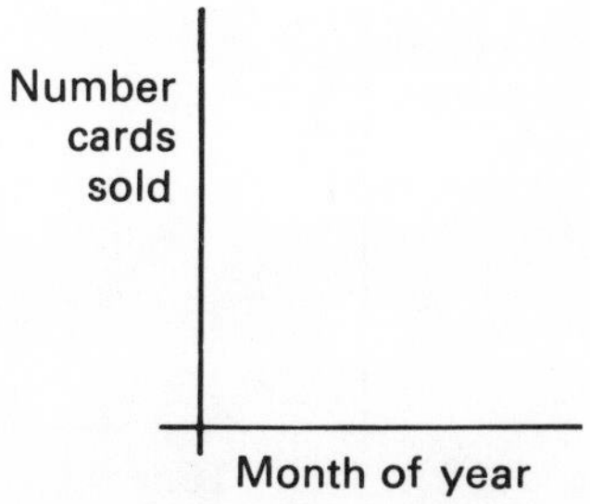

Number cards sold | Month of year

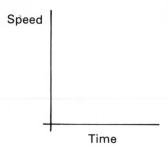

Speed

Time

10. If you drop a brick from the top of a tall building, the speed of the falling brick depends on how long it has been falling. Sketch a graph of speed versus time.

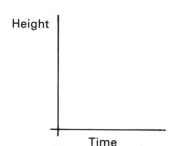

Height

Time

11. The height of a batted baseball depends on the length of time since it was hit. Sketch a graph of height versus time elapsed since hitting. State a reasonable domain and range for this relation.

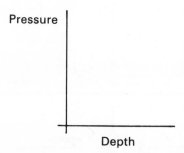

Pressure

Depth

12. The water pressure on the hull of a diving submarine depends on the depth of the submarine. Sketch a graph of pressure versus depth. State a reasonable domain and range for this relation.

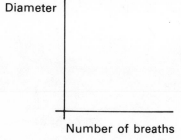

Diameter

Number of breaths

13. When you blow up a round balloon the diameter of the balloon depends on the number of breaths you have blown into it. Sketch a graph of diameter versus number of breaths. Comment on the domain and range of this relation.

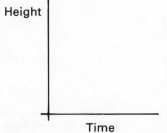

Height

Time

14. Suppose you are the last person to get on a ferris wheel. Once you are seated, the wheel starts to rotate. Your height above the ground depends on the length of time you have been riding. Sketch a graph of height versus time. State a reasonable domain and range for this relation.

4.6 FUNCTIONS

In Section 4.1 we defined a relation as a *set of ordered pairs*. In this section we will consider a special kind of relation called a *function*. The table shown gives the length of a year on the planets as compared to earth.

PLANET	LENGTH OF YEAR (compared to earth)
MERCURY	0.24
VENUS	0.62
EARTH	1
MARS	1.9
JUPITER	12
SATURN	29
URANUS	84
NEPTUNE	165
PLUTO	248

Express the length of year for each planet in terms of 1 "year" on Mercury.

This table may also be represented as a correspondence or mapping

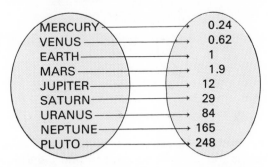

or as a set of ordered pairs {(MERCURY, 0.24), (VENUS, 0.62), (EARTH, 1), (MARS, 1.9), (JUPITER, 12), (SATURN, 29), (URANUS, 84), (NEPTUNE, 165), (PLUTO, 248)}.
Corresponding to each planet there is one and only one number. This relation describes a function.

A function is a relation such that for every first element there is one and only one second element.

{(3, 5), (7, 11), (8, 15), (9, 22)}	FUNCTION
{(3, 6), (4, 7), (4, 12), (5, 13)}	NOT A FUNCTION (why?)
{(6, 4), (7, 4), (8, 4), (9, 4)}	FUNCTION
{(3, 8), (3, 9), (3, 10), (3, 11)}	NOT A FUNCTION

EXAMPLE 1.

(a) *Illustrate the relation defined by*

$$\{(x, y) \mid y = 3x - 2, \ x \in \{1, 2, 3, 4\}\}$$

as a mapping.
(b) *State the domain and range of the relation.*
(c) *Is the relation a function? Explain.*

Solution

x	3x − 2	y
1	3(1) − 2	1
2	3(2) − 2	4
3	3(3) − 2	7
4	3(4) − 2	10

My father was 28 when I was 6. Now he is twice as old as I am. How old am I?

(a) Relation as a mapping.

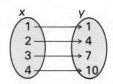

(b) Domain: {1, 2, 3, 4}
      Range: {1, 4, 7, 10}
(c) Yes. For every first element there is one and only one second element.
Another way to describe this function is by $(x, 3x - 2)$. This states that the first element is transformed or mapped into the second element by the operation indicated.

EXAMPLE 2.   *Given that* $x \in \{-2, -1, 0, 1, 2\}$,
(a) *Illustrate the relation defined by* (x, x^2) *as a mapping.*
(b) *State the domain and range.*
(c) *Is the relation a function? Explain.*

Solution

(a) The ordered pair (x, x^2) states that the first element is transformed or mapped into the second element by squaring the first element.

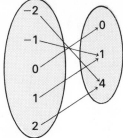

FUNCTION: For each element in the domain there is one element in the range.

(b) Domain: $\{-2, -1, 0, 1, 2\}$
    Range: $\{0, 1, 4\}$
(c) Yes. For every first element there is one and only one second element. (Only one arrow starts from each element of the domain.)

Another way to illustrate a function is by *arrow notation*. For example

$$f : x \rightarrow 2x - 1$$

This states that the first element is mapped or transformed into the second element by multiplying x by 2 then subtracting 1. The letter f, in $f : x$, is used for identification only (distinguishes one mapping from another). Examples of other mappings are

$$g : x \rightarrow x + 5$$
$$m : x \rightarrow x^2 + 3$$
$$h : x \rightarrow 2x^2 - 4$$

EXAMPLE 3. *Given $h : x \rightarrow 2x + 4$, $x \in \{0, 1, 2, 3, 4\}$,*
(*a*) *Illustrate the relation as a mapping.*
(*b*) *List the ordered pairs of h.*
(*c*) *State the domain and range of h.*
(*d*) *Is h a function? Explain.*

> A function is a mapping
>
> f maps or transforms one element x into an element y
> $f : x \rightarrow y$

Solution
(a)

```
0 ──── 2(0)+4 ───→ 4
1 ──── 2(1)+4 ───→ 6
2 ──── 2(2)+4 ───→ 8
3 ──── 2(3)+4 ───→ 10
4 ──── 2(4)+4 ───→ 12
```

(b) $\{(0, 4), (1, 6), (2, 8), (3, 10), (4, 12)\}$
(c) Domain: $\{0, 1, 2, 3, 4\}$
    Range: $\{4, 6, 8, 10, 12\}$
(d) Yes. For each element in the domain there is one element in the range.

EXERCISE 4-6

A **1.** State which of the following relations are functions. Explain your answer.
(a) $\{(1, 3), (2, 5), (3, 7), (4, 9), (5, 11)\}$
(b) $\{(-2, 0), (-1, 2), (0, 4), (1, 6), (2, 8)\}$
(c) $\{(-3, 4), (-1, 7), (1, 9), (1, 11)\}$
(d) $\{(5, 4), (7, 11), (6, 4), (2, 11)\}$
(e) $\{(3, 6), (4, 6), (9, 6), (10, 6)\}$
(f) $\{(-3, 5), (-3, 7), (-3, 9), (-3, 11)\}$
(g) $\{(8, -3), (9, -3), (7, 6), (8, -2)\}$
(h) $\{(red, 3), (green, 4), (blue, 5)\}$
(i) $\{(15, 33), (15\frac{1}{2}, 33), (16, 34), (16, 35)\}$
(j) $\{(4, 7), (-4, 7), (3, 7), (3, -7)\}$

Men's shirt sizes are examples of ordered pairs.

2. State which of the following relations are functions. Explain your answer.

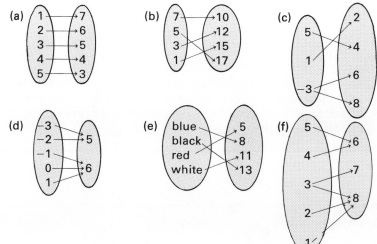

(a) (b) (c) (d) (e) (f)

3. Given that a mapping is defined by the ordered pair $(x, x+7)$, state the missing element in each of the following.
(a) $(5, \blacksquare)$ (b) $(0, \blacksquare)$, (c) $(-3, \blacksquare)$
(d) $(\blacksquare, 8)$ (e) $(\blacksquare, 21)$ (f) $(\blacksquare, 0)$
(g) $(-16, \blacksquare)$ (h) $(-5, \blacksquare)$ (i) $(\blacksquare, -8)$

4. Given that $f : x \rightarrow x - 4$, state the missing element in each of the following.
(a) $(6, \blacksquare)$ (b) $(14, \blacksquare)$ (c) $(10, \blacksquare)$
(d) $(\blacksquare, 5)$ (e) $(\blacksquare, 0)$ (f) $(\blacksquare, -3)$
(g) $(-5, \blacksquare)$ (h) $(-10, \blacksquare)$ (i) $(\blacksquare, -6)$

5. (a) In your mathematics class is the relation defined by (student, age) a function? Explain. (b) Is the relation (age, student) a function? Explain.

6. In your mathematics class is the relation defined by (eye colour, student) a function? Explain.

B **7.** (a) Illustrate the relation defined by $\{(x, y) \mid y = 2x - 3, x \in \{1, 2, 3, 4, 5\}\}$ as a mapping.
(b) State the domain and range of the relation.
(c) Is the relation a function? Explain.

8. (a) Illustrate the relation defined by $\{(x, y) \mid y = x^2 + 2, x \in \{-2, -1, 0, 1, 2\}\}$ as a mapping.
(b) State the domain and range of the relation.
(c) Is the relation a function? Explain.

9. Given that $x \in \{0, 1, 2, 3, 4\}$
(a) Illustrate the relation defined by $(x, 3x + 4)$ as a mapping.
(b) State the domain and range.
(c) Is the relation a function? Explain.

10. Given that $x \in \{1, 3, 5, 7, 9\}$
(a) Illustrate the relation defined by $\left(x, \dfrac{x+3}{2}\right)$ as a mapping.
(b) Is the relation a function? Explain.

11. Given $f : x \rightarrow 5x - 4$, $x \in \{0, 1, 2, 3, 4\}$
(a) List the ordered pairs of f.
(b) State the domain and range of f.
(c) Is f a function? Explain.

12. Given $g : x \rightarrow \frac{1}{2}x + 3$, $x \in \{0, 2, 4, 6\}$
(a) List the ordered pairs of g.
(b) Is g a function? Explain.

13. Given $h : x \rightarrow 2x^2 - 4$, $x \in \{-2, -1, 0, 1, 2\}$
(a) List the ordered pairs of h.
(b) Is h a function? Explain.

C **14.** List as a set of ordered pairs the possible "calls" of a baseball umpire. ((1, 2) means 1 ball and 2 strikes). Is the relation a function? Explain.

15. List the ordered pairs of the relation defined by $\{(x, y) \mid x = y^2, y \in \{-2, -1, 0, 1, 2\}\}$. Is the relation a function? Explain.

16. Express the following relations in the form
$$f : x \rightarrow \blacksquare.$$
(a) $y = 3x - 7$
(b) $y - 4x = 6$
(c) $5x + y = 13$
(d) $2x + 3y = 4$

Put the numbers from 1 to 9 in the spaces to make the statements true.
$$\square - \square + \square = 8$$
$$\square \div \square + \square = 8$$
$$\square \times \square + \square = 8$$

4.7 FUNCTION NOTATION

Function notation is another way to express a mapping, such as $f : x \rightarrow 2x + 5$. This mapping can be written as
$$f(x) = 2x + 5$$
where $f(x)$ is read "f of x" or "f at x".

If $f(x) = 2x + 5,$
then $f(3) = 2(3) + 5$
$= 6 + 5$
$= 11$

Note that $f(3)$ means the value of the function when $x = 3$.
This is a very convenient method of determining the ordered pairs of a function.

We now have several methods to name functions.

$$y = 2x + 5$$
$$\{(x, y) \mid y = 2x + 5\}$$
$$f : x \rightarrow 2x + 5$$
$$(x, 2x + 5)$$
$$f(x) = 2x + 5$$

Identifies the function

$f(x)$

States the variable used in the function.

EXAMPLE 1.   If $h(x) = 4x - 5$, find
(a) $h(6)$ (b) $h(-3)$ (c) $h(0)$ (d) $h(m)$
and state the ordered pair associated with each.

Solution

(a) $h(x) = 4x - 5$
$h(6) = 4(6) - 5$
$= 24 - 5$
$= 19$
ordered pair: (6, 19)

(b) $h(x) = 4x - 5$
$h(-3) = 4(-3) - 5$
$= -12 - 5$
$= -17$
ordered pair: (−3, −17)

(c) $h(x) = 4x - 5$
$h(0) = 4(0) - 5$
$= 0 - 5$
$= -5$
ordered pair: (0, −5)

(d) $h(x) = 4x - 5$
$h(m) = 4(m) - 5$
$= 4m - 5$
ordered pair: $(m, 4m - 5)$

EXAMPLE 2.   If $f(x) = 2x + 1$ and $g(x) = 1 - 2x$, find
(a) $f(2)$ (b) $g(-2)$ (c) $f[g(-1)]$

$f[g(x)]$ can be written
$(f \circ g)(x)$

Solution

(a) $f(x) = 2x + 1$
$f(2) = 2(2) + 1$
$= 4 + 1$
$= 5$

(b) $g(x) = 1 - 2x$
$g(-2) = 1 - 2(-2)$
$= 1 + 4$
$= 5$

(c) $g(x) = 1 - 2x$
$g(-1) = 1 - 2(-1)$
$= 1 + 2$
$= 3$

Since $g(-1) = 3$
then $f[g(-1)] = f(3)$
$= 2(3) + 1$
$= 6 + 1$
$= 7$

EXERCISE 4-7

A   **1.** If $f(x) = 4x + 3$, find
(a) $f(1)$ (b) $f(2)$ (c) $f(-2)$ (d) $f(0)$
(e) $f(10)$ (f) $f(-7)$ (g) $f(-100)$ (h) $f(50)$
(i) $f(6)$ (j) $f(-5)$ (k) $f(a)$ (l) $f(b)$

2. If $g(x) = 3x - 5$, find
(a) $g(2)$ (b) $g(7)$ (c) $g(-3)$ (d) $g(0)$
(e) $g(10)$ (f) $g(-10)$ (g) $g(-7)$ (h) $g(20)$
(i) $g(-4)$ (j) $g(m)$ (k) $g(t)$ (l) $g(a^2)$

3. If $h(x) = x^2$, $f(x) = 2x + 5$ and $g(x) = 1 + 3x$, find
(a) $h(2)$ (b) $g(-3)$ (c) $f(0)$ (d) $h(0)$
(e) $g(4)$ (f) $h(-2)$ (g) $f(-6)$ (h) $g(-4)$
(i) $f(4)$ (j) $h(\frac{1}{2})$ (k) $f(\frac{1}{2})$ (l) $g(-\frac{1}{3})$

Each letter represents
a different digit in
this addition

```
  T H I S
    I S
V E R Y
---------
E A S Y
```

B   **4.** If $f(x) = x^2 + 4$, find
(a) $f(2)$ (b) $f(-3)$ (c) $f(6)$ (d) $f(-2)$
and state the ordered pair associated with each.

5. If $g(x) = \frac{1}{2}x - 4$, find
(a) $g(2)$ (b) $g(-4)$ (c) $g(6)$ (d) $g(9)$
and state the ordered pair associated with each.

6. If $h(x) = x^2 - 3x + 7$, find
(a) $h(1)$ (b) $h(2)$ (c) $h(-3)$ (d) $h(0)$

7. Given $h(x) = (x + 1)^2$, find
(a) $h(2)$ (b) $h(4)$ (c) $h(-1)$ (d) $h(-4)$

8. If $g(x) = 4x - 7$, find
(a) $g(3) + g(2)$ (b) $g(7) + g(1)$ (c) $g(-2) - g(4)$
(d) $g(5) + g(-3) - g(6)$

9. Given $f(x) = x^2 + 1$ and $h(x) = (x - 1)^2$, find
(a) $f(4) + h(2)$ (b) $h(3) + f(-3)$
(c) $f(-2) - h(-1)$ (d) $h(-4) - f(2)$

10. If $m(x) = 5x - 4$ and $g(x) = 2x^2$, find
(a) $m(5) + g(3)$ (b) $g(-2) - m(1)$
(c) $2[m(-1)] + 3[g(-4)]$ (d) $4[g(-1)] - 3[m(-1)]$

C   **11.** Given $m(x) = 3x - 4$ and $n(x) = 1 - 2x$, find
(a) $m(-3)$ (b) $n(0)$ (c) $m[n(-1)]$
(d) $n[m(3)]$ (e) $m[m(2)]$ (f) $m[n(3)]$

12. Given $f(x) = x^2$ and $g(x) = x^2 + 2$ find
(a) $f(-4)$ (b) $g(2)$ (c) $f[g(0)]$ (d) $g[f(-2)]$

13. If $f(x) = 5x - 10$, find x so that
(a) $f(x) = 0$ (b) $f(x) = 25$ (c) $f(x) = -35$

14. If $g(x) = (x + 1)(x - 2)$, find x so that $g(x) = 0$.

15. If $f(x) = 3x + 2$, find
(a) $f(x + 1)$ (b) $f(x - 1)$ (c) $f(2x - 3)$

4.8 GRAPHING FUNCTIONS

Functions are special relations and are graphed in the same manner as the relations in Sections 4.3 and 4.4.

EXAMPLE 1. *Graph* $f: x \rightarrow 3x - 4$, $x \in \{-1, 0, 1, 2, 3\}$

Solution

x	3x − 4	y
−1	3(−1) − 4	−7
0	3(0) − 4	−4
1	3(1) − 4	−1
2	3(2) − 4	2
3	3(3) − 4	5

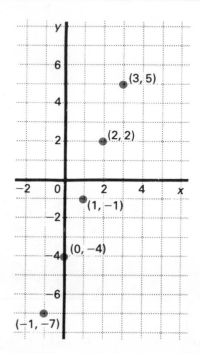

EXAMPLE 2. *Graph* $f(x) = 1 - 2x$, $x \in R$.

Solution

x	1 − 2x	y
−1	1 − 2(−1)	3
0	1 − 2(0)	1
1	1 − 2(1)	−1
2	1 − 2(2)	−3

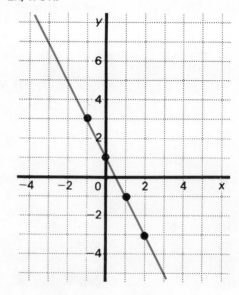

Functions have been defined as relations (sets of ordered pairs) where for every first element there is only one second element. Determining what relations are functions is done easily by examining the graph of the relation in question.

VERTICAL LINE TEST FOR A FUNCTION

Graph the relations.
(a) $S = \{(2, 2), (3, 4), (6, 1), (8, 5)\}$
(b) $T = \{(1, 4), (3, 2), (3, 6), (5, 5)\}$

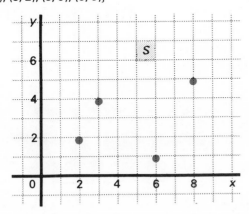

Relation S is a function since for every value of x there is only one value for y. In the graph of S you can see that no 2 points have the same x coordinate. If a vertical line were drawn through every point in S, no 2 points would lie on the same vertical line.

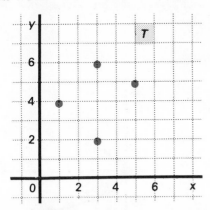

Relation T is not a function since the x coordinate 3 is paired with y coordinates 2 and 6. If a vertical line were drawn through (3, 2), (3, 6) would also lie on the same line.

Vertical Line Test For a Function
If any vertical line will cut the graph of a relation at most once, the relation is a function.

EXAMPLE 3. *Graph the following relations and use the vertical line test to determine whether or not each is a function.*

(a) $\{(x, y) \mid y = x^2, -3 \leq x \leq 3, x, y \in R\}$

(b) $\{(x, y) \mid x = y^2, -3 \leq y \leq 3, x, y \in R\}$

Solution

(a) $-3 \leq x \leq 3$ means that x may take on values between -3 and 3.

x	x^2	y
-3	$(-3)^2$	9
-2	$(-2)^2$	4
-1	$(-1)^2$	1
0	$(0)^2$	0
1	$(1)^2$	1
2	$(2)^2$	4
3	$(3)^2$	9

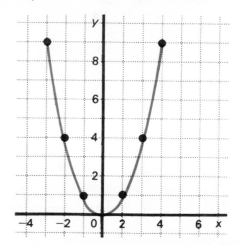

Since any vertical line will cut the graph at most once, the relation is a function.

(b) $-3 \leq y \leq 3$ means that y may take on values between -3 and 3.

y	y^2	x	Ordered Pair
-3	$(-3)^2$	9	$(9, -3)$
-2	$(-2)^2$	4	$(4, -2)$
-1	$(-1)^2$	1	$(1, -1)$
0	$(0)^2$	0	$(0, 0)$
1	$(1)^2$	1	$(1, 1)$
2	$(2)^2$	4	$(4, 2)$
3	$(3)^2$	9	$(3, 9)$

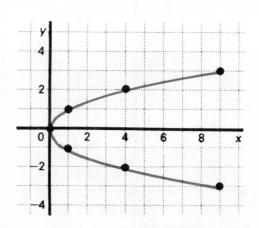

It is possible to draw a vertical line and cut the graph more than once, hence the relation is not a function.

EXERCISE 4-8

A **1.** Use the vertical line test to determine which of the following are graphs of functions.

(a)

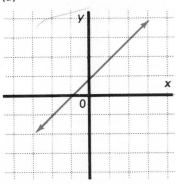

(b)

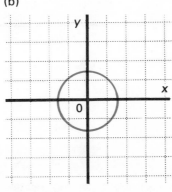

(c)

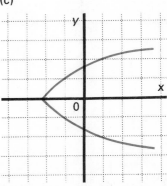

(d)

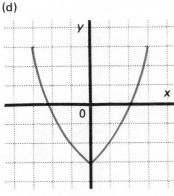

(e)

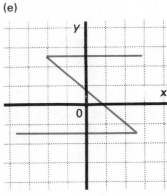

(f)

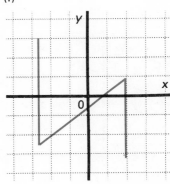

(g)

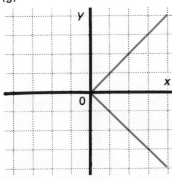

(h)

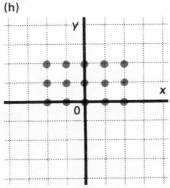

(i)

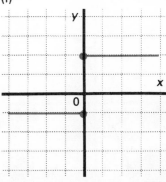

(j)

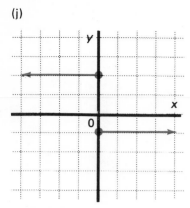

(k)

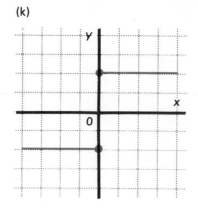

(l)

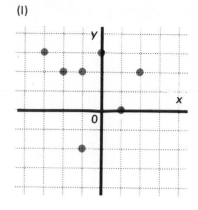

B **2.** State the domain and range of the following relations. Is the relation a function?

(a)

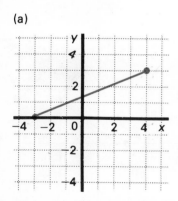

(b)

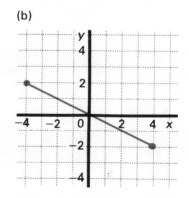

(c)

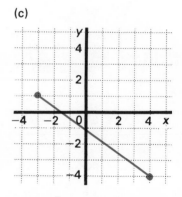

(d)

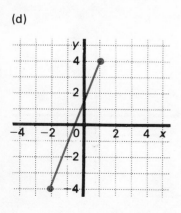

(e)

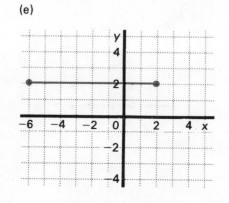

(f)

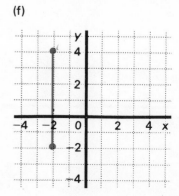

(g)

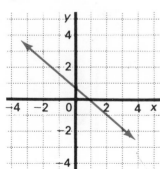

(h)

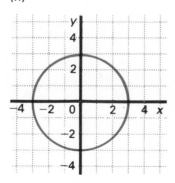

(i)

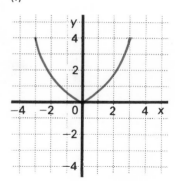

(j)

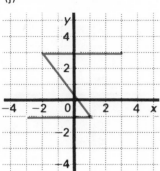

(k)

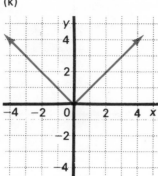

(l)

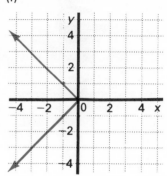

3. State the domain and range of each of the following relations. Is the relation a function?

(a)

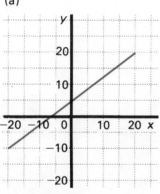

(b)

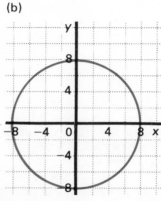

(c)

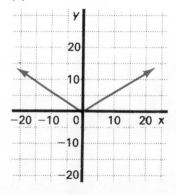

(d)

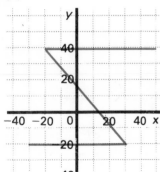

(e)

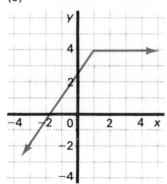

(f)

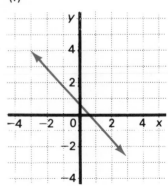

(g)

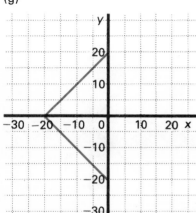

(h)

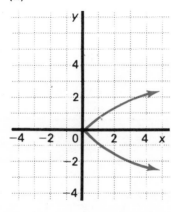

(i)

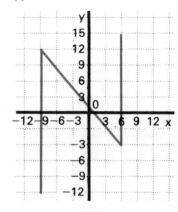

4. Graph the following functions.
(a) $f : x \rightarrow 2x + 3$, $x \in \{-2, -1, 0, 1, 2\}$
(b) $h : x \rightarrow 3x - 2$, $x \in \{-2, -1, 0, 1\}$
(c) $f(x) = 3x + 4$, $x \in R$
(d) $g : x \rightarrow 3 - 2x$, $x \in R$
(e) $m : x \rightarrow \frac{1}{2}x + 2$, $x \in R$
(f) $t : x = 5 - 3x$, $x \in R$
(g) $f(x) = \dfrac{x + 1}{2}$, $x \in R$
(h) $g(x) = \dfrac{5 - 2x}{3}$, $x \in R$

5. Graph the following relations and determine which are functions.
(a) $y = x^2$, $-2 \leqq x \leqq 2$, $x, y \in R$
(b) $y = -2x^2$, $-2 \leqq x \leqq 2$, $x, y \in R$
(c) $x = y^2$, $-2 \leqq y \leqq 2$, $x, y \in R$
(d) $\{(x, y) \mid y = 4, x, y \in R\}$
(e) $\{(x, y) \mid x = -2, x, y \in R\}$
(f) $x = -2y^2$, $-2 \leqq y \leqq 2$, $x, y \in R$

6. Graph the following relations and determine which are functions.

(a) $y = |x|$, $x, y \in R$

(b) $x = |y|$, $x, y \in R$

(c) $y = |x| + 1$, $x, y \in R$

(d) $x = |y| - 2$, $x, y \in R$

(e) $y = |x + 1|$, $x, y \in R$

(f) $x = |y - 2|$, $x, y \in R$

(g) $y = -|x| + 4$, $x, y \in R$

(h) $x = -|y| - 3$, $x, y \in R$

C **7.** Graph the following relations and determine which are functions.

(a) $|x| + |y| = 6$, $x, y \in R$

(b) $|x| + |y| = 9$, $x, y \in R$

(c) $|x| - |y| = 3$, $x, y \in R$

(d) $|y| - |x| = 4$, $x, y \in R$

8. Graph the following relations and determine which are functions.

(a) $\{(x, y) \mid x^2 + y^2 = 25, x, y \in R\}$

(b) $y = \sqrt{x}$, $x, y \in R$

(c) $x = \sqrt{y}$, $x, y \in R$

(d) $y = x^3$, $x, y \in R$

REVIEW EXERCISE

A **1.** State the domain and range of each of the following.

(a) $\{(5, 11), (6, 14), (7, 28), (9, 43)\}$

(b) $\{(-3, 4), (-1, 5), (0, 7), (3, 12)\}$

(c) $\{(-3, 6), (-3, 7), (-3, 8), (-3, 9), (-3, 10)\}$

(d) $\{(-5, -2), (-4, -2), (-3, -2)\}$

(e) $\{(5, -4), (5, -3), (6, -2), (6, -1), (7, 0)\}$

(f) $\{(a, b), (c, d), (e, f), (g, h)\}$

2. If $S = \{3, 4, 5, 6, 7\}$ and $T = \{5, 6, 7, 8\}$, which of the following belong to $T \times S$?

(a) $(4, 5)$ (b) $(5, 4)$ (c) $(5, 5)$ (d) $(4, 8)$ (e) $(7, 3)$

(f) $(7, 5)$

3. If $A = \{0, 1, 2, 3\}$, $B = \{0, 1, 2\}$, $C = \{6, 7\}$ and $D = \{-1, 0\}$,

(a) state the elements of $B \times D$.

(b) state the elements of $D \times B$.

(c) state the elements of $C \times D$.

(d) how many ordered pairs in the set

(i) $A \times B$

(ii) $C \times A$

(iii) $B \times D$

(iv) $A \times A$

How many words of four letters or more can you form using the letters in the word GEOMETRY?

4. If $A = \{1, 2, 3, 4\}$, state the elements of

(a) $\{(x, y) \mid y = x, x, y \in A\}$

(b) $\{(x, y) \mid y > x, x, y \in A\}$

(c) $\{(x, y) \mid y < x, x, y \in A\}$

(d) $\{(x, y) \mid x = 4, x, y \in A\}$

(e) $\{(x, y) \mid y = 2, x, y \in A\}$

5. State which of the following relations are functions.

(a) $\{(5, 6), (6, 8), (7, 10), (8, 13)\}$

(b) $\{(4, -3), (5, -3), (6, -3), (7, -3), (8, -3)\}$

(c) $\{(-1, 6), (-2, 7), (-1, 8), (-3, 9)\}$

(d) $\{(5, -4), (5, 0), (5, 4)\}$

(e) 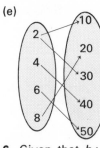　(f) 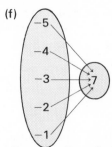　(g)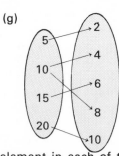

6. Given that $h : x \rightarrow x + 5$, state the missing element in each of the following.

(a) $(2, \blacksquare)$　　　(b) $(8, \blacksquare)$　　　(c) $(\blacksquare, 10)$　　　(d) $(\blacksquare, 4)$
(e) $(0, \blacksquare)$　　　(f) $(\blacksquare, 0)$　　　(g) $(-11, \blacksquare)$　　　(h) $(\blacksquare, -5)$

7. If $f(x) = 2x + 1$, $g(x) = 3x - 1$ and $h(x) = x^2$, find

(a) $f(2)$　　　(b) $g(4)$　　　(c) $h(2)$　　　(d) $g(20)$
(e) $h(-3)$　　(f) $h(0)$　　　(g) $f(-10)$　　(h) $g(-5)$
(i) $f(\tfrac{1}{2})$　　(j) $g(-\tfrac{1}{3})$　　(k) $f(a)$　　　(l) $g(b)$

B　**8.** State the domain and range of each of the following relations. Is the relation a function?

(a)

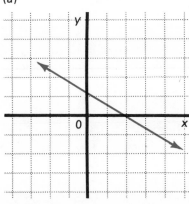

(b)

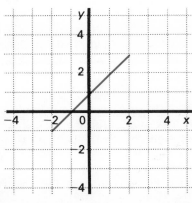

(c)

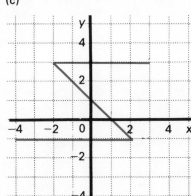

(d)

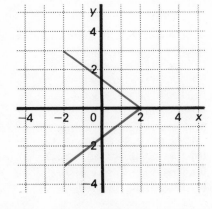

(e)

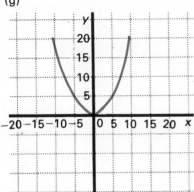

(f)

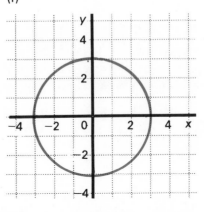

(g)

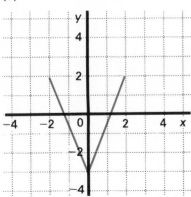

(h)

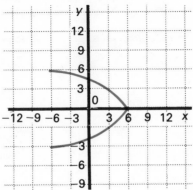

State the output of the
following flow chart.

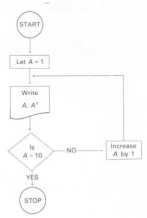

(i)

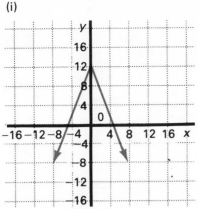

9. If $A = \{-1, 0, 1, 2, 3\}$, list and graph the following relations.

(a) $\{(x, y) \mid y = x, x, y \in A\}$

(b) $\{(x, y) \mid y > x, x, y \in A\}$

(c) $\{(x, y) \mid x - y = 2, x, y \in A\}$

(d) $\{(x, y) \mid x = 0, x, y \in A\}$

(e) $\{(x, y) \mid y = -1, x, y \in A\}$

relations and functions   105

10. Graph the following relations. Use at least 3 ordered pairs in each case.

(a) $\{(x, y) \mid y = 2x + 2, x, y \in R\}$

(b) $\{(x, y) \mid y = 3x - 4, x, y \in R\}$

(c) $\{(x, y) \mid y = 4x + 3, x, y \in R\}$

(d) $\{(x, y) \mid y = 5 - 3x, x, y \in R\}$

(e) $\{(x, y) \mid y = -x - 7, x, y \in R\}$

(f) $\{(x, y) \mid y = \dfrac{x - 3}{2}, x, y \in R\}$

(g) $\{(x, y) \mid y = -\tfrac{2}{3}x - 1, x, y \in R\}$

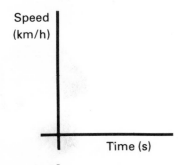

Speed
(km/h)

Time (s)

11. You are the driver of a car entered in a 200 m race. The track is straight. Sketch a graph of speed versus time from the start of the race to the finish. What is a reasonable domain and range for this relation?

Height
(m)

Time (s)

12. The height of a punted football depends on the number of seconds since it was punted. Sketch a graph of height versus time.

13. If $f(x) = 3x - 2$ and $h(x) = (x - 2)^2$, find

(a) $f(-4)$ (b) $h(-2)$ (c) $f(1) + h(1)$

(d) $h(4) - f(-2)$ (e) $2[f(4)] + 3[f(-1)]$ (f) $4[h(2)] - 2[f(-4)]$

14. Graph the following functions.

(a) $f(x) = 2x - 3, x \in R$

(b) $f : x \rightarrow 1 - 3x, x \in R$

(c) $h(x) = 3x + 5, x \in R$

(d) $m : x \rightarrow -\tfrac{1}{2}x - 4, x \in R$

(e) $g(x) = \dfrac{4 - 2x}{3}, x \in R$

15. Graph the following relations and determine which are functions.

(a) $y = 2x^2, -2 \le x \le 2, x, y \in R$

(b) $y = -x^2 + 4, -2 \le x \le 2, x, y \in R$

(c) $x = 2y^2, -2 \le y \le 2, x, y \in R$

(d) $y = |x| + 4, x, y \in R$

(e) $y = |x - 3|, x, y \in R$

(f) $x = |y| - 4, x, y \in R$

REVIEW AND PREVIEW TO CHAPTER 5

EXERCISE 1

GRAPHING ON A NUMBER LINE

1. Graph the solution set of the following.

(a) $2x+3\leqq11, x \in I$

(b) $3x-1>8, x \in I$

(c) $3-2x<15, x \in R$

(d) $4-x\leqq5, x \in R$

(e) $3x+5>x-11, x \in R$

(f) $2-3x\leqq2x+7, x \in R$

(g) $3(x-1)>5x-13, x \in R$

(h) $2(1-2x)<6-(x+1), x \in R$

2. Graph the solution set of the following, where $x \in R$

(a) $3x+1\geqq7$ and $2x-3\leqq7$

(b) $3x-1<8$ and $4x+1\geqq-7$

(c) $1-3x>2x-4$ or $1-x\leqq2x-5$

(d) $2(x-3)+7>3x+5$ and $7\leqq2(1-2x)+1$

(e) $5-(x-4)\geqq3(1-x)-4$ or $3x+2(x-1)\leqq8-(x+4)$

(f) $\dfrac{x-1}{2}\leqq5$ and $\dfrac{x-4}{3}>1$

(g) $2-(1-3x)<2(1+x)-6$ or $2x-3(x-4)<9$

EXERCISE 2

1. Express each of the following in terms of the indicated variable.

(a) If $A = lw$ then $l = $ ▨ and $w = $ ▨

(b) If $I = prt$ then $p = $ ▨ and $t = $ ▨

(c) If $C = 2\pi r$, then $r = $ ▨

(d) If $V = lwh$, then $l = $ ▨ and $w = $ ▨

(e) If $D = ST$ then $S = $ ▨ and $T = $ ▨

(f) If $A = \frac{1}{2}bh$, then $h = $ ▨ and $b = $ ▨

(g) If $P = 2(l+w)$, then $l = $ ▨ and $w = $ ▨

(h) If $A = \dfrac{h}{2}(a+b)$, then $h = $ ▨ and $b = $ ▨

(i) If $Ax + By + C = 0$, then $x = $ ▨ and $y = $ ▨

(j) If $A = \pi r^2$, then $r = $ ▨

CHAPTER 5

Equations of Lines

The human mind has never invented a labor-saving machine equal to algebra.

The Nation, Vol. 33.

5.1   RELATIONS DEFINED BY $y = mx + b$

An equation of degree one is called a *linear equation*.

Unless otherwise stated, $x, y \in R$

$3x + 5 = 14$ is called a linear equation in one variable.
$2x + 3y = 6$ is called a linear equation in two variables.

An equation of degree two is called a *quadratic equation*.

$x^2 + 7x + 12 = 0$ is a quadratic equation in one variable.
$x^2 + y^2 = 25$ is a quadratic equation in two variables.

An equation of degree three is called a *cubic equation*.

$x^3 - 27 = 0$ is a cubic equation in one variable.

In this section we shall study linear equations and inequalities in two variables.

In order to graph a linear equation such as $3x + 2y - 6 = 0$ we must find ordered pairs that satisfy the equation. Determining the ordered pairs is simplified if the equation is expressed in the form $y = mx + b$.

EXAMPLE 1. *Express the relation $3x + 2y - 6 = 0$ in the form $y = mx + b$ and then graph the relation.*

Solution

$$3x + 2y - 6 = 0$$
$$2y = -3x + 6$$
$$y = -\tfrac{3}{2}x + 3$$

x	$-\tfrac{3}{2}x + 3$	y
-2	$-\tfrac{3}{2}(-2) + 3$	6
0	$-\tfrac{3}{2}(0) + 3$	3
2	$-\tfrac{3}{2}(2) + 3$	0
4	$-\tfrac{3}{2}(4) + 3$	-3

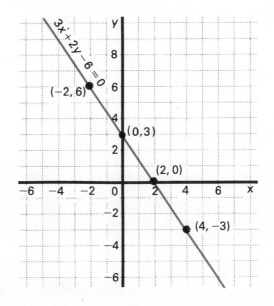

We may have expressed the equation in terms of x and found ordered pairs. However, as we shall see in Chapter 6, the $y = mx + b$ form of an equation can be used to determine important characteristics about the graph of a line.

EXERCISE 5-1

A **1.** State the degree of the following expressions and equations.

(a) $3x^2 + 5x - 4$
(b) $2a + 3b$
(c) $6x^3 - 5x^4 + 6$
(d) $3x + 7 = 10$
(e) $3a^3 - 5 = 0$
(f) $4x^2y^3 + 3xy$
(g) $2xy + 3x^2 - 4x$
(h) $3ab - 4a + 2b$
(i) $x^2 + y^2 = 16$
(j) $2m^2n + 3m^2 - 6$
(k) $12x^5 - 3x^3y^3 + 4$
(l) $2x^3 - 162 = 0$
(m) $y = 3x + 5$
(n) $y = 2x^2 + 3x - 4$
(o) $2x^2y - 3x^3 + 4x^2y^2$

B Express the following equations in the form $y = mx + b$.

2. (a) $y + 2x = 7$
(b) $y - 4x + 3 = 0$
(c) $y + 5x = 0$
(d) $y - 3 = 0$
(e) $2x = y + 7$
(f) $y - 6x = 0$
(g) $6 = 3x + y$
(h) $-3x = y - 4$

3. (a) $x - y = 6$
(b) $4x - y + 7 = 0$
(c) $-y - 3x = 5$
(d) $6x = 5 - y$
(e) $4x - y = 0$
(f) $2 - y = 0$
(g) $3 = 7x - y$
(h) $0 = -x - y$

How many words of four letters or more can you form using the letters in the word RATIONAL?

4. (a) $3x + 2y = 5$ (b) $5x + 4y = 3$
(c) $3y + 2x + 8 = 0$ (d) $2x + 7y = 0$
(e) $x + 3y - 3 = 0$ (f) $4x = 3 + 2y$
(g) $3 = 4x + 2y$ (h) $x + 4 = 3y$

5. (a) $2x - 3y = 7$ (b) $x - 4y + 5 = 0$
(c) $5x - 2y - 10 = 0$ (d) $2x - 2y = 7$
(e) $10x = 5y - 4$ (f) $7x - 2y = -6$
(g) $4x - 5y = 0$ (h) $5y - 1 = 0$

6. (a) $\frac{1}{2}x + 3y = 4$ (b) $\frac{1}{3}x + 2y = 8$

(c) $\dfrac{2x}{3} - \dfrac{y}{2} = 5$ (d) $\frac{1}{5}x - \frac{1}{2}y = \frac{3}{2}$

(e) $\dfrac{y}{4} - 3 = \dfrac{x}{5}$ (f) $3x - \frac{3}{4}y + 5 = 0$

7. Express the following relations in the form $y = mx + b$, and then graph the relation. Use at least 3 ordered pairs for each.
(a) $2x + y = 7$ (b) $3x + y = 4$
(c) $4x + y + 4 = 0$ (d) $2x - y = 5$ Unless otherwise
(e) $6x - 2y = 5$ (f) $3x - 2y + 6 = 0$ stated, $x, y \in R$.
(g) $5x - 2y = 0$ (h) $x + 3y = 0$
(i) $3y - 9x = -2$ (j) $4x = 7 - 3y$

5.2 GRAPHING USING INTERCEPTS

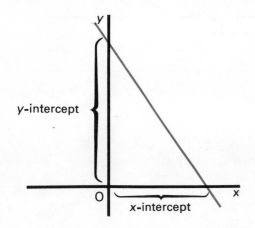

Relations may be graphed using the intercepts. The x-intercept of a relation is the x-coordinate of the point where the relation intersects the x-axis. The y-intercept of a relation is the y-coordinate of the point where the relation intersects the y-axis.

EXAMPLE 1. *Graph the relation* $4x - 3y = 12$, $x, y \in R$.

Solution
To find the x-intercept, let $y = 0$

$$4x - 3y = 12$$
$$4x - 3(0) = 12$$
$$4x = 12$$
$$x = 3$$

To find the y-intercept, let $x = 0$

$$4x - 3y = 12$$
$$4(0) - 3y = 12$$
$$-3y = 12$$
$$y = -4$$

3 is called the x-intercept and -4 the y-intercept.

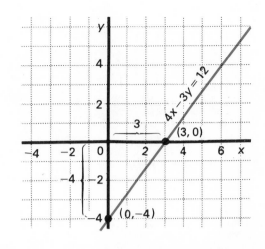

EXERCISE 5-2

A **1.** State the x-and y-intercepts of each of the following.
(a) $2x + 3y = 6$
(b) $4x + 3y = 12$
(c) $3x + y = 9$
(d) $x + 4y = 8$
(e) $5x - 2y = 10$
(f) $7x - 3y = 21$
(g) $4x - 5y = -20$
(h) $3x - 5y = -15$
(i) $7x + 2y - 14 = 0$
(j) $8x - 3y + 24 = 0$
(k) $y = 4x - 8$
(l) $y = -3x + 12$

State a relation that does not have an x-intercept.

Use the x-and y-intercepts to graph the following relations.

B **2.** (a) $4x + 5y = 20$
(b) $3x - 4y = 12$
(c) $2x + y = 4$
(d) $5x + 3y = 15$
(e) $x - y = -7$
(f) $5x + 2y = -10$
(g) $2x + 7y - 14 = 0$
(h) $x - 3y + 6 = 0$

3. (a) $y = 3x - 6$
(b) $y = -2x + 4$
(c) $y = -x - 3$
(d) $y = \frac{1}{2}x + 2$
(e) $y = -\frac{1}{3}x + 1$
(f) $\dfrac{x}{2} + \dfrac{y}{3} = 1$
(g) $\dfrac{x}{4} - \dfrac{y}{2} = 3$
(h) $\frac{2}{3}x - \frac{1}{4}y = -2$

State a relation that does not have a y-intercept.

C **4.** State (if any), the x-and y-intercepts of each of the following.
(a) $\{(x, y) \mid 2x - 3 = 0,\ x,\ y \in R\}$
(b) $\{(x, y) \mid y + 3 = 0,\ x,\ y \in R\}$
(c) $\{(x, y) \mid y = x^2 - 9,\ x,\ y \in R\}$
(d) $\{(x, y) \mid y = 2x^2 - 8,\ x,\ y \in R\}$
(e) $\{(x, y) \mid x^2 + y^2 = 25,\ x,\ y \in R\}$
(f) $\{(x, y) \mid 9x^2 + 4y^2 = 36,\ x,\ y \in R\}$

$$x^2 - 81 = 0$$
$$x^2 = 81$$
$$x = 9$$
or
$$x = -9$$

5.3 POSSIBLE VALUES OF A RELATION

Before proceeding with the graphing of inequalities, it is necessary to become proficient at determining which ordered pairs satisfy a relation and which do not.

5	14	12	28
9	22	17	░░
8	20	15	34
13	30	19	42

Determine the pattern.
Find the missing number.

EXAMPLE 1. *Does* (7, 2) *satisfy the relation* $3x - 5y = 11$?

Solution
When $x = 7$ and $y = 2$, L.S. $= 3x - 5y$
$$= 3(7) - 5(2)$$
$$= 21 - 10$$
$$= 11$$
R.S. $= 11$
L.S. $=$ R.S.

(7, 2) does satisfy the relation $3x - 5y = 11$.

EXAMPLE 2. *Does* (3, 6) *satisfy the relation* $y = 4x - 7$?

Solution
When $y = 6$, L.S. $= y$
$$= 6$$
When $x = 3$, R.S. $= 4x - 7$
$$= 4(3) - 7$$
$$= 12 - 7$$
$$= 5$$
L.S. $\neq$ R.S.

(3, 6) does not satisfy $y = 4x - 7$.

EXAMPLE 3. *Does* (3, 9) *satisfy the relation* $y \leq 2x + 4$?

Solution
When $y = 9$, L.S. $= y$
$$= 9$$
When $x = 3$, R.S. $= 2x + 4$
$$= 2(3) + 4$$
$$= 10$$
For (3, 9), L.S. $<$ R.S.
Since in $y \leq 2x + 4$, L.S. $\leq$ R.S.
(3, 9) satisfies the relation $y \leq 2x + 4$.

EXAMPLE 4. *Does* (−1, −2) *satisfy the relation* $2x - 5y > 9$?

Solution
When $x = -1$ and $y = -2$, L.S. $= 2x - 5y$
$$= 2(-1) - 5(-2)$$
$$= -2 + 10$$
$$= 8$$
R.S. $= 9$

For $(-1, -2)$ L.S. $<$ R.S.

Since in $2x-5y>9$, L.S. $>$ R.S.

$(-1, -2)$ does not satisfy the relation $2x-5y>9$.

EXERCISE 5-3

A **1.** State which of the following ordered pairs satisfy the relation $x+2y=12$.

(a) $(4, 4)$ (b) $(0, 5)$ (c) $(-2, 7)$ (d) $(12, 0)$

(e) $(1, 6)$ (f) $(14, -1)$ (g) $(16, -3)$ (h) $(5, 4)$

A litre bottle had all dimensions doubled. What is the new volume of the new bottle?

2. State which of the following ordered pairs satisfy the relation $3x-2y=12$.

(a) $(4, 0)$ (b) $(0, 6)$ (c) $(5, 1)$ (d) $(6, 3)$

(e) $(-1, -8)$ (f) $(2, -3)$ (g) $(-2, 8)$ (h) $(3, 1)$

3. Determine which of the following ordered pairs satisfy the relation $y=3x-6$.

(a) $(2, 0)$ (b) $(5, 8)$ (c) $(-1, -10)$ (d) $(-2, -12)$

(e) $(0, -5)$ (f) $(1, -2)$ (g) $(4, 8)$ (h) $(-3, -15)$

B **4.** Determine which of the following ordered pairs satisfy the relation $y<3x-5$.

(a) $(1, -4)$ (b) $(5, 9)$ (c) $(-2, -8)$ (d) $(1, -1)$

(e) $(3, 6)$ (f) $(-1, -9)$ (g) $(2, 0)$ (h) $(6, 14)$

5. State which of the following ordered pairs satisfy $4x+3y\geqq12$.

(a) $(1, 3)$ (b) $(4, -2)$ (c) $(-2, 7)$ (d) $(0, 4)$

(e) $(2, 1)$ (f) $(3, 0)$ (g) $(-1, 6)$ (h) $(4, -2)$

6. Determine whether the ordered pair satisfies the relation.

(a) $2x-3y>6$; $(-1, -3)$ (b) $5x+2y<10$; $(-1, 9)$

(c) $4x-3y>12$; $(1, -2)$ (d) $x+2y<6$; $(0, 3)$

(e) $5x-3y\leqq15$; $(3, 0)$ (f) $5x+4y\geqq20$; $(-1, 7)$

(g) $2x+9y>18$; $(1, 2)$ (h) $5x-2y\leqq10$; $(-1, -7)$

(i) $2x-y<1$; $(-2, 1)$ (j) $7x+3y\geqq21$; $(0, 6)$

(k) $4x-3y\leqq25$; $(4, -3)$ (l) $x-3y>0$; $(-4, -1)$

(m) $x+4y<7$; $(-2, 2)$ (n) $5x+y<2$; $(1, -2)$

7. Determine whether the ordered pair satisfies the relation.

(a) $y>3x+1$; $(-1, 1)$ (b) $y\leqq2x-4$; $(2, 0)$

(c) $y<x-5$; $(-1, -6)$ (d) $y>3x-4$; $(-1, -5)$

(e) $y\geqq2x+5$; $(1, 6)$ (f) $y\leqq4x-6$; $(1, 0)$

(g) $y<1-3x$; $(-1, 4)$ (h) $y\geqq2-4x$; $(-1, 6)$

(i) $y>5x+7$; $(3, 24)$ (j) $y<1-x$; $(-2, 3)$

(k) $y\leqq2x-1$; $(-1, -4)$ (l) $y>3x+2$; $(-4, -11)$

(m) $y<3x$; $(3, 9)$ (n) $y>-x-1$; $(1, -3)$

8. Find 5 ordered pairs that satisfy each of the following relations.

(a) $3x+2y\geqq6$ (b) $x-2y\leqq4$

(c) $y>2x+1$ (d) $y\leqq3x-7$

(e) $5x-2y>15$ (f) $y<-2x+4$

(g) $x-4y>1$ (h) $y>-3x+11$

(i) $3x-4y<-6$ (j) $y\leqq5-4x$

C **9.** Determine the value of *m* so that the given ordered pair satisfies the given relation.
(a) $mx + 3y = 12$; $(3, 2)$ (b) $mx - 2y = 18$; $(4, 1)$
(c) $3x + my = 22$; $(6, -1)$ (d) $5x + my = -22$; $(-2, -4)$
(e) $2x + my = -2$; $(-4, -2)$ (f) $mx + 5y + 7 = 0$; $(-3, 1)$
(g) $2x - 3y + m = 0$; $(-4, -2)$ (h) $4x + my - 10 = 0$; $(2, -4)$

Which of the following figures can you make from
the pattern above?

5.4 GRAPHING INEQUALITIES—PART I

The graph of a linear relation divides the plane into 3 distinct regions.
Consider the graph of the relation $y = x$, $x, y \in R$

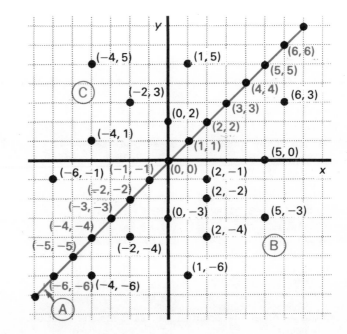

Region *A*: For every point here, $y = x$.
Region *B*: For every point here, $y < x$.
Region *C*: For every point here, $y > x$.

EXAMPLE 1. *Sketch the graph of $y = 2x + 1$ and indicate on the graph the regions*
(i) $y = 2x + 1$
(ii) $y > 2x + 1$
(iii) $y < 2x + 1$

Solution

The region where $y = 2x + 1$ is the straight line. In order to determine the regions $y > 2x + 1$ and $y < 2x + 1$ we select a test point $(-3, 4)$, not on the line, and determine which of the two remaining relations the test point satisfies.

For the relation $y = 2x + 1$
when $y = 4$, L.S. $= y$

$$= 4$$

when $x = -3$, R.S. $= 2x + 1$

$$= 2(-3) + 1$$

$$= -5$$

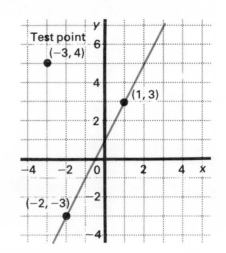

At the point $(-3, 4)$, since $4 > -5$

$$\text{L.S.} > \text{R.S.}$$

In the region of the test point,

$$y > 2x + 1.$$

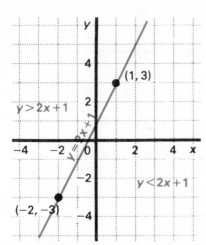

EXAMPLE 2. *Sketch the graph of $3x - 2y = 6$ and indicate the regions*

(i) $3x - 2y = 6$
(ii) $3x - 2y > 6$
(iii) $3x - 2y < 6$

Solution

For this example it is convenient to use the "intercept method" to draw the graph. In this case the point $(0, 0)$ is a convenient test point.

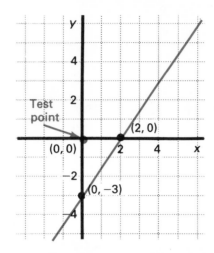

For the relation $3x - 2y = 6$
when $x = 0$ and $y = 0$, L.S. $= 3x - 2y$
$$= 3(0) - 2(0)$$
$$= 0$$
R.S. $= 6$

At the point $(0, 0)$, since $0 < 6$
$$\text{L.S.} < \text{R.S.}$$

In the region of the test point
$$3x - 2y < 6.$$

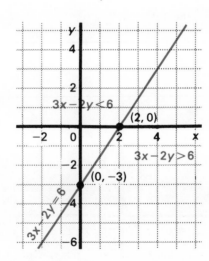

At the farm, Bill counted the heads and legs of the cows and chickens. He counted 78 legs and 35 heads. How many cows were there?

EXERCISE 5-4

B **1.** Draw the graph of each of the following relations and indicate the 3 regions associated with each for $x, y \in R$.

(a) $y = x + 2$ (b) $y = 3x - 4$

(c) $y = x - 5$ (d) $4x + 3y = 12$

(e) $5x - 2y = 10$ (f) $y = 3 - 2x$

(g) $x - 3y = 6$ (h) $2x - y = -4$

(i) $y = \dfrac{x+1}{2}$

(j) $y = \frac{1}{3}x - 1$

(k) $3x - y - 6 = 0$

(l) $x + y = 0$

2. Draw the graph of each of the following relations and indicate the 3 regions associated with each.

For $x = 3$, the regions are
(i) $x = 3$ (ii) $x > 3$ (iii) $x < 3$

(a) $\{(x, y) \mid x = 3, \ x, \ y \in R\}$
(b) $\{(x, y) \mid y = -4, \ x, \ y \in R\}$
(c) $\{(x, y) \mid x = -5, \ x, \ y \in R\}$
(d) $\{(x, y) \mid y = 0, \ x, \ y \in R\}$

5.5 GRAPHING INEQUALITIES—PART II

In the previous section we found that a line divides the plane into three regions. In this section we will graph one or two of these regions.

EXAMPLE 1. *Draw the graph of $y \leqq 2x - 3$*

Solution
In this problem we are asked to show two of the three regions, namely $y = 2x - 3$ and $y < 2x - 3$.

First, draw the boundary line $y = 2x - 3$. In this case the point $(0, 0)$ is a convenient test point.

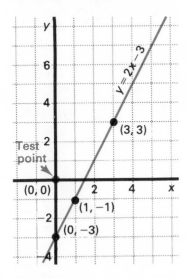

For the relation $y = 2x - 3$
when $y = 0$, L.S. $= y$
$= 0$
when $x = 0$, R.S. $= 2x - 3$
$= 2(0) - 3$
$= -3$
At the point $(0, 0)$, since $0 > -3$
L.S. $>$ R.S.

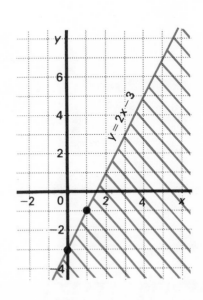

In the region of the test point $y > 2x - 3$

The region $y < 2x - 3$ is on the other side of the line. The graph of $y \leqq 2x - 3$ is shown at right. Some sort of markings or shading must be used to indicate the required region.

EXAMPLE 2. *Draw the graph of $2x + 3y > 6$*

Solution
Draw the boundary line $2x + 3y = 6$. The intercept method is convenient for this example. The test point selected lies anywhere except on the line. In this example we will use $(4, 3)$ as the test point.

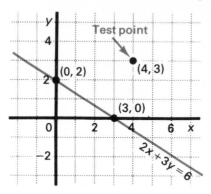

For the relation $2x + 3y = 6$
When $x = 4$ and $y = 3$, L.S. $= 2x + 3y$
$$= 2(4) + 3(3)$$
$$= 17$$
R.S. $= 6$
At the point $(4, 3)$, since $17 > 6$
$$\text{L.S.} > \text{R.S.}$$
In the region of the test point $2x + 3y > 6$.

The graph of $2x + 3y > 6$ is shown at right.

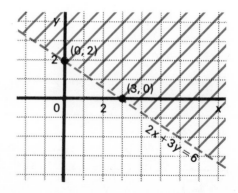

The line $2x + 3y = 6$ is shown as a broken line since it is not part of the solution.

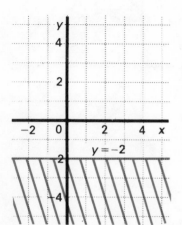

EXAMPLE 3. *Draw the graph of*
$$\{(x, y) \mid y \leq -2, \ x, y \in R\}$$

Solution
Draw the boundary line $y = -2$. A test point will show that the region where $y < -2$ is below the boundary line.

INVESTIGATION 5-5 *Inequalities Involving* $y = mx + b$

1. (a) Draw the graph of each of the following.

(i) $y > 2x + 1$

(ii) $y > 3x - 4$

(iii) $y > -x + 6$

(iv) $y > -3x - 1$

(b) For $y > mx + b$, is the required region above the line or below the line?

2. (a) Draw the graph of each of the following.

(i) $y < 3x + 4$

(ii) $y < 2x - 5$

(iii) $y < -x - 5$

(iv) $y < -2x + 3$

(b) *For* $y < mx + b$, is the required region above the line or below the line?

Use $+$, $-$, $\times$, $\div$, ( ) to make a true statement.

$$7 \ 1 \ 2 = 2 \ 2 \ 2$$

> For $y > mx + b$, the required region is above the line. For $y < mx + b$, the required region is below the line. These rules hold only when the defining relation is expressed in the form $y > mx + b$ or $y < mx + b$.

EXERCISE 5-5

B Draw the graph of each of the following for $x, y \in R$

1. (a) $y \geq 3x + 5$ (b) $y \leq 2x - 1$

(c) $y < 4 + 2x$ (d) $y > -3x + 2$

(e) $y \geq 5x - 1$ (f) $y \leq -x - 5$

(g) $y < -4x$ (h) $y > 4 - 3x$

2. (a) $2x - 3y \geq 6$ (b) $5x + 4y \leq 20$

(c) $4x - 3y > 12$ (d) $x + 3y < 9$

(e) $3x - 5y - 15 \geq 0$ (f) $x + 4y < 2$

(g) $9x - 2y > -18$ (h) $2y - 7x \geq 14$

3. (a) $\{(x, y) \mid x \geq 2, x, y \in R\}$ (b) $\{(x, y) \mid y < 3, x, y \in R\}$

(c) $\{(x, y) \mid x < -3, x, y \in R\}$ (d) $\{(x, y) \mid y \geq -2, x, y \in R\}$

(e) $\{(x, y) \mid x \geq 0, x, y \in R\}$ (f) $\{(x, y) \mid y \geq 0, x, y \in R\}$

4. (a) $y \geq \dfrac{x - 1}{3}$ (b) $y < \dfrac{1 - 2x}{2}$

(c) $y > -\tfrac{1}{2}x + 4$ (d) $\dfrac{x}{3} - \dfrac{y}{4} \leq 1$

(e) $y - 2 < 3x$ (f) $y - 2x \geq 0$

■■×■=■■

Put 5 different digits in the spaces to make the statement true. The digits must total 27.

5.6 INTERSECTION AND UNION OF LINEAR INEQUALITIES

In this section we shall determine the intersection or union of two or more linear inequalities. Recall that for an intersection we use "and" or "∩". For union we use "or" or "∪".

EXAMPLE 1. *Graph the following:*

$$\{(x, y) \mid y \geqq 2x - 1 \quad \text{and} \quad y \leqq -x + 2\}$$

Solution
Graph each relation on the same set of axes.

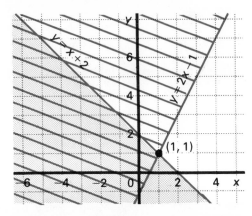

The intersection is the double shaded region which contains all the points that satisfy both inequalities.

EXAMPLE 2. *Graph the following:*

$$\{(x, y) \mid 2x - 3y < 6 \quad \text{and} \quad 5x + 3y \leqq 15\}$$

Solution
Graph each relation on the same set of axes.
  The intersection is the double shaded region. As indicated on the graph, the point $(3, 0)$ is not included in the intersection.

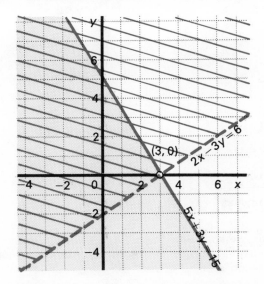

EXAMPLE 3. *Graph the following:*

$$\{(x, y) \mid x \leq 5 \cap x \geq -1 \quad \text{and} \quad y \leq 4 \cap y \geq -2\}$$

Solution
Graph each relation on the same set of axes. The required intersection is the shaded region.

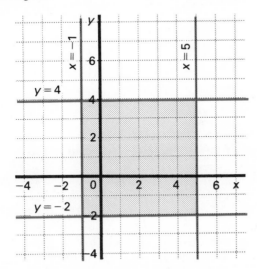

EXERCISE 5-6

A **1.** State the quadrant or quadrants defined by each of the following.
   (a) $\{(x, y) \mid y \geq 0 \quad \text{and} \quad x \geq 0\}$
   (b) $\{(x, y) \mid x \leq 0 \quad \text{and} \quad y \geq 0\}$
   (c) $\{(x, y) \mid x \geq 0 \quad \text{or} \quad y \geq 0\}$
   (d) $\{(x, y) \mid y \leq 0 \quad \text{and} \quad x \geq 0\}$
   (e) $\{(x, y) \mid x \leq 0 \quad \text{or} \quad y \leq 0\}$
   (f) $\{(x, y) \mid y \leq 0 \quad \text{and} \quad x \leq 0\}$
   (g) $\{(x, y) \mid x \leq 0 \quad \text{or} \quad y \geq 0\}$

B **2.** Graph the following.
   (a) $\{(x, y) \mid y \geq x + 3 \quad \text{and} \quad y \leq -x + 4\}$
   (b) $\{(x, y) \mid y \leq 2x + 1 \quad \text{and} \quad y \leq 3 - 2x\}$
   (c) $\{(x, y) \mid y > 3x + 2 \quad \text{or} \quad y \leq 2 - 2x\}$
   (d) $\{(x, y) \mid y < \frac{1}{2}x + 3 \quad \text{and} \quad y > x - 5\}$
   (e) $\{(x, y) \mid y \leq 2x \quad \text{and} \quad y \geq -3x\}$

3. Graph the following.
   (a) $\{(x, y) \mid x + 2y \leq 4 \quad \text{and} \quad x - 3y \geq 6\}$
   (b) $\{(x, y) \mid 2x + 3y \geq 6 \quad \text{and} \quad 4x + 3y \leq 12\}$
   (c) $\{(x, y) \mid x - y < 5 \quad \text{or} \quad x + 3y > 9\}$
   (d) $\{(x, y) \mid 2x - y \geq 8 \quad \text{and} \quad 2x + y < 6\}$
   (e) $\{(x, y) \mid 3x - y < 9 \quad \text{or} \quad x - 5y \leq -10\}$

	y	
Second quadrant		First quadrant
	0	x
Third quadrant		Fourth quadrant

Unless otherwise stated,
$x, y \in R$

Put the numbers from 1 to
9 in the spaces to make
the statements true.

$\square - \square + \square = 10$

$\square + \square - \square = 10$

$\square \div \square + \square = 10$

4. Graph the following.
(a) $\{(x, y) \mid x \geq 2$ and $y \leq 3\}$
(b) $\{(x, y) \mid y \geq -2$ and $x \leq -1\}$
(c) $\{(x, y) \mid x \leq 3$ and $x \geq -2\}$
(d) $\{(x, y) \mid y < 4$ and $y > -2\}$
(e) $\{(x, y) \mid x < 3$ or $y \leq 2\}$

5. Graph the following.
(a) $\{(x, y) \mid x \leq 4$ and $y \leq 3$ and $x \geq -2$ and $y \geq -5\}$
(b) $\{(x, y) \mid x \leq -1$ and $x \geq -4$ and $y \leq 6$ and $y \geq 1\}$
(c) $\{(x, y) \mid x \geq 5$ or $y \geq 4$ or $x \leq -3\}$
(d) $\{(x, y) \mid x > 4$ and $x < 7$ and $y > -2$ and $y < 5\}$
(e) $\{(x, y) \mid x \leq -2$ and $x > -6$ and $y \leq -1$ and $y > -5\}$
(f) $\{(x, y) \mid y < 3$ and $x \leq -2$ and $x \geq -5\}$

6. Graph the following.
(a) $\{(x, y) \mid 5x + 2y \leq 10$ and $x \geq 0$ and $y \geq 0\}$
(b) $\{(x, y) \mid 3y - 4x \leq 12$ and $x \leq 0$ and $y \geq 0\}$
(c) $\{(x, y) \mid 6x - 5y \leq 30$ and $3x - 2y \leq 6$ and $x \geq 0 \cap y \geq 0\}$
(d) $\{(x, y) \mid 7x + 5y \leq 35$ and $x - y \leq 1$ and $5y - 6x \leq 30\}$
(e) $\{(x, y) \mid 7x + 3y \leq 21$ and $4x + 5y \leq 20$ and $x \geq 0$ and $y \geq 0\}$
(f) $\{(x, y) \mid 5x + 4y \leq 20$ and $3y - 4x \leq 12$ and $y \geq 0\}$
(g) $\{(x, y) \mid 4x + 5y \leq 20$ and $5y - 6x \leq 30$ and $y \geq -3\}$

C **7.** Graph the following.
(a) $\{(x, y) \mid |x| \leq 3$ and $|y| \leq 2\}$
(b) $\{(x, y) \mid |y| \geq 2$ and $|x| \geq 3\}$
(c) $\{(x, y) \mid |x| \geq 2$ and $y > 4\}$
(d) $\{(x, y) \mid |y| \leq 3$ and $x \geq -2\}$
(e) $\{(x, y) \mid |x| + |y| \leq 6\}$

REVIEW EXERCISE

A **1.** State the degree of the following expressions and equations.
(a) $4x + 5y = 14$
(b) $3x^2 + 4xy - 2y^3$
(c) $x^3 - 8 = 0$
(d) $5xy - 4x + y$
(e) $2x^2y - 3x^2 + 4$
(f) $y = 2x^2 + 6x - 7$
(g) $x^4y - 3x^2y^2 + y^4$
(h) $x^2 + 7x + 10 = 0$
(i) $3a^3b^2 - 4a^3b^3 + 5a^2b^3$

$1^3 + 6^3 + 8^3 = 9^3$
Find another set of num-
bers, each less than 10,
with this characteristic

2. State the x and y intercepts of the following.
(a) $4x + 5y = 20$
(b) $x + 2y = 10$
(c) $3x - y = 6$
(d) $7x - 2y = 14$
(e) $2x - 3y = -6$
(f) $y = 4x - 4$
(g) $2x + 9y - 18 = 0$
(h) $y = -4x + 12$
(i) $6x - 5y + 30 = 0$

3. State which of the following ordered pairs satisfy the equation $2x + 3y = 24$.
(a) $(12, 0)$
(b) $(2, 6)$
(c) $(0, 9)$
(d) $(1, 7)$
(e) $(3, 6)$
(f) $(6, 4)$
(g) $(10, 2)$
(h) $(-1, 9)$

4. State which of the following ordered pairs satisfy the equation $y = 4x - 6$.
(a) $(1, -3)$
(b) $(-2, -14)$
(c) $(0, -6)$
(d) $(3, 7)$
(e) $(2, 2)$
(f) $(-1, -7)$
(g) $(10, 36)$
(h) $(-5, -26)$

5. Express the following in the form $y = mx + b$.
(a) $3x + y = 14$
(b) $4x + 2y = 9$
(c) $5x - 3y = 6$
(d) $7x - 2y + 4 = 0$

(e) $x - y - 7 = 0$
(f) $\dfrac{x}{2} - \dfrac{y}{3} = 2$

6. Express each of the following in the form $y = mx + b$ and then graph the relation.
(a) $3x + y = 4$
(b) $2x - y = 5$
(c) $4x - 2y = 7$
(d) $2x - 4y - 3 = 0$
(e) $4x - 3y = 0$
(f) $\frac{1}{2}x - 2y + 3 = 0$

Unless otherwise stated, $x, y \in R$

7. Use the x-and y-intercepts to graph the following relations.
(a) $7x + 2y = 14$
(b) $5x - 3y = 15$
(c) $x - y = -4$
(d) $4x - 3y - 12 = 0$

(e) $y = 4x + 8$
(f) $\dfrac{x}{2} - \dfrac{y}{3} = 2$

NINE Each letter repre-
FOUR sents a different
FIVE digit in this
      subtraction

8. Determine whether the ordered pair satisfies the relation.
(a) $3x - 2y \geq 6$; $(1, -3)$
(b) $7x + 2y < 10$; $(-1, 8)$
(c) $3x - y > 4$; $(-1, -6)$
(d) $y \geq 2x - 5$; $(1, -2)$
(e) $5x + 3y < 2$; $(1, -1)$
(f) $y < 1 - 4x$; $(-2, 8)$
(g) $3y - 2x < -2$; $(2, 0)$
(h) $6x + 7y > -3$; $(-3, 2)$

9. Draw the graph of each of the following.
(a) $y \geq 2x - 4$
(b) $y < 3x + 5$
(c) $2x - 3y \leq 12$
(d) $4x + 5y > 20$
(e) $y > -2x + 3$
(f) $3x - 4y < -24$
(g) $\{(x, y) \mid x \geq -2, x, y \in R\}$
(h) $\{(x, y) \mid y < 3, x, y \in R\}$

10. Graph the following.
(a) $\{(x, y) \mid y \geq x + 1$ and $y \leq -2x + 7\}$
(b) $\{(x, y) \mid y < 2x + 8$ and $y \geq 3 - 3x\}$
(c) $\{(x, y) \mid y > 2x - 3$ and $y < x + 5\}$
(d) $\{(x, y) \mid 2x + 3y \leq 6$ and $5x - 2y \geq 20\}$
(e) $\{(x, y) \mid x - 3y > 12$ or $2x + y > 6\}$
(f) $\{(x, y) \mid x \geq 3$ and $y \geq -2\}$
(g) $\{(x, y) \mid 4x - 3y \leq 24$ and $y < 6 - 3x\}$

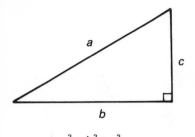

$$a^2 = b^2 + c^2$$

REVIEW AND PREVIEW TO CHAPTER 6

EXERCISE 1

PYTHAGORAS

Use the Pythagorean relationship to determine the missing dimension in each of the following.

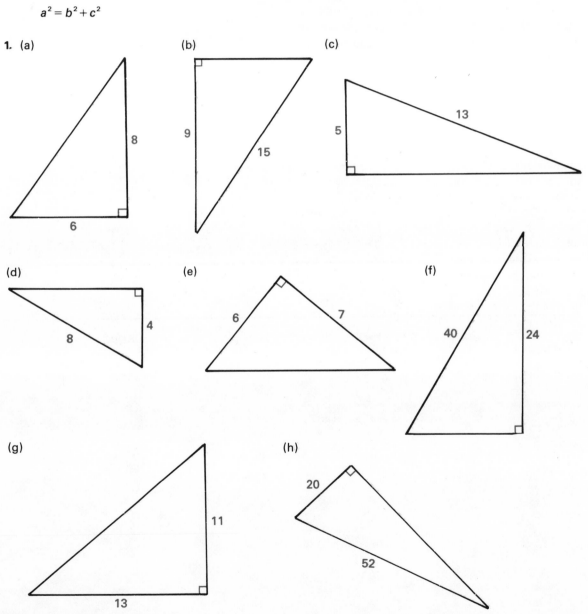

1. (a)

8

6

(b)

9

15

(c)

13

5

(d)

8

4

(e)

6

7

(f)

40

24

(g)

11

13

(h)

20

52

2. (a)

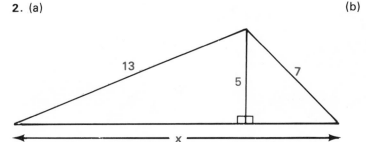

(b)

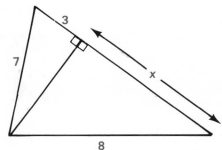

(c)

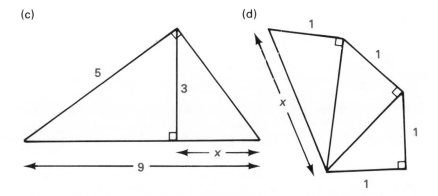

(d)

n	$\sqrt{n}$
1	1.000
2	1.414
3	1.732
4	2.000
5	2.236
6	2.449
7	2.645
8	2.828
9	3.000
10	3.162
11	3.316
12	3.464
13	3.605
14	3.741
15	3.872
16	4.000
17	4.123
18	4.242
19	4.358
20	4.472
21	4.582
22	4.690
23	4.795
24	4.898
25	5.000
26	5.099
27	5.196
28	5.291
29	5.385
30	5.477
31	5.567
32	5.656
33	5.744
34	5.830
35	5.916
36	6.000
37	6.082
38	6.164
39	6.244
40	6.324
41	6.403
42	6.480
43	6.557
44	6.633
45	6.708
46	6.782
47	6.855
48	6.928
49	7.000

EXERCISE 2

$y = mx + b$

1. Express each of the following in the form $y = mx + b$ and state the value of m and b.

(a) $2x + y = 7$

(b) $3x + 2y = 4$

(c) $x - y = 4$

(d) $5x + 3y - 5 = 0$

(e) $x + 3y - 7 = 0$

(f) $4x + 7 = 3y$

(g) $5x - 2 - 3y = 0$

(h) $2y - 11 = 6x$

(i) $5 = 2x - 5y$

(j) $7x = 4 - 3y$

EXERCISE 3

State the x-and y-intercepts of each of the following.

1. (a) $2x + y = 6$

(b) $4x + 3y = 12$

(c) $3x - 2y = 12$

(d) $5x - 3y = 15$

(e) $7x + 2y - 14 = 0$

(f) $5x - 4y + 20 = 0$

(g) $2x + 3y = 0$

(h) $3x = 2y - 6$

(i) $2y = x - 4$

(j) $y = 5x - 10$

(k) $y = -2x + 6$

(l) $y = -x - 3$

CHAPTER 6

Slope and Equations of Lines

The advancement and perfection of mathematics are intimately connected with the prosperity of the State.

Napoleon

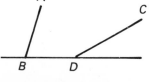

AB has a greater slope (or steepness) than CD.

6.1   SLOPE

The slope of a line is the measure of the amount of steepness of the line. The slope of a line is defined to be the quotient of the vertical change (called the rise) divided by the horizontal change (called the run).

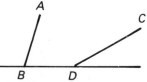

rise

run

$$\text{Slope} = \frac{\text{rise}}{\text{run}} = \frac{\text{vertical change}}{\text{horizontal change}}$$

EXAMPLE 1.   *Find the slope of the line through A(2, 1) and B(6, 4).*

Solution
The vertical change or rise of AB is 3 (the difference in the y coordinates). The horizontal change or run is 4 (the difference in the x coordinates).

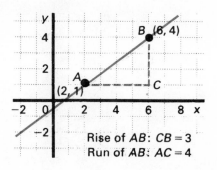

Rise of AB: $CB = 3$
Run of AB: $AC = 4$

$$\text{Slope of line} = \frac{\text{rise of } AB}{\text{run of } AB} = \frac{3}{4}$$

The rise is the vertical change or the difference in the y coordinates and is denoted by Δy (read "delta y"). Similarly the run, the difference in the x coordinates, is denoted by Δx. The letter m is used to denote slope.

$$\text{Slope} = \frac{\text{rise}}{\text{run}} = \frac{\Delta y}{\Delta x} = m$$

EXAMPLE 2. *Find the slope of the line segment joining $A(3, -2)$ to $B(6, 5)$.*

Solution

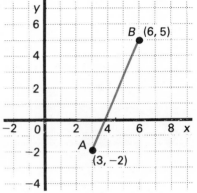

$$m_{AB} = \frac{\Delta y}{\Delta x} \qquad \text{or} \qquad m_{BA} = \frac{\Delta y}{\Delta x}$$

$$= \frac{5 - (-2)}{6 - 3} \qquad\qquad = \frac{-2 - 5}{3 - 6}$$

$$= \frac{7}{3} \qquad\qquad\qquad = \frac{-7}{-3}$$

$$\qquad\qquad\qquad\qquad = \frac{7}{3}$$

The slope of AB is the same as the slope of BA.

EXAMPLE 3. *Find the slope of the line l through $A(4, -2)$ and $B(-5, 6)$.*

Solution
Since the slope of a line is the same as the slope of any segment of the line, to find the slope of l, all we need do is find the slope of AB.

$$m_{AB} = \frac{\Delta y}{\Delta x}$$

$$= \frac{6 - (-2)}{-5 - 4}$$

$$= \frac{8}{-9}$$

$$= -\frac{8}{9}$$

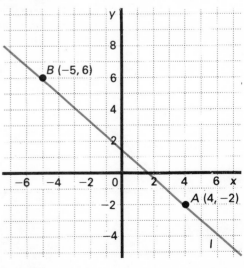

In going from left to right, if a line falls its slope is a negative number.
In going from left to right, if a line rises its slope is a positive number.

EXAMPLE 4. *Find the slope of the line through $P(x_1, y_1)$ and $Q(x_2, y_2)$.*

Solution

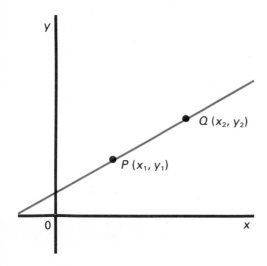

$$m = \frac{\Delta y}{\Delta x}$$

$$= \frac{y_2 - y_1}{x_2 - x_1}$$

Given two points on a line, the slope of the line may be found using
$$m = \frac{y_2 - y_1}{x_2 - x_1}$$

EXERCISE 6-1

A **1.** For the two points indicated on each line,
(i) state the rise
(ii) state the run
(iii) determine the slope of the line.

(a)

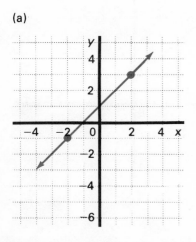

(b)

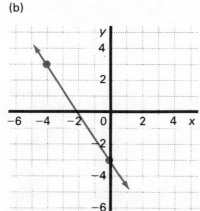

(c)

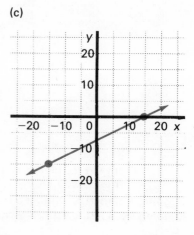

(d)

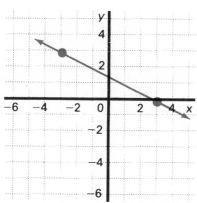

(e)

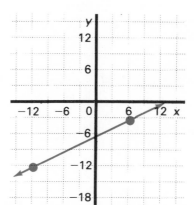

(f)

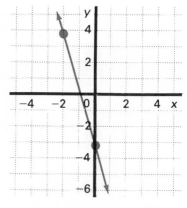

(g)

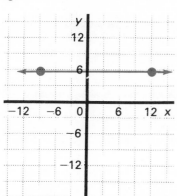

(h)

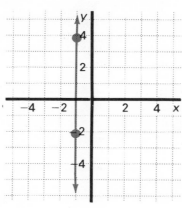

(i)

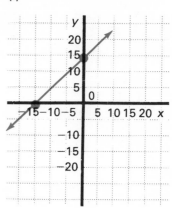

B **2.** Determine the slopes of the lines through the following points.
(a) $A(1, 1)$, $B(4, 3)$
(b) $C(0, 2)$, $D(4, 6)$
(c) $E(5, 7)$, $F(9, 11)$
(d) $G(0, 0)$, $H(5, 6)$
(e) $K(5, 3)$, $L(7, 3)$
(f) $M(-3, 4)$, $N(5, -2)$
(g) $P(-3, -1)$, $Q(-5, 7)$
(h) $R(2, -3)$, $S(0, 4)$

Horizontal lines have a slope of 0.

Vertical lines have no slope.

3. Determine the slopes of the line segments joining the following pairs of points.
(a) $A(6, -8)$, $B(-3, 2)$
(b) $C(7, -3)$, $D(8, -3)$
(c) $E(5, 7)$, $F(5, -2)$
(d) $G(-2, -1)$, $H(-5, -4)$
(e) $K(-6, 7)$, $L(-6, -5)$
(f) $M(8, 0)$, $N(0, 8)$
(g) $R(\frac{1}{2}, 3)$, $S(2, -3)$
(h) $P(\frac{1}{3}, \frac{1}{2})$, $Q(2, 2\frac{1}{2})$
(i) $W(2\frac{1}{5}, -3)$, $R(-3\frac{1}{2}, \frac{1}{2})$
(j) $B(-\frac{1}{2}, 3)$, $A(-\frac{1}{2}, -4)$
(k) $A(3.2, -4.6)$, $B(-2.4, 8.8)$
(l) $C(1.75, -0.3)$, $D(-2.25, -1.7)$
(m) $E(-1.86, -2.14)$, $F(3.58, -0.72)$
(n) $G(11.9, -9.3)$, $H(15.4, 6.7)$

slopes and equations of lines 129

4. Sketch the graph of each of the following and then determine the slope of each line, for $x, y \in R$.

(a) $y = 3x - 2$ (b) $y = 4 - x$

(c) $2x + 3y = 6$ (d) $5x - 3y = 15$

(e) $y = \dfrac{x-1}{3}$ (f) $2x - y - 4 = 0$

(g) $f(x) = 2x - 7$ (h) $f : x \rightarrow 2 - 3x$

C   **5.** (a) A line through $(3, 1)$ and $(4, y)$ has a slope $m = 7$. Find y.

(b) A line through $(6, -2)$ and $(3, y)$ has a slope $m = 2$. Find y.

(c) A line through $(4, -7)$ and $(-2, y)$ has a slope $m = -\frac{2}{3}$. Find y.

(d) A line through $(-2, -3)$ and $(x, 5)$ has a slope $m = 2$. Find x.

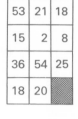

Determine the pattern. Find the missing number.

6.2 LINEAR EQUATION—POINT SLOPE FORM

In this section we will find equations of lines. The slope of a line is equal to the slope of any line segment contained in the line. By using the definition of slope we can determine the equation of a line, given the slope of the line and any point on the line.

EXAMPLE 1. (a) *Determine an equation of a line through* $(3, 1)$ *with slope* $m = 2$.

(b) *Express the equation in the form* $Ax + By + C = 0$

Solution

(a) We must find an equation in x and y that satisfies the given conditions.

Let (x, y) be any point on the line, other than $(3, 1)$. The slope of the line is 2.

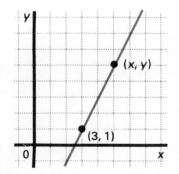

$$m = \frac{\Delta y}{\Delta x}$$

or

$$\frac{\Delta y}{\Delta x} = m$$

then

$$\frac{(y - 1)}{(x - 3)} = 2$$

and

$$(y - 1) = 2(x - 3)$$

(b) It is often convenient to express equations in the form

$$Ax + By + C = 0$$

where $A, B, C \in R$. This is called the standard form of a linear equation.

$$(y - 1) = 2(x - 3)$$

$$y - 1 = 2x - 6$$

$$2x - 6 - y + 1 = 0$$

$$2x - y - 5 = 0$$

EXAMPLE 2. Find the equation of the line through (x_1, y_1) with slope m.

Solution
Let (x, y) be any point on the line other than (x_1, y_1). The slope of the line is m.

$$\frac{\Delta y}{\Delta x} = m$$

then

$$\frac{(y - y_1)}{(x - x_1)} = m$$

and

$$y - y_1 = m(x - x_1)$$

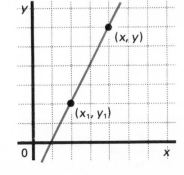

LINEAR EQUATION—POINT SLOPE FORM

Given a point on the line, (x_1, y_1) and the slope of the line m, an equation of the line may be expressed as

$$y - y_1 = m(x - x_1)$$

EXAMPLE 3. (a) *Find an equation of the line through $(2, -3)$ with slope $m = -2$. Express the equation in standard form.*
(b) *Use this equation to find two other points on the line. Check your solutions.*

Solution
(a)

$$y - y_1 = m(x - x_1)$$
$$(x_1, y_1) = (2, -3) \quad \text{and} \quad m = -2$$
$$y - (-3) = -2(x - 2)$$
$$y + 3 = -2(x - 2)$$
$$y + 3 = -2x + 4$$
$$2x + y - 1 = 0$$

(b) To find other points on the line, it is convenient to express the equation in the form $y = mx + b$.

$$2x + y - 1 = 0$$
$$y = -2x + 1$$

when $x = 1$, $y = -2(1) + 1$
$$= -2 + 1$$
$$= -1$$
when $x = 3$, $y = -2(3) + 1$
$$= -6 + 1$$
$$= -5$$

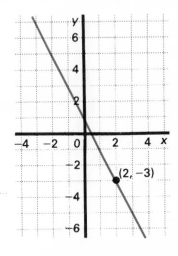

$$Ax + By + C = 0$$
$$By = -Ax - C$$
$$y = -\frac{A}{B}x - \frac{C}{B}$$
$$y = mx + b$$

Two other points on the line are $(1, -1)$ and $(3, -5)$. We check our solutions by showing that the points satisfy the equation of the line.

checking $(1, -1)$

$\text{L.S.} = 2x + y - 1$
$= 2(1) + (-1) - 1$
$= 2 - 1 - 1$
$= 0$
$\text{R.S.} = 0$

checking $(3, -5)$

$\text{L.S.} = 2x + y - 1$
$= 2(3) + (-5) - 1$
$= 6 - 5 - 1$
$= 0$
$\text{R.S.} = 0$

EXERCISE 6-2

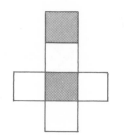

Which of the following figures can you make from the pattern above?

A **1.** State the following equations in standard form $(Ax + By + C = 0)$ and state the values of A, B, and C.
(a) $5x + 3y = 7$
(b) $3x = 2y - 4$
(c) $4x = 3 - 5y$
(d) $7x + 2 = -3y$
(e) $5y = 2 - 3x$
(f) $2y - 3 = 7x$
(g) $5 = 3y - 4x$
(h) $3x - 4y = 0$
(i) $2x + 7 = 0$
(j) $3 - 4y = 0$
(k) $0 = 2 - 3y + 4x$
(l) $y = 2x - 7$

B **2.** Determine an equation of the line through the given point having the given slope. Express the equation in standard form.
(a) $(3, 2)$, $m = 4$
(b) $(5, 7)$, $m = 2$
(c) $(-5, 2)$, $m = -3$
(d) $(-4, -1)$, $m = -1$
(e) $(-6, -4)$, $m = 3$
(f) $(4, -2)$, $m = -6$
(g) $(6, 8)$, $m = \frac{1}{2}$
(h) $(-3, 5)$, $m = -\frac{1}{3}$
(i) $(\frac{1}{2}, -2)$, $m = -\frac{1}{2}$
(j) $(\frac{1}{4}, -\frac{1}{5})$, $m = \frac{2}{3}$
(k) $(0.2, 0.6)$, $m = 0.1$
(l) $(2.8, -3.6)$, $m = -1.2$
(m) $(3, -5.7)$, $m = 6.1$
(n) $(-4.1, -3.8)$, $m = 4.6$

3. Find an equation of the line through the given point and having the given slope. Use the equation to find two other points on the line.
(a) $(1, 2)$, $m = 2$
(b) $(-1, -3)$, $m = 6$
(c) $(3, -4)$, $m = -2$
(d) $(-5, 2)$, $m = -3$
(e) $(0, 1)$, $m = 3$
(f) $(6, 0)$, $m = \frac{1}{2}$
(g) $(-2, -1)$, $m = -\frac{1}{2}$
(h) $(5, -3)$, $m = \frac{1}{3}$
(i) $(0.6, 0.3)$, $m = -0.1$
(j) $(-0.8, 1.2)$, $m = -1.4$

4. Determine an equation of the line with slope $m = 2$ and having the same x-intercept as $3x + 5y = 15$.

5. Determine an equation of the line with slope $m = -3$ and having the same y-intercept as $2x - 3y = 6$.

6. Determine an equation of the line through $(-5, 6)$ and
(a) having slope $m = 4$
(b) parallel to the x-axis
(c) parallel to the y-axis.

7. Determine the equation of the x-axis.

8. Determine the equation of the y-axis.

9. Determine an equation of the line through $(-5, 2)$ and having the same slope as the line $2x - y + 7 = 0$.

6-3 LINEAR EQUATION—SLOPE Y–INTERCEPT FORM

A straight line can be described by writing its equation in the form $y = mx + b$.

EXAMPLE 1. *Find an equation of the line through* $(0, -3)$ *with* $m = -4$.

Solution

$$y - y_1 = m(x - x_1)$$
$$y - (-3) = -4(x - 0)$$
$$y + 3 = -4x$$
$$y = -4x - 3$$

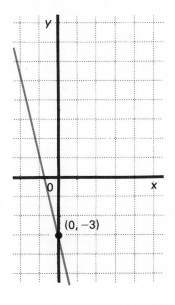

EXAMPLE 2. *Find an equation of the line through* $(0, b)$ *with slope* *m*.

Solution

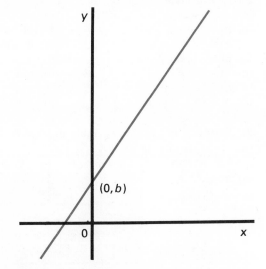

$$y - y_1 = m(x - x_1)$$
$$y - b = m(x - 0)$$
$$y - b = mx$$
$$y = mx + b$$

Linear Equation—Slope *y*-intercept form

The graph of the equation of a line expressed in the form

$$y = mx + b, \ x, y \in R$$

has a slope *m* and a *y*-intercept *b*.

---

slopes and equations of lines   133

EXAMPLE 3. *State the slope and y-intercept of the line* $2x - 3y = 7$

Solution
Express the equation in the form $y = mx + b$

$$2x - 3y = 7$$
$$-3y = -2x + 7$$
$$\frac{-3y}{-3} = \frac{-2x}{-3} + \frac{7}{-3}$$
$$y = \tfrac{2}{3}x - \tfrac{7}{3}$$
$$y = mx + b$$

The slope $m = \tfrac{2}{3}$ and

$$y\text{-intercept } b = -\tfrac{7}{3}$$

EXERCISE 6-3

A **1.** State the slope and y-intercept of each of the following.
(a) $y = 4x + 6$
(b) $y = x - 4$
(c) $y = -2x - 3$
(d) $y = -7x + 4$
(e) $y = \tfrac{1}{2}x - 6$
(f) $y = -\tfrac{2}{3}x + 7$
(g) $y + 7 = 3x$
(h) $y - 6 = -2x$
(i) $y = 5$
(j) $x = 3$
(k) $y = -2$
(l) $x = -4$
(m) $3x + y = 2$
(n) $y - 2x = 0$
(o) $2x + y - 5 = 0$

Use $+$, $-$, $\times$, $\div$, $(\ )$ to make a true statement.

$3 \ 2 \ 5 = 4 \ 2 \ 1$

2. State a linear equation of a line whose graph has the given slope and y-intercept.
(a) $m = 2$, $b = 3$
(b) $m = 4$, $b = -2$
(c) $m = -2$, $b = -4$
(d) $m = 0$, $b = 3$
(e) $m = -1$, $b = 0$
(f) $m = -\tfrac{1}{2}$, $b = -2$
(g) $m = 0.2$, $b = 1.7$
(h) $m = -1.5$, $b = -4.6$
(i) $m = -\tfrac{4}{5}$, $b = 0$
(j) $m = 0$, $b = -\tfrac{1}{5}$
(k) $m = 15.3$, $b = -45.6$
(l) $m = -9.8$, $b = 23.1$

B **3.** Complete the following table in your notebook.

EQUATION	$y = mx + b$	SLOPE	y-intercept
(a) $3x + y = 7$			
(b) $x + 2y = 4$			
(c) $2x + 3y = 9$			
(d) $4x - y = 5$			
(e) $3x - 2y = -4$			
(f) $2x + 6y - 5 = 0$			
(g) $4x - 3y + 2 = 0$			
(h) $5y - 4x - 1 = 0$			
(i) $3x + 2y = 0$			
(j) $y + 7 = 0$			

4. State the slope and y-intercept of each of the following.
(a) $2x + 3y = 8$
(b) $3x - 2y = 5$
(c) $5x + 2y - 4 = 0$
(d) $2x + 5y = 0$

(e) $7x - 3y + 2 = 0$

(f) $2y - 4 = 7x$

(g) $2y - 7 = 0$

(h) $3x + 5 = 0$

(i) $3x + 0.5y = 4$

(j) $1.2x - 0.3y = 0.12$

(k) $0.4x + 0.5y - 0.2 = 0$

(l) $14.4x + 1.2y = 0$

Put the numbers from 1 to 9 in the spaces to make the statements true.

$$\square - \square + \square = 4$$
$$\square + \square \div \square = 4$$
$$\square \times \square \div \square = 4$$

5. Sketch the graphs of the lines with the following slopes and y-intercepts.

(a) $m = 2, b = 4$

(b) $m = 3, b = -2$

(c) $m = -2, b = 5$

(d) $m = -4, b = -6$

(e) $m = \frac{1}{2}, b = 1$

(f) $m = -\frac{1}{3}, b = -2$

C **6.** Find an equation of the line through $(a, 0)$ with slope m.

6.4 LINEAR EQUATION—TWO POINT FORM

We can determine the equation of a line given two points on the line.

EXAMPLE 1. *Find the equation of the line through $(-1, -3)$ and $(5, 6)$. Express the equation in standard form.*

Solution
Since we know two points on the line we can determine the slope of the line.

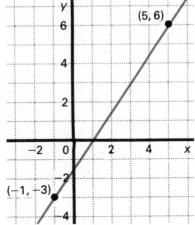

$$m = \frac{\Delta y}{\Delta x}$$

$$= \frac{6 - (-3)}{5 - (-1)}$$

$$= \frac{9}{6}$$

$$= \frac{3}{2}$$

We now have the slope of the line $(m = \frac{3}{2})$ and a point on the line, $(5, 6)$ or $(-1, -3)$

$$y - y_1 = m(x - x_1)$$
$$y - 6 = \frac{3}{2}(x - 5)$$
$$y - 6 = \frac{3}{2}x - \frac{15}{2}$$
$$2y - 12 = 3x - 15$$
$$3x - 2y - 3 = 0$$

Using the point $(-1, -3)$ and the slope $m = \frac{3}{2}$ will give the same result.

slopes and equations of lines   135

EXERCISE 6-4

B **1.** Find an equation of the line through the following pairs of points. Express the equation in standard form.

(a) (2, 3) and (3, 5)

(b) (1, 4) and (3, 10)

(c) (−1, −5) and (−3, 5)

(d) (−3, −2) and (−6, 7)

(e) (−1, 0) and (3, −16)

(f) (4, 2) and (2, 1)

(g) (−5, 2) and (1, 4)

(h) (6, 4) and (−5, 4)

(i) (3, −5) and (3, 6).

(j) $(2, \frac{1}{2})$ and (3, −4)

(k) (1.5, 3) and (2.5, 7)

(l) (−0.8, −0.3) and (−1, −0.6)

(m) (−2.2, 5.4) and (−3.4, 7.2)

(n) (15.4, −47.5) and (−3.6, 0)

2. Determine an equation of the line through (−4, 2) and (−2, 10). Use the equation to determine two other points on the line.

3. Find an equation of the line through (4, −1) and having the same y–intercept as $2x + 3y = 6$. Express the equation in standard form.

4. Find an equation of the line having the same x–intercept as $2x − 5y = 10$ and the same y–intercept as $4x − 3y − 12 = 0$.

5. Find an equation of the line having the same y–intercept as $5x − 3y − 15 = 0$ and the same x–intercept as $x + 3y − 1 = 0$.

6. Find an equation of the line through $(a, 0)$ and $(0, b)$.

6.5 PARALLEL AND PERPENDICULAR LINES

In this section we will investigate the slopes of parallel and perpendicular lines.

INVESTIGATION 6.5

1. (a) Draw the graph of each of the following on the same set of axes.

(i) $y = 2x$

(ii) $y = 2x + 3$

(iii) $y = 2x − 3$

(iv) $y = 2x + 6$

(b) How are the graphs of these four lines related?

(c) State the slope of each line.

(d) What conclusion can you draw about the slopes of parallel lines?

How many jumps will it take a frog to move 10 m up an incline, if every jump is 1 m long and if the frog slides back 0.5 m after each jump?

2. (a) Draw the graphs of the following pairs of lines. Use a different set of axes for each pair of lines.

(i) $y = 2x + 2$ and $y = −\frac{1}{2}x − 3$

(ii) $y = 3x − 4$ and $y = −\frac{1}{3}x + 2$

(iii) $y = −x + 5$ and $y = x − 3$

(iv) $y = −4x + 1$ and $y = \frac{1}{4}x − 2$

(b) What is the degree measure of the angle formed by each pair of lines?

(c) Complete the following table in your notebook.

EQUATIONS OF LINES	SLOPE OF FIRST LINE m_1	SLOPE OF SECOND LINE m_2	$m_1 \times m_2$
(i) $y = 2x + 2$ $y = -\frac{1}{2}x - 3$			
(ii) $y = 3x - 4$ $y = -\frac{1}{3}x + 2$			
(iii) $y = -x + 5$ $y = x - 3$			
(iv) $y = -4x + 1$ $y = \frac{1}{4}x - 2$			

(d) What conclusion can you draw about the slopes of perpendicular lines?

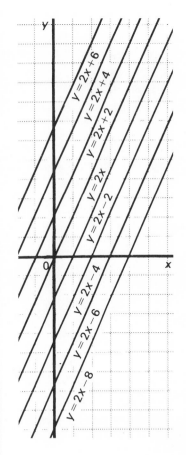

Parallel Lines: two lines are parallel if they have the same slope.

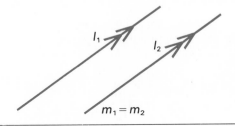

$m_1 = m_2$

Perpendicular Lines: two lines are perpendicular if the product of their slopes is −1.

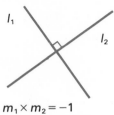

$m_1 \times m_2 = -1$

Lines parallel to the y axis are not included in the above statements since lines parallel to the y axis have no slope.

For perpendicular lines,

$$m_1 = -\frac{1}{m_2}$$

EXAMPLE 1. *Determine an equation of a line through* $(-4, 1)$ *and perpendicular to the line* $6x - 3y = 7$.

Solution
In order to use $y - y_1 = m(x - x_1)$ to determine the equation we must know a point on the line and the slope of the line. A point on the line is $(-4, 1)$. To find the required slope we first find the slope of $6x - 3y = 7$.

$$6x - 3y = 7$$
$$-3y = -6x + 7$$
$$y = 2x - \tfrac{7}{3}$$

The slope of $6x - 3y = 7$ is 2. The slope of lines perpendicular to this line is $-\frac{1}{2}$ since $2(-\frac{1}{2}) = -1$.

$$y - y_1 = m(x - x_1)$$
$$y - 1 = -\tfrac{1}{2}(x + 4)$$
$$y - 1 = -\tfrac{1}{2}x - 2$$
$$2y - 2 = -x - 4$$
$$x + 2y + 2 = 0$$

The equation is $x + 2y + 2 = 0$

EXERCISE 6-5

A **1.** Given the slopes of two lines, determine whether the lines are (i) parallel (ii) perpendicular (iii) neither perpendicular nor parallel.
(a) $m_1 = \frac{2}{3}, m_2 = \frac{3}{2}$
(b) $m_1 = \frac{7}{2}, m_2 = -\frac{2}{7}$
(c) $m_1 = \frac{1}{2}, m_2 = \frac{5}{10}$
(d) $m_1 = 2, m_2 = -\frac{4}{8}$
(e) $m_1 = -\frac{3}{2}, m_2 = \frac{3}{2}$
(f) $m_1 = -1, m_2 = 1$
(g) $m_1 = \frac{4}{5}, m_2 = \frac{16}{20}$
(h) $m_1 = \frac{1}{3}, m_2 = -\frac{3}{9}$
(i) $m_1 = -\frac{2}{7}, m_2 = \frac{21}{6}$
(j) $m_1 = \frac{4}{20}, m_2 = \frac{10}{50}$
(k) $m_1 = 1\frac{1}{3}, m_2 = -\frac{8}{6}$
(l) $m_1 = 0, m_2 = -1$
(m) $m_1 = 0.5, m_2 = -2$
(n) $m_1 = 0.25, m_2 = 4$
(o) $m_1 = 0.1, m_2 = 1$
(p) $m_1 = -0.8, m_2 = 1.25$

B **2.** State the slope of a line (i) parallel to and (ii) perpendicular to the following lines.
(a) $y = 2x + 5$
(b) $y = 3x - 2$
(c) $y = -3x + 1$
(d) $y = -x + 4$
(e) $y = \frac{1}{2}x + 7$
(f) $y = -\frac{2}{3}x - 4$
(g) $y = -\frac{3}{4}x$
(h) $y = \frac{5}{4}x + 3$
(i) $y + 7x = 4$
(j) $y - 3x + 6 = 0$
(k) $3x + y - 4 = 0$
(l) $5x + 2y = 7$
(m) $5x - 4y + 3 = 0$
(n) $3x - y = 4$
(o) $5x - 4 = 7y$
(p) $2y - 4 = -3x$

3. Determine an equation of the line through $(-2, 4)$ and parallel to $2x - y - 4 = 0$.

The difference of the squares of two positive whole numbers is 215. Find the numbers.

4. Determine an equation of the line through $(-3, -1)$ and parallel to $4x + 2y = 5$.

5. Find an equation of the line perpendicular to $2x - y + 4 = 0$ and through $(-5, 6)$.

6. Find an equation of the line through $(-6, 0)$ and perpendicular to $4x + 3y - 7 = 0$.

7. (a) Plot the points $A(4, 2), B(-2, 1)$ and $C(2, -2)$.
   (b) Determine an equation of the line through A and parallel to BC.
   (c) Determine an equation of the line through B and perpendicular to AC.

8. Prove that the following points are the vertices of a right angled triangle.
(a) $A(-2, 5), B(6, 8), C(1, -3)$.
(b) $P(-6, 1), Q(-2, -7), R(-4, -8)$.

9. Prove that the following points are the vertices of a parallelogram.
(a) $A(2, 1), B(14, 11), C(6, 5), D(-6, -5)$
(b) $P(-5, -2), Q(1, -1), R(4, 4), S(-2, 3)$

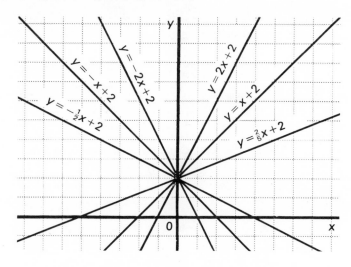

6.6 LENGTH OF A LINE SEGMENT

The length of a horizontal line segment may be determined by calculating $|\Delta x|$ for the line.

length of AB; $l_{AB} = |\Delta x|$
$$= |4 - (-5)|$$
$$= 9$$

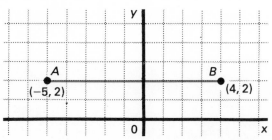

The length of a vertical line segment may be determined by calculating $|\Delta y|$ for the line.

length of CD; $l_{CD} = |\Delta y|$
$$= |(-2) - 5|$$
$$= 7$$

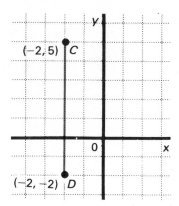

Arrange 9 coins in 6 rows of 3 coins each.

The length of a line segment that is neither horizontal nor vertical may be found using the Pythagorean theorem.

EXAMPLE 1. *Find the length of the line segment joining $A(3, 2)$ to $B(10, 6)$.*

Solution

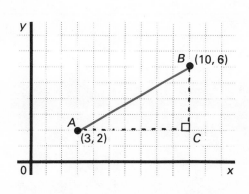

Draw line segment AB.
Construct right triangle ABC.
length of $BC = |\Delta y|$
$$= |6 - 2|$$
$$= 4$$

length of $AC = |\Delta x|$
$$= |10 - 3|$$
$$= 7$$

By Pythagoras, $(AB)^2 = (AC)^2 + (BC)^2$
$$AB = \sqrt{(AC)^2 + (BC)^2}$$
$$= \sqrt{7^2 + 4^2}$$
$$= \sqrt{49 + 16}$$
$$= \sqrt{65}$$

Since $(AC)^2 = (\Delta x)^2$ and $(BC)^2 = (\Delta y)^2$ the length formula may be generalized as follows.

Length of a line segment
$l = \sqrt{(\Delta x)^2 + (\Delta y)^2}$

EXAMPLE 2. *Find the length of the line segment joining C(2, −3) to D(−3, 1).*

Solution

$$l_{CD} = \sqrt{(\Delta x)^2 + (\Delta y)^2}$$
$$= \sqrt{(-5)^2 + (4)^2}$$
$$= \sqrt{25 + 16}$$
$$= \sqrt{41}$$

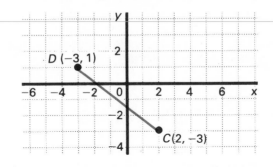

8	3	2	12
15	2	5	6
16	3	4	

EXERCISE 6-6

A **1.** Determine the length of the line segment joining the two given points.

(a) (3, 2) and (3, 7)
(b) (4, 8) and (10, 8)
(c) (−3, 7) and (8, 7)
(d) (9, −3) and (−2, −3)
(e) (7, −4) and (7, −11)
(f) (−5, 0) and (12, 0)
(g) (0, −9) and (0, 6)
(h) (−5, 4) and (−5, −6)
(i) (1, −5) and (−7, −5)
(j) (2, −8) and (2, −9)
(k) (1.4, −3.2) and (−2.6, −3.2)
(l) (−1.3, 0.8) and (−1.3, −2.4)

Determine the pattern. Find the missing number.

B **2.** Calculate the lengths of the following line segments.

(a) $A(4, 2), B(7, 9)$
(b) $R(2, 1), T(10, 6)$
(c) $S(−3, 5), M(2, 8)$
(d) $P(−4, 6), Q(−7, −9)$
(e) $D(−5, 0), E(7, −11)$
(f) $K(0, 0), L(−7, −6)$
(g) $C(−3, −8), F(2, 7)$
(h) $R(−1, 3), S(6, −5)$
(i) $M(0, −2), N(4, −3)$
(j) $A(−1, 1), B(1, −1)$
(k) $C(1.2, −0.8), D(2.2, 1.2)$
(l) $R(1.5, 15.5), T(−3.5, 7.5)$
(m) $E(6.6, −0.1), F(4.2, 0.9)$
(n) $G(−1.3, 4.5), H(−7.4, 8)$

3. Find the lengths of the sides of a triangle with vertices $A(5, 6)$, $B(−1, 2)$, and $C(1, −3)$.

4. A quadrilateral has vertices $A(4, 6)$, $B(−3, 2)$, $C(−5, −5)$, and $D(6, −1)$. Find the lengths of the diagonals.

5. Prove that $C(−1, 2)$ is the mid point of the line segment joining $A(−5, 7)$ and $B(3, −3)$.

6. The coordinates of the end points of a diameter of a circle are (5, 2) and (−3, −4). What is the length of the radius of the circle?

7. (a) Graph the quadrilateral $A(5, 5), B(−1, 1), C(−3, −5)$ and $D(3, −1)$.
(b) Show that $ABCD$ is a parallelogram by finding the slopes of the sides.
(c) Show that $AB = DC$ and $BC = AD$.

8. (a) Graph the triangle $A(2, 8), B(−4, −2)$ and $C(4, −4)$.
(b) Find the equation of the line through A and B.
(c) Show that $S(−1, 3)$ is on AB.
(d) Show that S is the mid point of AB.

(e) Find the equation of the line through *A* and *C*.
(f) Show that *T*(3, 2) is on *AC*.
(g) Show that *T* is the midpoint of *AC*.
(h) Prove that *ST* is parallel to *BC*.
(i) Find the lengths of *ST* and *BC*. How are they related?
(j) How is the line joining the mid points of 2 sides of a triangle related to the third side?

6.7 APPLICATIONS

In this section we will see how a linear function can be used as a *mathematical model* for some practical problems. We will take some liberties in using mathematical equations and graphs to solve problems. Not all mathematical models fit real world situations exactly. However the "fit" is usually close enough "for all practical purposes".

EXAMPLE 1. *The Arco Chemical Supply Co. sells distilled water to be used in chemistry experiments. Sample prices that appear in their catalogue are:*

$$2\ell \ cost \ \$1.75$$
$$5\ell \ cost \ \$4.00$$

You can buy any amount up to and including 10ℓ.
(a) *Plot a graph of this relation.*
(b) *Find an equation for this relation expressing price in terms of litres.*
(c) *Use the equation to determine the price of 8ℓ of water.*
(d) *What quantity does the slope of the relation represent?*
(e) *Determine the y-intercept. What meaning does the intercept have?*

Solution
(a)

If it is 18:00 in Los Angeles, what time is it in Moscow?

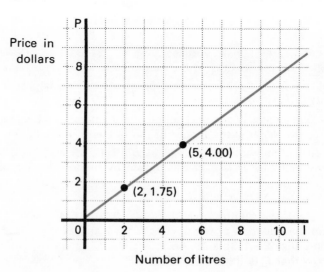

(b) In this problem we will replace x by ℓ (litres) and y by p (price).

$$\text{Slope } m = \frac{\Delta y}{\Delta x} = \frac{\Delta p}{\Delta \ell}$$

$$= \frac{4.00 - 1.75}{5 - 2}$$

$$= \frac{2.25}{3}$$

$$= 0.75$$

$y - y_1 = m(x - x_1)$ becomes $p - p_1 = m(\ell - \ell_1)$

Using $m = 0.75$ and the point $(5, 4.00)$

$$p - p_1 = m(\ell - \ell_1)$$

$$p - 4.00 = 0.75(\ell - 5)$$

$$p - 4.00 = 0.75\,\ell - 3.75$$

$$p = 0.75\,\ell + 0.25$$

(c) $p = 0.75\,\ell + 0.25$

$\quad = 0.75(8) + 0.25$

$\quad = 6.00 + 0.25$

$\quad = 6.25$

8 ℓ will cost $6.25.
(d) The slope represents the price per litre.
(e) The y-intercept is 0.25. This probably represents a handling charge that the company puts on all orders.

38	47	29	73
24	28	18	21
48	25	░░	36
68	55	78	49

Determine the pattern. Find the missing number.

EXERCISE 6-7

For the following problems, assume that a linear relation is the best mathematical model that fits the situation. When the domain is N it will be convenient to draw the graph as though $x \in R$ instead of indicating the relation as a series of points on the plane.

1. The Vasco Restaurant has banquet facilities for 300 people. When the owner quotes a price for a banquet he is including the room rent plus the cost of the meal. A banquet for 50 people costs $800. One hundred people will cost $1250.
(a) Plot a graph of this relation (use a solid line instead of a series of points even though $x \in N$).
(b) Find an equation for this relation expressing cost in terms of people.
(c) From the graph, determine the cost of a banquet for 200 people.
(d) Use the equation to determine the cost of a banquet for 150 people.
(e) What quantity does the slope of the relation represent?

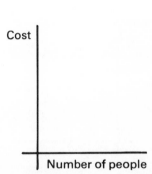

Cost

Number of people

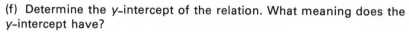

(f) Determine the y-intercept of the relation. What meaning does the y-intercept have?

(g) Use the equation of the relation to determine how many people could attend if you paid $2330.

(h) Why is the graph of the relation limited to the first quadrant?

(i) State the domain and range of the relation.

2. The Ace Plumbing Supply Company advertises that it will take approximately 4 h for its 180 ℓ home hot water tank to heat cold water to the required hot water temperature. An inspector filled the tank with cold water and found that after 2 h the temperature of the water was 35°C and after 3 h, 47.5°C.

(a) Plot a graph of this relation.

(b) Find an equation for this relation expressing temperature in terms of time.

(c) What quantity does the slope of the relation represent?

(d) What will be the water temperature after 1 h of heating?

(e) Determine the y-intercept. What meaning does the intercept have?

(f) Determine, from the graph, how long will it take for the water to reach 50°C.

(g) Why is the graph of the relation limited to the first quadrant?

(h) State the domain and range of the relation.

(i) Why would a maximum limit be put on the water temperature?

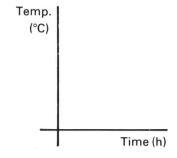

3. The student council decides to provide a band and a lunch for the graduation dance. If 200 people attend, the cost will be $1600. If 300 people attend, the price increase to $1900.

(a) Plot a graph of this relation.

(b) Find an equation of this relation expressing cost in terms of the number of students attending.

(c) The fire regulations will permit a maximum or 500 people at the dance. State the domain and range of the relation.

(d) From the graph, determine the cost of the dance if 400 people attend.

(e) From the equation, determine how many people should attend if the council can only afford to spend $2350.

(f) What quantity does the slope of the relation represent?

(g) Determine the y-intercept. What meaning does the intercept have?

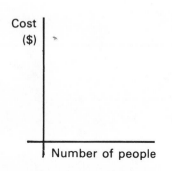

4. In order to determine the gasoline consumption of a new car, the company representative filled the tank with gasoline and proceeded to drive around the test track at a constant speed. After driving 100 km, 80 ℓ of gas remained in the tank. After 300 km, 40 ℓ of gas remained.

(a) Plot a graph of this relation.

(b) Find an equation of this relation expressing litres of gasoline remaining in terms of kilometres driven.

(c) What quantity does the slope of the relation represent?

(d) From the graph, determine how many litres of gasoline remain after 400 km of driving.

(e) What is the capacity of the gas tank (in litres)?

(f) How many kilometres could you expect to drive on a full tank of gasoline?

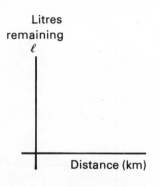

(g) How many litres of gasoline will the car use in going 350 km?
(h) State the domain and range of this relation.

5 Since light travels much faster than sound, you will see the lightning before you hear the thunderclap. If the storm is 660 m away the time difference between flash and thunderclap is 2 s. The time difference is 5.4 s for a distance of 1782 m.

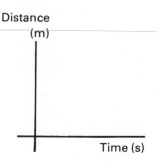

(a) Plot a graph of this relation.
(b) Find an equation for this relation expressing distance in terms of time.
(c) What quantity does the slope of the relation represent?
(d) Use the equation to determine the distance from the storm if the time interval is 6.2 s.
(e) What factors affect the domain and range of this relation?
(f) Why are both intercepts zero?
(g) Why do you put lightning rods on houses?

REVIEW EXERCISE

A **1.** State the slope and y intercept of each of the following.
(a) $y = 7x + 6$ (b) $3x + y = 14$ (c) $4x - y - 7 = 0$
(d) $y = \frac{1}{3}x - 4$ (e) $4x + 2y - 7 = 0$ (f) $x = 7$
(g) $y = -4$ (h) $3x - 5y = 9$ (i) $4x - 7y + 11 = 0$

2. Determine the length of the line segment joining the two given points.
(a) $(5, 2)$ and $(5, 7)$ (b) $(3, 8)$ and $(5, 8)$
(c) $(-2, 8)$ and $(-2, 15)$ (d) $(-4, 16)$ and $(-4, 0)$
(e) $(7, -4)$ and $(1, -4)$ (f) $(3, 4)$ and $(3, -7)$
(g) $(-4, -6)$ and $(-11, -6)$ (h) $(5, -12)$ and $(5, 3)$

B **3.** Determine the slopes of the line segments joining the following pairs of points.
(a) $A(5, -3)$, $B(-4, 6)$ (b) $C(-1, 7)$, $D(-4, 8)$
(c) $E(-3, -5)$, $F(5, -9)$ (d) $G(0, -11)$, $H(1, -5)$
(e) $K(1.2, -5.6)$, $L(0.2, 0.4)$ (f) $M(3, -2.5)$, $N(4, -7.5)$

4. Determine an equation of the line through the given point having the given slope.
(a) $(4, 6)$, $m = 7$ (b) $(-3, -5)$, $m = -1$
(c) $(-5, 8)$, $m = -2$ (d) $(3, -7)$, $m = \frac{1}{2}$
(e) $(-4, 0)$, $m = -1.4$ (f) $(1.4, -0.8)$, $m = -0.2$

5. Determine an equation of the line through $(-4, -5)$ and
(a) having slope $m = -2$,
(b) parallel to the y-axis,
(c) parallel to the x-axis.

6. Find an equation of the line through the following pairs of points
(a) $(3, 4)$ and $(1, -1)$ (b) $(-4, -6)$ and $(5, -2)$
(c) $(3, -7)$ and $(-2, 5)$ (d) $(1.2, -0.6)$ and $(-0.8, 0.4)$

7. Find an equation of the line through (6, −5) and parallel to $4x - 2y + 7 = 0$.

8. Find an equation of the line through (−3, −4) and perpendicular to $4x + 2y - 6 = 0$.

9. Calculate the lengths of the following line segments
(a) $A(5, 6), B(-4, 3)$ (b) $C(-3, 7), D(-6, 4)$
(c) $G(-11, 5), H(4, -1)$ (d) $M(1.4, -0.6), N(-0.6, 3.4)$

10. A quadrilateral has vertices $A(4, 6)$, $B(-5, 2)$, $C(-6, -7)$ and $D(8, -3)$. Find the lengths of the diagonals.

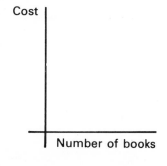

11. The Barko Publishing Company specializes in printing student yearbooks. An order of 400 books costs $3000. An order of 600 books costs $4000.
(a) Plot a graph of this relation.
(b) Find an equation of this relation expressing cost in terms of the number of books ordered.
(c) What quantity does the slope of the relation represent?
(d) From the graph determine the cost of 300 books.
(e) From the equation determine the cost of 200 books.
(f) If an order costs $3500, how many books were ordered?
(g) Determine the y-intercept of the relation.
(h) What meaning does the y-intercept have?

REVIEW AND PREVIEW TO CHAPTER 7

EXERCISE 1

Solve the following equations:

1. (a) $x - 3 = 12$ (b) $w + 7 = 11$ (c) $3x = 15$
(d) $\frac{1}{2}b = 6$ (e) $2x + 1 = 15$ (f) $2x - 3 = 13$

(g) $\frac{x}{3} = 5$ (h) $-3d = -21$ (i) $-3 + 4n = 17$

2. (a) $3m + 1 = 16$ (b) $2t - 4 = -20$ (c) $5y - 10 = -10$
(d) $3 - d = 4$ (e) $5 = 2a + 1$ (f) $4x + 16 = 0$

(g) $\frac{x}{4} = -5$ (h) $-6 = -3x - 9$ (i) $2b + 7 = -13$

EXERCISE 2

Solve the following equations:

1. (a) $4x + 7 = 2x - 3$ (b) $3a - 14 = 6 - 2a$
(c) $5b + 6 = 7b - 2$ (d) $4x - 3 = 6x - 11$
(e) $2 + 3y - 4 = -5y + 6$ (f) $-6x - 4 = 6 + 4x + 20$

2. (a) $5(x - 3) = 2(x + 6)$ (b) $6(m + 2) = 4(m - 3)$
(c) $2(2b - 1) + 4 = 5(b + 1)$ (d) $5(a - 3) - 2a = -6$
(e) $7 - 2(1 - 3x) + 16 = 8x + 11$ (f) $4b - (3b - 1) - 3 + 6(b - 2) = 0$

EXERCISE 3

Solve the following equations:

1. (a) $\dfrac{x}{3} = \dfrac{1}{2}$ (b) $\dfrac{m - 1}{3} = 6$

(c) $\dfrac{x}{3} - \dfrac{1}{2} = \dfrac{1}{4}$ (d) $\dfrac{a + 2}{2} = \dfrac{a - 1}{3}$

(e) $\dfrac{x + 1}{2} + \dfrac{x + 1}{3} = 5$ (f) $\dfrac{2m + 1}{3} - \dfrac{m + 1}{4} = 3$

(g) $\dfrac{a + 7}{6} + \dfrac{1}{2} = \dfrac{a - 2}{4}$ (h) $\dfrac{1 - 3x}{4} - \dfrac{x - 1}{3} = -x$

2. (a) $2(x^2 + 2x + 1) = 2(x^2 + x + 4)$
(b) $(x - 3)(2x + 1) - 2x^2 = 2$
(c) $4a^2 - (2a - 1)(2a + 1) = a$
(d) $(b - 3)(b + 4) - (b + 2)(b + 1) = -16$
(e) $(m - 3)(2m + 1) - 2m^2 = 2$
(f) $(y + 1)(y + 2) + (y - 1)(y - 3) = (2y - 1)(y + 1)$
(g) $(2x - 3)(x - 1) - 2(x + 2)(x + 3) = 6$
(h) $(2m - 3)(m - 2) - 2(m^2 - 1) = -6$

CHAPTER 7

Systems of Equations

A mathematician, like a painter or poet, is a maker of patterns. If his patterns are more permanent than theirs, it is because they are made with *ideas.*

G. H. Hardy

Pierre Fermat (1601–1665)

Fermat was not a professional mathematician. He was a French lawyer and civil servant whose hobby was mathematics. Whenever he had some spare time he did mathematics for the fun of it. But he found enough spare time to invent two of the major areas of mathematics; analytic geometry and differential calculus. Not bad for an amateur! Fermat never published his discoveries, and so although he invented analytic geometry at the same time as Descartes, he did not receive credit for it at the time. Fermat was also one of the founders of two other areas of mathematics: probability theory and number theory. A major concern in number theory is to solve equations allowing only integers as solutions. For example, the problem known as Fermat's Last Theorem states that if n is an integer larger than 2, then there are no integers x, y, z such that $x^n + y^n = z^n$. (Of course for $n = 2$ we know some solutions such as $x = 3$, $y = 4$, $z = 5$. The assertion is that for $n > 2$ the equation $x^n + y^n = z^n$ has no solution in integers. For example, for $n = 3$ it says that no perfect cube can be expressed as the sum of two perfect cubes.) Fermat claimed that he had proved this theorem. In the margin of a book he wrote, "I have discovered a truly remarkable proof which this margin is too small to contain." However he never published a proof, and to this day nobody has been able to prove or disprove it, although certain special cases have been proved. (For example Euler gave proofs for the cases $n = 3$ and 4 and later mathematicians have shown that it is true when $n \leqq 619$.) Fermat's Last Theorem is still the most famous unsolved problem in mathematics!

7.1 ORDERED PAIRS AS SOLUTION SETS

An equation in one variable such as $2x + 3 = 11$ has *one* real value as a solution. In this case {4} is the solution set. The solution of an equation in two variables, such as $x + y = 7$, is an infinite set of ordered pairs. Some of the ordered pairs are (1, 6), (7, 0), (−3, 10) and (8, −1).

EXERCISE 7-1

A **1.** Check the ordered pairs following the equation to see whether or not the pair is an element of the solution set.

(a) $x + y = 14$; (2, 12), (0, 14), (−1, 16), (4, 9), (−7, 19), (20, −6)
(b) $2x + y = 13$; (0, 12), (1, 11), (7, −1), (5, 2), (−3, 20), (10, −7)
(c) $x − y = 8$; (9, 1), (4, 4), (2, −6), (13, 4), (−6, −14), (3, −5)
(d) $x − y = −2$; (4, 6), (3, 6), (−3, 5), (−3, −5), (−3, −1), (−2, 0)
(e) $2x − y = 7$; (1, 9), (5, 3), (−2, −11), (0, −7), (5, −3), (−1, −9)
(f) $y = x + 4$; (2, 6), (−3, 2), (8, 12), (−6, −1), (5, 9), (−4, 0)
(g) $y = 3x − 1$; (1, 1), (−1, −4), (5, 14), (−2, −8), (−3, −11), (0, −1)
(h) $x = 5y + 3$; (8, 1), (6, −2), (−12, −3), (3, 0), (12, 2), (−19, −5)

2. State the missing element of each ordered pair so that the ordered pair belongs to the solution set of the equation.

(a) $x + y = 9$; (4, ▨), (▨, 1), (−3, ▨), (▨, −5), (12, ▨)
(b) $x − y = 6$; (9, ▨), (▨, 2), (5, ▨), (▨, −3), (−8, ▨)
(c) $2x + y = 15$; (1, ▨), (5, ▨), (7, ▨), (▨, 3), (▨, −5)
(d) $y = 2x + 1$; (3, ▨), (−2, ▨), (▨, 13), (6, ▨), (▨, 9)
(e) $3x + 2y = 6$; (2, ▨), (▨, 3), (4, ▨), (▨, 9), (▨, −3)

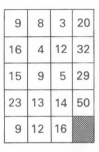

9	8	3	20
16	4	12	32
15	9	5	29
23	13	14	50
9	12	16	▨

Determine the pattern. Find the missing number.

There are an infinite number of ordered pairs that satisfy the equation $x + y = 6$. Some of them are (5, 1), (4, 2), (3, 3), (2, 4). Similarily there are an infinite number of different ordered pairs that satisfy the equation $x − y = 2$. Examples are (5, 3), (4, 2), (6, 4) and (1, −1).

There is just *one* ordered pair, (4, 2), that satisfies both equations.

3. In each case, state the ordered pair that satisfies both equations.

(a) $x + y = 4$
$\quad x − y = 2$ (2, 2), (5, 3), (3, 1), (1, 3)

(b) $x − y = 1$
$\quad x + y = 7$ (3, 2), (9, −2), (12, −5), (4, 3)

(c) $2x + y = 7$
$\quad x + y = 5$ (1, 5), (2, 3), (0, 7), (−2, 7)

(d) $2x + 3y = 16$
$\quad 5x − 2y = 2$ (8, 0), (−2, −6), (5, 2), (2, 4)

4. State the missing element(s) in the ordered pair so that the ordered pair satisfies both equations.

(a) $x + y = 9$
$\quad x − y = 3$ (▨, 3)

(b) $x + y = 11$
$\quad x − y = 3$ (7, ▨)

(c) $x − y = 4$
$\quad x + y = 10$ (▨, ▨)

(d) $x − y = 6$
$\quad x + y = 8$ (▨, ▨)

(e) $x − y = 0$
$\quad x + y = 10$ (▨, ▨)

(f) $x + y = 12$
$\quad x − y = 2$ (▨, ▨)

(g) $x + y = 13$
$\quad x − y = 5$ (▨, ▨)

(h) $x + y = −3$
$\quad x − y = 7$ (▨, ▨)

7.2 GRAPHICAL SOLUTION OF A LINEAR SYSTEM

When you find all the ordered pairs that satisfy both equations, such as $y = 2x + 1$ and $y = −x + 7$, you have solved a system of linear equations. In this section we will deal with graphical solutions.

EXAMPLE 1. *Find the point of intersection of the graphs defined by* $y = 2x + 1$ *and* $y = -x + 7$.

Solution

$y = 2x + 1$

x	y
0	1
1	3
2	5
3	7

$y = -x + 7$

x	y
0	7
2	5
4	3
6	1

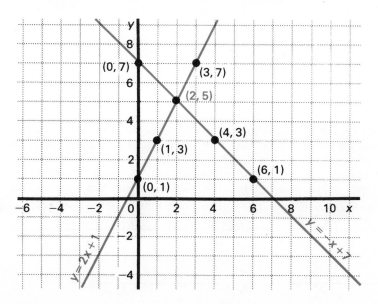

From the graph, we see that the point of intersection is (2, 5)

Check in $y = 2x + 1$

L.S. = y
    = 5

R.S. = 2x + 1
    = 2(2) + 1
    = 5

check in $y = -x + 7$

L.S. = y
    = 5

R.S. = -x + 7
    = -(2) + 7
    = 5

Since the point (2, 5) satisfies both equations, we say that the solution of this linear system is (2, 5).

EXAMPLE 2. *Solve the following graphically.*

$y + 2x = -5$ ①   *These equations are also*
$y - 3x = 5$ ②   *called simultaneous equations.*
                                They are numbered for easy
                                identification.

Solution

$$y + 2x = -5$$
$$y = -2x - 5$$

x	y
1	-7
0	-5
-1	-3

$$y - 3x = 5$$
$$y = 3x + 5$$

x	y
1	8
0	5
-1	2

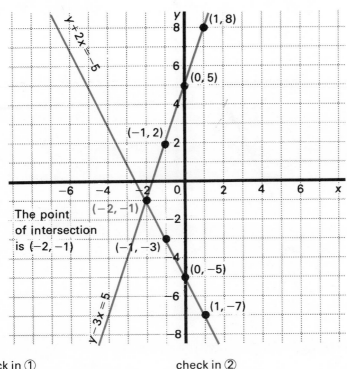

The point of intersection is $(-2, -1)$

check in ①

L.S. $= y + 2x$

$= (-1) + 2(-2)$

$= -1 - 4$

$= -5$

R.S. $= -5$

check in ②

L.S. $= y - 3x$

$= (-1) - 3(-2)$

$= -1 + 6$

$= 5$

R.S. $= 5$

The solution is $(-2, -1)$

EXAMPLE 3. *Solve the following graphically .(Check your solution.)*

$$2x + 3y = -12 \quad ①$$
$$2x - y = -4 \quad ②$$

Solution

In this case, it is convenient to use the *intercept method* to draw the graphs of the relations.

Which of the following figures can you make from the pattern above?

For $2x + 3y = -12$, when $x = 0$, $y = -4$

when $y = 0$, $x = -6$

Two ordered pairs are $(0,-4)$ and $(-2,0)$

For $2x - y = -4$, when $x = 0$, $y = 4$

when $y = 0$, $x = -2$

Two ordered pairs are $(0, 4)$ and $(0, -2)$

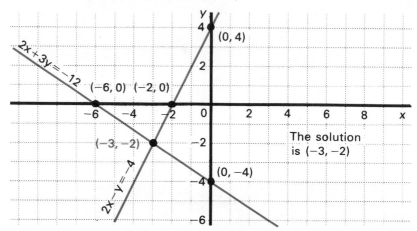

check in ①

L.S. $= 2x + 3y$

$= 2(-3) + 3(-2)$

$= -6 - 6$

$= -12$

R.S. $= -12$

check in ②

L.S. $= 2x - y$

$= 2(-3) - (-2)$

$= -6 + 2$

$= -4$

R.S. $= -4$

EXERCISE 7-2

A **1.** State 3 ordered pairs that satisfy each of the following.

(a) $y = x + 3$ (b) $y = 2x - 1$ (c) $y = 3x + 1$

(d) $y = 2 - x$ (e) $y = -x + 4$ (f) $y = -2x - 1$

(g) $y = 4x + 2$ (h) $y = 3x$ (i) $y = -x$

2. Use the "intercept method" to find two ordered pairs that satisfy each of the following.

(a) $2x + 3y = 6$ (b) $4x + 5y = 20$ (c) $x + 2y = 8$

(d) $3x + y = 9$ (e) $5x - 3y = 15$ (f) $3x - 4y = -12$

(g) $x + y = 7$ (h) $x - y = 4$ (i) $x - y = -3$

B **3.** Solve the following graphically.

Use the intercept method to draw the graphs.

(a) $y = x + 2$ (b) $y = 2x - 1$

$y = 4 - x$ $y = 8 - x$

(c) $y = 1 - 2x$ (d) $y = x + 8$

$y = x + 7$ $y = -3x$

(e) $y = 2x - 1$ (f) $y = -3x + 10$

$y = 4x - 3$ $y = 2x + 5$

4. Solve the following graphically. Check your solution.

(a) $x - y = -4$
$x + 2y = 2$

(b) $3x - 2y = 12$
$2y - x = -8$

(c) $2x + y = 12$
$3x - 2y = 18$

(d) $5x - 2y = 10$
$x + 2y = 2$

C **5.** Solve the following graphically and answer the question below.

(a) $y = x + 4$
$y = x - 2$

(b) $2x + 3y = 6$
$4x + 6y = 12$

(c) $y = -2x + 2$
$y = -2x - 4$

(d) $4x - 3y = 12$
$12x - 9y = 36$

How many points of intersection are there for each pair of equations?

LINEAR SYSTEMS	
1. A linear system may have exactly one solution. This is true when the lines determining the system intersect at a point. Such a system is said to be *consistent*.	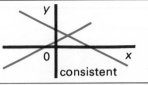
2. A linear system may have no solution. This is true when the lines determining the system are parallel. Such a system is said to be *inconsistent*.	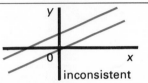
3. A linear system may have an unlimited number of solutions. This is true when the two equations defining the system determine the same straight line. Such a system is said to be *dependent*.	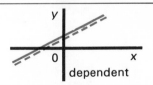

6. Determine, by inspection, the characteristic of each of the following linear systems (consistent, inconsistent, or dependent).

(a) $y = 2x + 1$
$y = -3x + 2$

(b) $x - 2y = 3$
$3x - 6y = 9$

(c) $x + 2y = 6$
$x + 2y = 12$

(d) $y = -4x + 3$
$y = -4x - 6$

(e) $y = 3x - 4$
$y = -x + 7$

(f) $y = x + 4$
$2y = 2x + 8$

(g) $4x + 2y = 7$
$4y = -8x + 3$

(h) $2x - 3y = 7$
$5x + 2y = 10$

(i) $2y = 6x - 4$
$y - 3x = -2$

(j) $4x - 3y = 9$
$8x - 6y = 18$

7.3 ALGEBRAIC SOLUTION OF A LINEAR SYSTEM—COMPARISON

This section deals with the first of three algebraic methods of solving a linear system. Previously we solved linear equations in one variable using algebra.

$$2x + 3 = 9$$
$$2x = 6$$
$$x = 3$$

We now take two equations in two variables, which form a linear system, and combine them in order to eliminate one of the variables. The first method of eliminating one variable is called *comparison*.

Equations are numbered for easy identification

EXAMPLE 1. *Solve* $y = 2x + 3$ ①
$$y = x + 4 \qquad ②$$

Solution
At the point of intersection of the two lines, the x-coordinate of the equation ① must equal the x co-ordinate of equations ②. Similarly, the y-coordinate of equation ① must equal the y-coordinate of equation ②.

Since $y = 2x + 3$ ①

and $y = x + 4$ ②

and $y = y$ at the point of intersection

then $2x + 3 = x + 4$
$$2x - x = 4 - 3$$
$$x = 1$$

substituting $x = 1$ in $y = 2x + 3$

$$y = 2x + 3$$
$$y = 2(1) + 3$$
$$y = 2 + 3$$
$$y = 5$$

check in ①   check in ②
   L.S. = y L.S. = y
      = 5   = 5

Use $+$, $-$, $\times$, $\div$, ( ) to make a true statement.
$$6\ 3\ 4 = 2\ 3\ 0$$

R.S. = $2x + 3$ R.S. = $x + 4$
     = 2(1) + 3   = 1 + 4
     = 5   = 5

The solution is $(1, 5)$.

EXAMPLE 2. *Solve by comparison*

$$3x + 2y = 12 \qquad ①$$
$$2x + 3y = 13 \qquad ②$$

Solution
Solve both equations for the same variable, y.

In ①, $3x + 2y = 12$

$$2y = -3x + 12$$

$$y = \frac{-3x + 12}{2}$$

In ②, $2x + 3y = 13$

$$3y = -2x + 13$$

$$y = \frac{-2x + 13}{3}$$

At the point of intersection,

$$y = y$$

$$\frac{-3x + 12}{2} = \frac{-2x + 13}{3}$$

clearing fractions

$$6\left[\frac{-3x + 12}{2}\right] = 6\left[\frac{-2x + 13}{3}\right]$$

L.C.D. of 2 and 3 is 6

$$3(-3x + 12) = 2(-2x + 13)$$

$$-9x + 36 = -4x + 26$$

$$-9x + 4x = 26 - 36$$

$$-5x = -10$$

$$x = 2$$

Substitute $x = 2$ in ①

$$3x + 2y = 12$$

$$3(2) + 2y = 12$$

$$6 + 2y = 12$$

$$2y = 6$$

$$y = 3$$

check in ①

L.S. $= 3x + 2y$

$\quad = 3(2) + 2(3)$

$\quad = 6 + 6$

$\quad = 12$

R.S. $= 12$

check in ②

L.S. $= 2x + 3y$

$\quad = 2(2) + 3(3)$

$\quad = 4 + 9$

$\quad = 13$

R.S. $= 13$

The solution is $(2, 3)$

To begin your solution it is not always necessary to solve both equations for y. All that is required is that both equations be solved for the same variable.

EXAMPLE 3. *Solve by comparison*

$$2a + 3b = 16 \qquad ①$$

$$5a - 2b = 2 \qquad ②$$

Solution
Solve both equations for the same variable.

Put the numbers from 1 to 9 in the spaces to make the statements true.

$$\square \div \square + \square = 5$$

$$\square + \square - \square = 5$$

$$\square \times \square - \square = 5$$

In ①, $2a + 3b = 16$ In ②, $5a - 2b = 2$

$$2a = -3b + 16 \qquad\qquad 5a = 2b + 2$$

$$a = \frac{-3b + 16}{2} \qquad\qquad a = \frac{2b + 2}{5}$$

For a common solution,

$$a = a$$

$$\frac{-3b + 16}{2} = \frac{2b + 2}{5}$$

$$10\left[\frac{-3b + 16}{2}\right] = 10\left[\frac{2b + 2}{5}\right]$$

$$5(-3b + 16) = 2(2b + 2)$$

$$-15b + 80 = 4b + 4$$

$$-19b = -76$$

$$b = 4$$

Substitute in ①

$$2a + 3b = 16$$

$$2a + 3(4) = 16$$

$$2a + 12 = 16$$

$$2a = 4$$

$$a = 2$$

check in ①   check in ②

$$\begin{aligned} \text{L.S.} &= 2a + 3b \\ &= 2(2) + 3(4) \\ &= 4 + 12 \\ &= 16 \end{aligned} \qquad \begin{aligned} \text{L.S.} &= 5a - 2b \\ &= 5(2) - 2(4) \\ &= 10 - 8 \\ &= 2 \end{aligned}$$

$$\text{R.S.} = 16 \qquad\qquad\qquad \text{R.S.} = 2$$

The solution is $a = 2$ and $b = 4$

EXERCISE 7-3

A   **1.** Solve each of the following equations for the indicated variable.

(a) $3x + y = 7$

     $y = \blacksquare$

(b) $x + 2y = 4$

     $x = \blacksquare$

(c) $2x + 3y = 2$

     $y = \blacksquare$

(d) $3x + 2y = 4$

     $x = \blacksquare$

(e) $5x + 2y = 20$

     $y = \blacksquare$

(f) $5x + 2y = 20$

     $x = \blacksquare$

(g) $3x - 2y = 12$

     $x = \blacksquare$

(h) $3y - 4x = 11$

     $y = \blacksquare$

(i) $5x - y = 7$

     $y = \blacksquare$

(j) $2y - x = 4$

     $x = \blacksquare$

(k) $2a+3b+4=0$
　　 $a=$ ▨
(l) $5a-3b-2=0$
　　 $b=$ ▨
(m) $2x-3y-4=0$
　　 $y=$ ▨
(n) $-3x+2y-3=0$
　　 $x=$ ▨
(o) $3b-5a-6=0$
　　 $a=$ ▨
(p) $3m-7n=4$
　　 $n=$ ▨

```
  DOG
  DOG
   GO
 WOOF
```
DOG Each letter repre-
DOG sents a different
GO digit in this
WOOF addition.

B　**2.** Solve by comparison.

(a) $y=3x+2$
　　 $y=x+6$

(b) $y=2x-3$
　　 $y=3x-4$

(c) $y=-4x+7$
　　 $y=2x-5$

(d) $y=5x+9$
　　 $y=-x-9$

(e) $x=2y+3$
　　 $x=y-4$

(f) $x=3-4y$
　　 $x=2y-9$

(g) $a=3b+7$
　　 $a=2b-4$

(h) $n=4m-3$
　　 $n=2-m$

3. Solve by comparison and check your solution.

(a) $y=3x-4$
　　 $3y-x=4$

(b) $x=2y+6$
　　 $2x+y=2$

(c) $y=2x.-3$
　　 $x+2y=4$

(d) $y=3x-1$
　　 $3y-2x=4$

4. Solve by comparison and check your solution.

(a) $2x+3y=6$
　　 $2x+4y=8$

(b) $2x-3y=2$
　　 $5x+6y=5$

(c) $5x+3y=7$
　　 $8x+9y=7$

(d) $2x-4y=5$
　　 $5x+12y=7$

(e) $2x-4y-5=0$
　　 $3x+8y-4=0$

(f) $3b-2a-4=0$
　　 $6a-5b+12=0$

(g) $3m=5-2n$
　　 $15m+4n-1=0$

(h) $2a=5-3b$
　　 $4a=9b+5$

(i) $2x+3y-4=0$
　　 $3x+15y+1=0$

(j) $2m+3n=0$
　　 $m-6n=-5$

7-4 ALGEBRAIC SOLUTION OF A LINEAR SYSTEM—SUBSTITUTION

The ordered pair $(1,9)$ is one of many ordered pairs that satisfies
$$y-2x=7$$
This may be checked as follows.

　　L.S. $=y-2x$ 　　　　R.S. $=7$

　　　　 $=9-2(1)$

　　　　 $=9-2$

　　　　 $=7$

Since 　　　　　　　　 $y-2x=7$

then 　　　　　　　　 $y=2x+7$

We now have another ordered pair that satisfies the equation, namely
$(x, 2x+7)$.

This pair may be checked

$$\text{L.S.} = y - 2x \qquad\qquad \text{R.S.} = 7$$
$$= (2x + 7) - 2x$$
$$= 2x + 7 - 2x$$
$$= 7$$

We now use this idea to solve the system

$$y - 2x = 7 \qquad ①$$
$$y + x = 4 \qquad ②$$

We know that $(x, 2x + 7)$ satisfies equation ①. At the point of intersection of the two lines, $(x, 2x + 7)$ must also satisfy ②.

$$y + x = 4$$
$$(2x + 7) + x = 4$$
$$2x + 7 + x = 4$$
$$3x + 7 = 4$$
$$3x = -3$$
$$x = -1$$

From ① we have $y = 2x + 7$
$$= 2(-1) + 7$$
$$= -2 + 7$$
$$= 5$$

The solution is $(-1, 5)$

EXAMPLE 1. *Solve by substitution.*

$$2x + y = 6 \qquad ①$$
$$3x - 2y = 2 \qquad ②$$

Solution
From ① $2x + y = 6 \qquad\qquad y = 6 - 2x$

Substituting in ② $\qquad\qquad 3x - 2y = 2$
$$3x - 2(6 - 2x) = 2$$
$$3x - 12 + 4x = 2$$
$$7x = 14$$
$$x = 2$$

Substitute $x = 2$ in ①

$$2x + y = 6$$
$$2(2) + y = 6$$
$$4 + y = 6$$
$$y = 2$$

check in ①   check in ②

$$\begin{aligned} \text{L.S.} &= 2x + y \\ &= 2(2) + 2 \\ &= 4 + 2 \\ &= 6 \\ \text{R.S.} &= 6 \end{aligned}$$

$$\begin{aligned} \text{L.S.} &= 3x - 2y \\ &= 3(2) - 2(2) \\ &= 6 - 4 \\ &= 2 \\ \text{R.S.} &= 2 \end{aligned}$$

The solution is $(2, 2)$

EXERCISE 7-4

B   **1.** Solve by substitution.

(a) $2x + y = 6$
    $3x + 2y = 10$

(b) $3x + y = 2$
    $5x + 2y = 3$

(c) $x + 4y = 3$
    $2x + 5y = 3$

(d) $x - 2y = 4$
    $2x - 3y = 7$

(e) $x - 2y = 3$
    $5x + 4y = 8$

(f) $2a + b = 2$
    $3a - 2b = 3$

(g) $m + 3n = 2$
    $3m - 6n = 1$

(h) $x + 2y = 4$
    $2x - 6y = 3$

C   **2.** Solve by substitution. Check your solution.

(a) $3x + 4y = 9$
    $5x - 8y = 4$

(b) $5x + 4y = 5$
    $3x - 2y = 3$

(c) $2x + 5y = 6$
    $4x + 15y = -8$

(d) $2a + 3b = 3$
    $10a + 6b = -3$

(e) $3m - 2n = 5$
    $4m + 14n = 15$

(f) $3x + 2y = 12$
    $2x + 3y = 13$

(g) $5a - 8b = 8$
    $10a + 4b = 1$

(h) $3m - 4n - 10 = 0$
    $5m - 12n - 6 = 0$

7.5 ALGEBRAIC SOLUTION OF A LINEAR SYSTEM—ADDITION OR SUBTRACTION

Another way to eliminate one of the variables in a linear system of 2 variables is by addition or subtraction.

EXAMPLE 1. *Solve* $x + y = 9$ ①
                     $x - y = 3$ ②

Solution

$$\begin{aligned} x + y &= 9 \quad ① \\ x - y &= 3 \quad ② \\ \hline 2x &= 12 \\ x &= 6 \end{aligned}$$

Adding

If $a = b$ and $c = d$ then
$a + c = b + d$

Substitute in ①

$$x + y = 9$$
$$6 + y = 9$$
$$y = 3$$

check in ①

L.S. $= x + y$
$= 6 + 3$
$= 9$
R.S. $= 9$

check in ②

L.S. $= x - y$
$= 6 - 3$
$= 3$
R.S. $= 3$

The solution is (6, 3)

If $18x = 18 + x$ then $x = $ ▨

EXAMPLE 2. *Solve*

$$x + 5y = 4 \qquad ①$$
$$x + 3y = 2 \qquad ②$$

Solution
Adding will not eliminate one of the unknowns. Subtracting will.

If $a = b$ and $c = d$ then
$a - c = b - d$

$$x + 5y = 4 \qquad ①$$
$$\underline{x + 3y = 2} \qquad ②$$

subtracting

$$2y = 2$$
$$y = 1$$

substitute in ①

$$x + 5y = 4$$
$$x + 5(1) = 4$$
$$x + 5 = 4$$
$$x = -1$$

check in ①

L.S. $= x + 5y$
$= (-1) + 5(1)$
$= -1 + 5$
$= 4$
R.S. $= 4$

check in ②

L.S. $= x + 3y$
$= (-1) + 3(1)$
$= -1 + 3$
$= 2$
R.S. $= 2$

The solution is (−1, 1)

EXAMPLE 3. *Solve*

$$3x + 2y = 34 \qquad ①$$
$$5x - 3y = -13 \qquad ②$$

Solution
Neither addition nor subtraction eliminates one of the variables if the equations are left in their present form. Elimination will not occur until either the x terms or y terms are identical or opposites. To achieve this we can multiply both sides of an equation by the same number.

160   fmt : introduction

| Solution 1 (eliminating y) | Solution 2 (eliminating x) | The ordered pairs that satisfy $x+y=6$ are the same ordered pairs that satisfy $2x+2y=12$. Multiplying both sides of an equation by the same number does not change the relation. |

Solution 1
(eliminating y)

$$3x+2y=34 \quad ①$$
$$5x-3y=-13 \quad ②$$

$①\times 3 \quad 9x+6y=102$
$②\times 2 \quad 10x-6y=-26$

Adding $19x=76$
$$x=4$$

substitute in $①$

$$3x+2y=34$$
$$3(4)+2y=34$$
$$12+2y=34$$
$$2y=22$$
$$y=11$$

check in $②$ L.S. $=5x-3y$
$$=5(4)-3(11)$$
$$=20-33$$
$$=-13$$
R.S. $=-13$

Solution 2
(eliminating x)

$$3x+2y=34 \quad ①$$
$$5x-3y=-13 \quad ②$$

$①\times 5 \quad 15x+10y=170$
$②\times 3 \quad 15x-9y=-39$

Subtracting $19y=209$
$$y=11$$

substitute in $②$

$$5x-3y=-13$$
$$5x-3(11)=-13$$
$$5x-33=-13$$
$$5x=20$$
$$x=4$$

check in $①$ L.S. $=3x+2y$
$$=3(4)+2(11)$$
$$=12+22$$
$$=34$$
R.S. $=34$

The ordered pairs that satisfy $x+y=6$ are the same ordered pairs that satisfy $2x+2y=12$. Multiplying both sides of an equation by the same number does not change the relation.

The solution is $(4, 11)$.

EXERCISE 7-5

A Solve for x and y.
1. (a) $x+y=6$
$\quad\;\; x-y=4$

(b) $x-y=3$
$\quad\;\; x+y=7$

(c) $x+y=8$
$\quad\;\; x-y=-2$

(d) $x+y=8$
$\quad\;\; -x+y=6$

(e) $2x+y=5$
$\quad\;\; x+y=4$

(f) $x+2y=4$
$\quad\;\; x+y=2$

(g) $3x+y=6$
$\quad\;\; 2x-y=4$

(h) $3x+2y=2$
$\quad\;\; x-2y=2$

(i) $x+3y=7$
$\quad\;\; x+y=3$

B Solve and check.
2. (a) $x+3y=10$
$\quad\;\; 3x+2y=16$

(b) $3x+y=12$
$\quad\;\; 2x+5y=21$

(c) $2a+b=10$
$\quad\;\; 3a-2b=8$

(d) $x-3y=1$
$\quad\;\; 3x-2y=17$

(e) $2a+5b=19$
$\quad\;\; 3a-b=3$

(f) $4x-y=7$
$\quad\;\; 6x+5y=17$

3. (a) $3x-2y=5$
$\quad\;\; 2x+3y=12$

(b) $m-2n=3$
$\quad\;\; 2m-3n=4$

(c) $3x-2y=-8$
$\quad\;\; 4x+3y=-5$

(d) $2a+3b=11$
$\quad\;\; 3a-2b=-16$

(e) $5x+3y+19=0$
$\quad\;\; 2x-5y=11$

(f) $5m+2n-5=0$
$\quad\;\; 2m+3n-13=0$

(g) $3x=4y+5$
$\quad\;\; 5x+3y+11=0$

(h) $10=3x-4y$
$\quad\;\; 5x-12y=6$

4. (a) $4x-9y=4$
$\quad\;\; 6x+15y=-13$

(b) $8x-9y=41$
$\quad\;\; 4x+3y=3$

(c) $8x+3y=-14$
$7y-12x=21$

(d) $3a-2b+26=0$
$5a+b+26=0$

(e) $3b-2a+2=0$
$7a-6b=-11$

(f) $4x+3y+3=0$
$8x=9y-1$

(g) $2x-8y+1=0$
$6x=7-16y$

(h) $6x-2y=1$
$9x-4y=4$

EXAMPLE 4. *Solve the following for x, y, t.*

$$3x-2y+4t=11 \qquad ①$$
$$2x+3y-t=5 \qquad ②$$
$$x+4y-2t=3 \qquad ③$$

Solution

Eliminate y from ① and ②

$$3x-2y+4t=11 \quad ①$$
$$2x+3y-t=5 \quad ②$$

①×3 $\quad 9x-6y+12t=33$
②×2 $\quad \underline{4x+6y-2t=10}$
Adding $\quad 13x+10t=43$ ④

Eliminate y from ② and ③

$$2x+3y-t=5 \quad ②$$
$$x+4y-2t=3 \quad ③$$

②×4 $\quad 8x+12y-4t=20$
③×3 $\quad \underline{3x+12y-6t=9}$
Subtracting $5x+2t=11$ ⑤

Eliminate t from ④ and ⑤

$$13x+10t=43 \quad ④$$
$$5x+2t=11 \quad ⑤$$
$$13x+10t=43$$
⑤×5 $\quad \underline{25x+10t=55}$
Subtracting $-12x=-12$
$$x=1$$

Substitute $x=1$ in ④

$$13x+10t=43$$
$$13(1)+10t=43$$
$$13+10t=43$$
$$10t=30$$
$$t=3$$

Substitute $x=1$, $t=3$ in ①

$$3x-2y+4t=11$$
$$3(1)-2y+4(3)=11$$
$$3-2y+12=11$$
$$-2y=-4$$
$$y=2$$

check in ②

$$\text{L.S.}=2x+3y-t$$
$$=2(1)+3(2)-(3)$$

Cross all the dots with six straight lines without lifting your pencil

$$= 2 + 6 - 3$$

$$= 5$$

$$\text{R.S.} = 5$$

The solution is $x = 1$, $y = 2$, $t = 3$.

C **5.** Solve the following.

(a) $2a + 3b + c = 15$
$3a + 2b - c = 10$
$4a + b + 2c = 15$

(b) $4x - 2y + 3t = 27$
$2x + 3y - 4t = -6$
$3x + 5y - 2t = 12$

(c) $3a - 2b - 3c = 22$
$2a - 3b + 4c = 0$
$4a + b - 2c = 16$

(d) $2x + 5y - 3m = -7$
$3x - 2y - 4m = 16$
$5x + 2y - 5m = 4$

(e) $3a + 4b - 2c = -5$
$5a + 7b + 6c = 1$
$2a - 13b + 5c = 3$

(f) $2x - 2y - 2d = 9$
$3x + 4y - 4d = 0$
$x - y + 2d = 3$

(g) $2a + b - 2c + d = 7$
$3a + 2b + 2c - d = 12$
$2a + 3b - c + 2d = 10$
$4a - b + 3c - 2d = 12$

(h) $x - y = 1$
$x + m = 2$
$m - y = 7$

7.6 LINEAR SYSTEMS WITH RATIONAL COEFFICIENTS

EXAMPLE 1. *Solve* $\dfrac{x}{2} - \dfrac{y}{3} = 3$ ①

$$2x - \frac{y}{2} = 7 \quad ②$$

Solution
Clear fractions before attempting solution.

$$\frac{x}{2} - \frac{y}{3} = 3 \quad ①$$

$$2x - \frac{y}{2} = 7 \quad ②$$

$$① \times 6 \quad 3x - 2y = 18$$

$$② \times 2 \quad 4x - y = 14$$

$$3x - 2y = 18$$

$$② \times 2 \quad \underline{8x - 2y = 28}$$

$$-5x = -10$$

$$x = 2$$

Substituting

$$3x - 2y = 18$$

$$3(2) - 2y = 18$$

$$6 - 2y = 18$$

$$-2y = 12$$

$$y = -6$$

check in ②

$$\text{L.S.} = 2x - \frac{y}{2}$$

$$= 2(2) - \frac{(-6)}{2}$$

$$= 4 + 3$$

$$= 7$$

$$\text{R.S.} = 7$$

The solution is $(2, -6)$.

EXERCISE 7-6

B   Solve the following.

1. (a) $\dfrac{x}{3} + \dfrac{y}{4} = 2$

$\dfrac{2x}{3} - \dfrac{y}{2} = 0$

(b) $\dfrac{4a}{3} - \dfrac{b}{4} = 9$

$\dfrac{5a}{6} + b = 1$

(c) $x - y = 6$

$\dfrac{2x}{3} + \dfrac{y}{3} = 1$

(d) $\dfrac{x}{3} - \dfrac{y}{6} = -\dfrac{2}{3}$

$\dfrac{x}{12} - \dfrac{y}{4} = 1\tfrac{1}{2}$

(e) $\tfrac{1}{2}x + y = -4$

$\dfrac{x}{2} - \dfrac{3y}{2} = 1$

(f) $\tfrac{1}{3}m - \tfrac{1}{6}n = \tfrac{1}{2}$

$\dfrac{m}{5} - \dfrac{3n}{10} = \dfrac{1}{2}$

2. (a) $0.2x - 0.3y = -0.1$
$0.5x - 0.4y = 0.8$

(b) $0.2x - 0.3y = -0.6$
$0.5x + 0.2y = 2.3$

(c) $0.3a - 0.5b = 1.2$
$0.7a - 0.2b = -0.1$

(d) $1.2m + 0.6n = 0$
$3.5m + 1.7n = 0.01$

(e) $4x + 5y = -0.5$
$3x + 7y = 0.6$

(f) $7c - 2d = -4.3$
$8c - 5d = -4.1$

(g) $0.5x - 1.3y = 1.23$
$4x - 2y = 0.6$

(h) $3x + 2y = 2$
$4x - 3y = 7.2$

3. (a) $5(x - 3) + 2(y + 4) = 10$
$3(x + 4) - 4(y + 3) = -21$

(b) $2(3x - 1) - (y + 4) = -7$
$4(1 - 2x) - 3(3 - y) = -12$

(c) $2(x - 1) - 3(y - 3) = 0$
$3(x + 2) - (y - 7) = 20$

(d) $4(x - 4) - (y - 3) = -18$
$5(x + 1) + 2(y - 2) = -28$

(e) $5(x + 5) - 2(y - 3) = 62$
$4(x - 7) - (y + 4) = -9$

(f) $3(x + 3) - (y + 6) = -2$
$5(2x - 1) - 3(3x - 2) = 7$

(g) $3(x - 15) - (2y - 3) = -2$
$4(2x - 35) - 3(1 - 2y) = 77$

(h) $3(x + 5) + 2(y - 3) = 9$
$5(2x - 1) - 3(2y - 3) = 4$

C   **4** (a) $\dfrac{x - 2}{3} + \dfrac{y + 1}{5} = 2$

$\dfrac{x + 2}{7} - \dfrac{y + 5}{3} = -2$

(b) $\dfrac{x - 5}{3} + \dfrac{y + 1}{2} = 1$

$\dfrac{x - 1}{5} + \dfrac{y + 2}{3} = 2$

Subtract one three digit number from another and get all the digits from 1 to 9.

e.g.
$$\begin{array}{r} 918 \\ -542 \\ \hline 376 \end{array}$$

(c) $\dfrac{3(x-2)}{2} - \dfrac{y-2}{4} = 11$

$\dfrac{2(x+2)}{5} - \dfrac{y}{3} = 6$

(d) $\dfrac{2x-1}{5} - \dfrac{3y+2}{4} = -2$

$\dfrac{3x+1}{5} + \dfrac{5y-3}{3} = 14$

(e) $\dfrac{2}{3}x + \dfrac{y-1}{4} = 6$

$\dfrac{5x}{6} - \dfrac{y+3}{4} = 2$

(f) $\dfrac{x-1}{3} + \dfrac{y+2}{4} = 4$

$\dfrac{x+1}{2} - \dfrac{y-2}{2} = 2$

7.7 LINEAR SYSTEMS WITH LITERAL COEFFICIENTS

In this section we will use the method of elimination by addition or subtraction to solve linear systems with literal coefficients.

EXAMPLE 1. *Solve for x and y.*

$$ax - 2by = 3ab \quad ① $$
$$2ax + by = ab \quad ②$$

Solution

$$ax - 2by = 3ab \quad ①$$
$$2ax + by = ab \quad ②$$

$①\times 2 \qquad 2ax - 4by = 6ab$

$\underline{\qquad\quad 2ax + by = ab}$

subtracting $\quad -5by = 5ab$

$\qquad\qquad\quad y = -a, \qquad b \neq 0$

substitute in $①$
$$ax - 2by = 3ab$$
$$ax - 2b(-a) = 3ab$$
$$ax + 2ab = 3ab$$
$$ax = ab$$
$$x = b, \qquad a \neq 0$$

The solution is $(b, -a)$.

EXAMPLE 2. *Solve for x and y.*

$$ax + by = c \quad ①$$
$$dx + ey = f \quad ②$$

Solution $\qquad ax + by = c \qquad\qquad ①$

$\qquad\qquad\qquad dx + ey = f \qquad\qquad ②$

$①\times e \qquad aex + bey = ce$

$②\times b \qquad \underline{bdx + bey = bf}$

Subtracting $\quad aex - bdx = ce - bf$

$$x(ae - bd) = ce - bf$$

$$(ae - bd)x = ce - bf$$

$$x = \frac{(ce - bf)}{(ae - bd)}, \qquad (ae - bd) \neq 0$$

The value of y may be found by substitution. However, it may be simpler, in cases similar to this example, to start again and eliminate x by addition or subtraction.

$$\left.\begin{array}{l} x = \dfrac{ce - bf}{ae - bd}, \qquad ae - bd \neq 0 \\[4mm] y = \dfrac{cd - af}{bd - ae}, \qquad bd - ae \neq 0 \end{array}\right\} \quad \begin{array}{l} \text{GENERAL SOLUTION} \\ \text{OF LINEAR SYSTEM} \\ \text{IN TWO UNKNOWNS} \end{array}$$

EXERCISE 7-7

A **1.** Solve the following for x.

(a) $ax = b$

(b) $mx = n$

(c) $nx = a + b$

(d) $(m + n)x = a + b$

Find a three digit number that is the sum of the cubes of its digits.

(e) $\dfrac{x}{a} = b$

(f) $\dfrac{x}{m} = -n$

(g) $(a + b)x = 4$

(h) $x(m - n) = -2y$

(i) $ax + bx = 6$

(j) $cx - dx = t$

(k) $gx - hx = c + d$

(l) $bx - ax = t - s$

(m) $2ax + bx = m$

(n) $4cx - 3tx = b - a$

B Solve for x and y.

2. (a) $x - y = a + b$
  $x + y = a - b$

(b) $bx + ay = 2ab$
  $bx - ay = 4ab$

(c) $6mx + 13ny = 4mn$
  $2mx + 5ny = 2mn$

(d) $2ax + 3by = ab$
  $3ax + 4by = 3ab$

(e) $ax - 3by = 2ab$
  $3ax + 4by = 5ab$

(f) $2x + y = a - b$
  $x - y = a + b$

3. (a) $2ax + y = m$
  $bx - y = n$

(b) $ax + y = 3$
  $x + by = 2$

(c) $3x + ay = 4$
  $ax + 2y = 6$

(d) $ax + y = 2$
  $bx - y = 4$

(e) $mx + ny = g$
  $dx + ey = h$

(f) $ax - by = c$
  $dx - ey = f$

7.8 SOLVING LINEAR SYSTEMS BY MATRICES

All of the following systems of equations are equivalent. On the left is an algebraic solution of a linear system. On the right is the corresponding matrix solution.

$$\begin{array}{l} x + 2y = 5 \\ 3x - 4y = -5 \end{array} \qquad \begin{pmatrix} 1 & 2 & 5 \\ 3 & -4 & -5 \end{pmatrix}$$

$$\begin{array}{l} 2x + 4y = 10 \\ 3x - 4y = -5 \end{array} \qquad \begin{pmatrix} 2 & 4 & 10 \\ 3 & -4 & -5 \end{pmatrix}$$

$$\begin{array}{l} 5x \quad\;\; = 5 \\ 3x - 4y = -5 \end{array} \qquad \begin{pmatrix} 5 & 0 & 5 \\ 3 & -4 & -5 \end{pmatrix}$$

$$\begin{array}{l} x \quad\;\; = 1 \\ 3x - 4y = -5 \end{array} \qquad \begin{pmatrix} 1 & 0 & 1 \\ 3 & -4 & -5 \end{pmatrix}$$

$$\begin{array}{l} x \quad\;\; = 1 \\ \quad -4y = -8 \end{array} \qquad \begin{pmatrix} 1 & 0 & 1 \\ 0 & -4 & -8 \end{pmatrix}$$

$$\begin{array}{l} x \quad\;\; = 1 \\ \quad\;\; y = 2 \end{array} \qquad \begin{pmatrix} 1 & 0 & 1 \\ 0 & 1 & 2 \end{pmatrix}$$

In the algebraic solution the symbols x, y, and $=$ play a minor role. We operate on the numerical coefficients of x and y and the constant terms. This suggests that a solution may be found without writing the variables and the equal sign. This was done in the matrix solution. Each matrix can be considered an abbreviation of the corresponding system of equations.

The goal in solving a system of two equations by matrices is to operate on its elements until the matrix has the following form.

$$\begin{pmatrix} 1 & 0 & C_1 \\ 0 & 1 & C_2 \end{pmatrix}$$

This is called the *row reduced form* of a matrix. The solution (C_1, C_2) can be read directly from the matrix.

Three operations are permitted when solving a system of linear equations by matrices.

① Multiplication of all elements of a row by the same non-zero number

② Addition of the same multiple of the elements of one row to the corresponding elements of another row

③ Interchanging rows.

EXAMPLE 1. *Solve the following system by matrices.*

$$\begin{array}{l} 3x + 2y = 4 \\ 2x - 3y = 7 \end{array}$$

Solution

Express the system in matrix form.

$$\begin{array}{l} \text{row ①} \\ \text{row ②} \end{array} \begin{pmatrix} 3 & 2 & 4 \\ 2 & -3 & 7 \end{pmatrix}$$

Multiply row ① by $\frac{1}{2}$ $\begin{pmatrix} \frac{3}{2} & 1 & 2 \\ 2 & -3 & 7 \end{pmatrix}$

Add $3\times$ row ① to row ② $\begin{pmatrix} \frac{3}{2} & 1 & 2 \\ \frac{13}{2} & 0 & 13 \end{pmatrix}$

Multiply row ② by $\frac{2}{13}$ $\begin{pmatrix} \frac{3}{2} & 1 & 2 \\ 1 & 0 & 2 \end{pmatrix}$

Solve mentally

$$3761x + 4283y = 8044$$
$$4283x + 3761y = 8044$$

Add $-\frac{3}{2} \times$ row ② to row ① $\begin{pmatrix} 0 & 1 & -1 \\ 1 & 0 & 2 \end{pmatrix}$

Interchange rows $\begin{pmatrix} 1 & 0 & 2 \\ 0 & 1 & -1 \end{pmatrix}$

$\therefore \quad x = 2$ and $y = -1$

EXERCISE 7-8

B **1.** Solve the following systems of equations using matrices.

(a) $x + y = 5$
$2x - y = 4$

(b) $x + 2y = 6$
$x + 3y = 7$

(c) $2x - 3y = 12$
$x + 4y = -5$

(d) $2x + y = 13$
$3x - 2y = 9$

(e) $4x - y = 5$
$2x + 5y = -14$

(f) $4x - y = -2$
$7x - 2y = -5$

(g) $2x + 5y = -10$
$5x - 3y = -9$

(h) $3x + 2y = 1$
$4x - 3y = 24$

(i) $3x + 5y = 11$
$4x + 3y = 0$

(j) $4x + 5y + 6 = 0$
$3x - 2y = -16$

To solve $ax + by = c$
$\qquad\quad dx + ey = f$

C **2.** Use the matrix method to solve the following systems of equations.

(a) $2x + y + 3z = 13$
$3x - 2y + z = 2$
$x + 3y - 2z = 1$

(b) $3x + y + 2z = -4$
$2x + 3y - 2z = 11$
$x + 2y + 3z = -1$

(c) $x + 3y + 2z = 6$
$3x - 2y + 3z = 2$
$2x + 4y + z = 14$

(d) $3x + 2y + z = 8$
$2x - 4y + 3z = 3$
$4x + 3y + 2z = 10$

REVIEW EXERCISE

A **1.** State 3 ordered pairs that satisfy each of the following.

(a) $y = x + 4$

(b) $y = x - 7$

(c) $y = -x + 1$

(d) $y = 2x - 3$

(e) $y = -4x$

(f) $y = 3 - x$

2. Use the *intercept method* to determine 2 points that satisfy each of the following.

(a) $4x + 3y = 12$

(b) $2x + y = 6$

(c) $3x - 2y = 6$

(d) $5x - 2y = 10$

(e) $7x - 3y = -21$

(f) $x - y = 4$

3. Solve each of the following equations for the indicated variable.

(a) $2x + y = 4; y$

(b) $x - 3y = 7; x$

(c) $3x + 2y = 5; y$

(d) $2a + 3b = 4; a$

(e) $3m - 2n = 2; m$

(f) $4d - 3e = 7; e$

(g) $4x - 3y = 0; x$

(h) $2x + 3y - 4 = 0; y$

B **4.** Solve the following graphically.

(a) $y = x + 3$
$y = -x + 1$

(b) $x + y = 7$
$x - y = 3$

(c) $y = 2x - 1$
$y = 3x - 4$

(d) $x + 2y = 0$
$2x - y = -10$

START

Read
a, b, c, d, e, f

ae = bd ——YES—

NO

Let
$x = \dfrac{ce - bf}{ae - bd}$

$y = \dfrac{af - cd}{ae - bd}$

Write
x, y

Write
"No Real Roots"

STOP

STOP

5. Classify each of the following linear systems as consistent, inconsistent or dependent.

(a) $y = 3x + 4$
$y = 3x - 7$

(b) $x + 2y = 6$
$2x + 4y = 12$

(c) $x - 3y = 7$
$x + 4y = 17$

(d) $2x - y = 4$
$2x - y = 15$

(e) $7x + 5y = 21$
$7x + 6y = 21$

(f) $2x = 3y + 7$
$6x - 9y - 21 = 0$

6. Solve. Check your solution.

(a) $5x - 2y = -9$
$3x + 7y = 11$

(b) $3x + y = 13$
$2x + 3y = 18$

(c) $5x - 4y + 13 = 0$
$7x - y + 9 = 0$

(d) $2x - 3y = -10$
$4x + y = 1$

(e) $2x + 3y = -18$
$3x - 5y = 11$

(f) $x + 5y = 16$
$2x + 3y = 11$

(g) $4x = 3y + 1$
$8x + 15y = 9$

(h) $2x - y - 15 = 0$
$5x + 4y - 18 = 0$

(i) $6x = 5y - 3$
$3x + 10y + 4 = 0$

(j) $7x + 8y = 1$
$14x - 10y + 11 = 0$

7. Solve

(a) $\frac{2}{3}x + \frac{1}{4}y = 3$

$\frac{1}{3}x - \frac{1}{2}y = -1$

(b) $\frac{3x}{2} - \frac{2y}{3} = 2$

$\frac{3x}{4} - \frac{y}{6} = 2$

(c) $\frac{7x}{10} - y = -13$

$\frac{3}{5}x + \frac{1}{6}y = -5$

(d) $\frac{x}{4} + \frac{y}{6} = 1\frac{1}{4}$

$\frac{x}{5} - \frac{y}{2} = -\frac{9}{10}$

(e) $4x + 3y = -1.9$
$2x - 7y = 3.3$

(f) $0.1x - 0.4y = 1.9$
$0.4x + 0.5y = -0.8$

(g) $2x - 5y = -3.1$
$x + 7y = 3.2$

(h) $0.4x - 0.3y = 2.4$
$0.6x + 0.7y = -1$

8. Solve. Check your solution.

(a) $2(x - 1) - 3(y + 2) = 18$
$3(x + 4) + 4(y - 3) = -12$

(b) $2(y - 3) - 3(2 - x) = -29$
$5(x + 3) - 4y = -6$

(c) $2(2x - 1) - (y - 4) = 1$
$5(1 - 3x) + 2(2y + 1) = 10$

(d) $2(4x - 1) - (3 - y) = -4$
$3(6x - 1) + 2(1 - y) = 14$

9. Solve for x and y.

(a) $ax + by = 4ab$
$ax - by = 2ab$

(b) $4ax - 3by = 6ab$
$2ax - 2by = 7ab$

(c) $2ax - y = 4ab$
$3ax + y = 6ab$

(d) $ax + by = c$
$mx - ny = d$

C **10.** (a) $2a + 3b - 4c = 21$
$3a - 2b + 2c = -4$
$4a + 5b + 3c = 17$

(b) $5a - 3b + 4c = -3$
$6a + 2b - 3c = -26$
$2a - 5b - 11c = 14$

(c) $a + b = -1$
$b + c = -2$
$a + c = 9$

(d) $2a + 3b + 2c - 4d = 8$
$3a - b + 3c - 2d = 19$
$4a + 2b + c + d = 6$
$2a + b - 4c + 2d = -12$

REVIEW AND PREVIEW TO CHAPTER 8

EXERCISE 1

PER CENT IN PRACTICAL PROBLEMS

1. John bought a portable radio that was priced at $152.00. If the rate of sales tax was 7%, how much did he pay for the radio?

2. Stephanie bought a new car that listed at $5550.00 If the rate of sales tax was 7%, how much did she pay for the car?

3. A credit union offers a 9% interest rate on deposits of multiples of $500 if they are left in the credit union for one year. The students' council deposits $1500. What is the interest after one year?

3. A salesman sells a car for $7550.00. If his commission is 5%, how much does he receive for this sale?

5. Terry Zobic sells real estate. Her commission is 6% on each sale. If she sells a property for $156 000.00, what is her commission?

6. A large department store has a "10% Day" when everything is discounted 10%. If you buy a pair of shoes priced at $32.50, how much is the discount?

7. A new car dealer pays you a salary of $100 a week plus commission of 3% on all sales. If your sales total $12 250.00 for the week, how much would you earn?

8. A variety store sells pens priced at $3.00. If the rate of sales tax is 7%, how much would you pay for a pen?

9. A jeweller bought a diamond ring for $1500.00. If his rate of mark up is 80% of his cost price, what would you pay for the ring?

10. A large department store has a "10% Day" when everything bought on this day is discounted 10%. If you buy a sweater priced at $40.00, what will you pay for the sweater if the rate of sales tax is 7%?

11. The science club decides to set up a tropical fish aquarium. The local pet store delivered, on request, the following items:

> tank: $75.00
> tank stand: $35.00
> gravel: $8.00
> pump: $22.00
> filter: $15.00

If the rate of sales tax is 7%, how much is the bill from the pet shop?

12. A bank offers an interest rate of 11% on deposits left in the bank for one year. If you deposit $1200.00 under these conditions, what will the interest amount to after one year?

13. Sarah purchased the following items from a department store: a blouse priced at $10.37, slacks priced at $25.33, and a jacket priced at $41.30. If the rate of sales tax is 7%, how much was her total bill?

14. A variety store oner buys bread from a bakery for $0.70 a loaf. If his rate of markup is 20%, what will you pay for a loaf of bread?

15. A television set priced at $780.00 is put on sale at 25% off. If the rate of sales tax is 7%, what would you pay for the set?

16. A new car lists for $6780.00. If you have a trade in valued at $2100.00 and the rate of sales tax is 7%, what will you pay for the car?

17. A bank pays interest of 12.5% on deposits left in the bank for one year. If you deposit $2500.00, how much is the interest after one year?

18. A car dealer pays you $200.00 a week plus 2% of your total sales. If your sales totalled $8100.00 for the week, how much would you be paid?

19. Mario's weekly sales for a four week period were $8900.00, $12 100.00, $14 700.00, and $7900.00. If he is paid $150.00 a week plus 3% of sales, how much did he earn in the four weeks?

20. Marina bought the following items at a hardware store.

        (i)   a hammer priced at $8.57
        (ii) nails priced at $2.36
        (iii) paint priced at $18.07
        (iv) a paint brush priced at $4.00

If the rate of sales tax is 7%, what was her total bill?

CHAPTER 8

Word Problems

Beside the mathematical arts there is no infallible knowledge, except it be borrowed from them.

Robert Recorde

8.1 TRANSLATING WORDS INTO MATHEMATICAL EXPRESSIONS

Many problems can be solved using mathematical methods. In order to do this, we must be able to change words into mathematical expressions and equations.

9	8	6	4	7
3	6	7	11	5
4	5	9	3	6
31	53	51	47	

Determine the pattern. Find the missing number.

EXERCISE 8-1

B **1.** Write the following as algebraic expressions in one variable.
(a) 3 times a number.
(b) a number increased by 4.
(c) a number decreased by 3.
(d) the length increased by 5 m.
(e) Mary's age 2 years ago.
(f) John's age 5 years from now.
(g) Twice the width increased by 3.
(h) One-half the speed.
(i) Eight points less than the winner.
(j) Three times the volume decreased by 20.
(k) The value, in cents, of x quarters.
(l) One-half Susan's age 6 years ago.
(m) One third of Tom's age 10 years from now.
(n) Six times a number decreased by 2.
(o) Four times as many people.
(p) The value, in cents, of y dimes.
(q) Nine per cent of the selling price.
(r) Twelve per cent of the cost price.
(s) Interest, after one year, from an investment at 10% per annum.
(t) Interest, after one year, from an investment at 12% per annum.

1. Introduce the variable.
2. Set up the equation.
3. Solve the equation.
4. State your solution.
5. Check your solution.

2. Find the unknown quantity using an equation in one variable and the 5 steps shown in the margin.
(a) A number increased by 35 is 82.
(b) Five times a number is 185.
(c) Four times a number less 47 is 293.
(d) When 57 is added to 9 times a number the result is 795.
(e) Six times the number of students less 87 is 999.
(f) Sam's age 5 years ago was 17.
(g) Sue's age 13 years from now will be 27.

(h) Three times Bill's age five years ago was 48.
(i) Five times Tom's age plus 13 is 163.
(j) Twice the length increased by 4 is 26.
(k) Three times the width decreased by 7 is 92.
(l) One half the length plus 11 is 43.
(m) Twice the car's speed increased by 31 is 165.
(n) John drove 400 km in 8 h. Find his speed.
(o) Mary averaged 60 km/h for 7.5 h. How far did she drive?
(p) How long will it take to drive 490 km at 35 km/h?
(q) 5% of the total price is $30.
(r) 7% of the cost price is $1.40.
(s) The bag of quarters had a total value of $17.75.

3. Write the following as expressions in two variables.
(a) the sum of the length and the width.
(b) twice the length added to three times the width.
(c) three times the length decreased by the width.
(d) the sum of Sam's age and 3 times Maria's age.
(e) the value of x nickels and y dimes.
(f) the value of x nickels and y quarters.
(g) the value of x $2 bills and y $5 bills.
(h) five times Paul's age decreased by 4 times Hal's age.
(i) twice the length increased by 3 plus 4 times the width.

4. Write the following as algebraic equations in 2 variables.
(a) The sum of 2 numbers is 50.
(b) The difference between 2 numbers is 40.
(c) There are a total of 35 boys and girls in the class.
(d) Tom counted 8 more cars than trucks.
(e) Sam's history and physics marks totalled 170.
(f) Twice one number plus 3 times another is 48.
(g) Four times the number of dimes less twice the number of quarters is 33.
(h) The sum of Susan's and Bob's age is 35.
(i) Eight times Tom's age plus Harry's age 2 years ago is 251.
(j) The length plus 3 times the width is 48.
(k) Seven times the length less 5 times the width is 38.
(l) Twelve times the length less 5 times the width is 487.
(m) The value of the dimes and quarters was 180 cents.
(n) The $10 bills and $5 bills had a total value of $765.
(o) The nickels and dimes had a total value of 795 cents.
(p) The total interest from one investment at 8% and another at 9% was $195.
(q) The total interest from 2 investments at 12% and 9% is $240.

8.2 PROBLEMS IN TWO VARIABLES—I

Some problems of business and industry are solved by expressing the problems as a system of equations. We will limit our problems to those that can be expressed as two equations with two variables. Although these problems could be solved using one variable and one equation, it is often simpler to use two equations and two variables.

To determine if $m > 2$ is prime

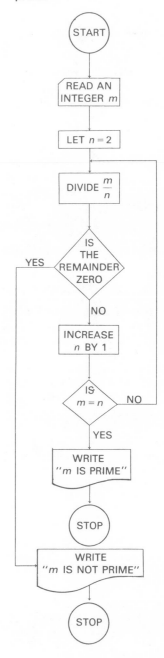

EXAMPLE 1. *The sum of two numbers is 340 and their difference is 174. Find the numbers.*

Solution

Introduce the variables.

Let x represent the larger number.
Let y represent the smaller number.

Translate the words to equations.

$$x + y = 340 \quad ①$$
$$x - y = 174 \quad ②$$

Solve the system of equations.

Adding
$$2x = 514$$
$$x = 257$$

Substitute in ① $x + y = 340$
$$257 + y = 340$$
$$y = 83$$

Check the solution.

Check in the original statement of the problem.
The sum of two numbers is 340.

$$257 + 83 = 340$$

The difference between them is 174.

$$257 - 83 = 174$$

State the solution.

Therefore the numbers are 257 and 83.

EXAMPLE 2. *When 4 times the larger of 2 numbers is added to 3 times the smaller the result is 68. Seven times the larger less 5 times the smaller is 37. Find the numbers.*

Solution

A book costs $3.00 plus one half its price. How much does it cost?

Let x represent the larger number.
Let y represent the smaller number.

$$4x + 3y = 68 \quad ①$$
$$7x - 5y = 37 \quad ②$$

①×5 $\quad 20x + 15y = 340$
②×3 $\quad 21x - 15y = 111$
Adding $\quad\quad 41x = 451$
$$x = 11$$

Substitute in ①

$$4x + 3y = 68$$
$$4(11) + 3y = 68$$
$$44 + 3y = 68$$
$$3y = 24$$
$$y = 8$$

Check: 4 times the larger plus 3 times the smaller is 68.

$$4(11)+3(8)$$
$$=44+24$$
$$=68$$

7 times the larger less 5 times the smaller is 37.

$$7(11)-5(8)$$
$$=77-40$$
$$=37$$

The numbers are 11 and 8.

EXAMPLE 3. *The vending machine contains a total of 395 quarters and dimes. The total value of the coins is $66.80. How many of each are there?*

Solution
Let x represent the number of quarters.
Let y represent the number of dimes.

$$x+y=395 \qquad ①$$
$$25x+10y=6680 \qquad ②$$

$① \times 10$
$$10x+10y=3950$$
$$25x+10y=6680$$
Subtracting
$$-15x=-2730$$
$$x=182$$

Substitute in ①
$$x+y=395$$
$$182+y=395$$
$$y=213$$

Check: There are 395 coins

$$182+213=395$$

Their total value is $66.80

$$182(\$0.25)+213(\$0.10)$$
$$=\$45.50+\$21.30$$
$$=\$66.80$$

There are 182 quarters and 213 dimes.

Write the value equation in terms of cents.

EXERCISE 8-2

B **1.** The sum of 2 numbers is 84. The difference between them is 18. Find the numbers.

2. The sum of 2 numbers is 255. When the smaller is subtracted from the larger the result is 39. Find the numbers.

3. The sum of 2 numbers is 1584. Their difference is 58. Find the numbers.

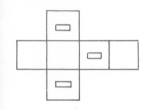

Which of the following figures can you make from the pattern above?

4. The sum of 2 numbers is 1211 and their difference is 283. Find the numbers.

5. The sum of 2 numbers is 249. Twice the larger plus 3 times the smaller is 591. Find the numbers.

6. When 6 times the larger of 2 numbers is added to 7 times the smaller the result is 114. Ten times the larger less 9 times the smaller is 66. Find the numbers.

7. Six times the larger of 2 numbers plus 5 times the smaller is 145. Eight times the larger increased by 4 times the smaller is 164. Find the numbers.

8. Seven times the smaller of 2 numbers plus 9 times the larger is 178. When 10 times the larger is increased by 11 times the smaller the result is 230. Find the numbers.

9. Seven times the larger of 2 numbers decreased by 5 times the smaller is 42. Nine times the larger increased by 8 times the smaller is 186. Find the numbers.

10. When the larger of 2 numbers is multiplied by 9 and added to 10 times the smaller, the result is 389. Seven times the larger diminished by 4 times the smaller is 67. Find the numbers.

11. The difference in 2 numbers is 92. When the larger is subtracted from 4 times the smaller the result is 151. Find the numbers.

12. The sum of 2 numbers is 188. The larger number is 24 more than 3 times the smaller. Find the numbers.

13. Two numbers have a difference of 123. The larger is 22 more than twice the smaller. Find the numbers.

14. Two numbers have a difference of 218. The larger is 140 less than twice the smaller. Find the numbers.

15. The sum of 2 numbers is 46. When 30 is subtracted from 5 times the smaller the result is 3 times the larger. Find the numbers.

16. Sam has a total of $113 made up of $2 bills and $5 bills. If there are 31 bills in all, how many $2 bills does he have?

17. Mary has $300 made up of $5 and $10 bills. If there are 39 bills in all, how many $5 bills does she have?

18. Pete has twice as many $2 bills as $5 bills. Together they total $153. How many $5 bills does he have?

19. I have 6 more $5 bills than $10 bills. In all, I have $255. How many $5 bills do I have?

20. The pop machine contained $3.05 made up of dimes and quarters. There are 20 coins in all. How many dimes are there?

21. A parking meter contained 78 coins made up of dimes and nickels. The total value of the coins was $5.20. How many dimes does it contain?

22. A vending machine contained dimes and quarters. The number of quarters is 7 more than twice the number of dimes. The coins have a total value of $20.35. How many of each coin are there?

23. The athletic department bought a total of 29 basketballs and footballs at a cost of $1000. If basketballs cost $30 each and footballs $40 each, how many footballs were bought?

24. A movie theatre sold twice as many adult tickets as student tickets. The total receipts were $2299. If adult tickets cost $7 and students $5, how many of each were sold?

25. There were 296 tickets sold for the school athletic banquet. Adult tickets cost $10, student tickets $5. The receipts totalled $1910. How many student tickets were sold?

26. The school bookstore ordered a total of 130 mathematics and history books. A math book costs $9.50 and a history book $8.10. If the total bill was $1137.00 how many math books were bought?

27. A hockey team played a total of 41 games. The number of games lost was 10 less than one-half the number of games won. How many games were won?

28. The length of a rectangle is 85 m longer than the width. If the perimeter is 402 m, find the dimensions of the rectangle.

29. The length of a rectangle is 4 times the width. If the perimeter is 400 m, find the dimensions of the rectangle.

30. The length of a rectangle is 5 m more than 7 times the width. If the perimeter is 74 m, find the dimensions of the rectangle.

31. A storeroom is in the shape of a rectangle. The width is 3 m less than one-half the length. If the perimeter is 60 m, find the dimensions of the room.

32. The sum of Mary's age and her father's age is 67. Three times Mary's age increased by 7 is her father's age. How old is Mary?

33. Sam's father is 3 times as old as he is. In 6 years the sum of their ages will be 68. How old is Sam?

34. If you double Lucien's age and then subtract 6 you have Paul's age. Two years ago the sum of their ages was 29. How old is Lucien?

35. Twice Sally's age increased by 3 times Sue's age is 103. Five times Sally's age decreased by 4 times Sue's age is 16. How old will Sally be 10 years from now?

C **36.** One half of Bob's age plus one third of Terry's age is 24. One fifth of Bob's age less one ninth of Terry's age is 3. How old is Terry?

37. The perimeter of a rectangle is 140 m. If the length were tripled and the width cut in half the perimeter would be 370 m. Find the dimensions of the original rectangle.

38. Hans has some $2 bills and $5 bills which have a total value of $81. If he replaced the $2 bills with the same number of 5s and the $5 bills with the same number of 10s, he would have $175. How many $2 bills does he have?

39. The gate receipts for a baseball game were $57 000. Adult tickets sold for $5.50 and students for $2.50. If the game had been a playoff game ticket prices would have been increased by 50¢ each, and the same crowd would have paid a total of $63 000. How many student tickets were sold?

If a brick has a mass of 10 kg and half a brick, what is the mass of a brick and a half?

Use $+$, $-$, $\times$, $\div$, $(\ )$ to make a true statement.

11 1 1 = 2 2 2 2

8.3 PROBLEMS IN TWO VARIABLES—II

In this section we will deal with special types of problems that can be solved with 2 equations in 2 variables.

EXAMPLE 1. *Mike invested $8000, part at 9%/a and the remainder at 12%/a. After one year the total interest earned on these investments was $810. How much did he invest at each rate?*

Solution
Let x be the amount invested at 9%.
Let y be the amount invested at 12%.

$$x + y = 8000 \qquad ① \qquad \text{Total money invested}$$

$$0.09x + 0.12y = 810 \qquad ② \qquad \text{Total interest earned}$$

$$x + y = 8000$$

$② \times 100 \qquad 9x + 12y = 81\,000 \qquad$ clearing decimal fractions

$① \times 9 \qquad 9x + 9y = 72\,000$

$$\overline{ 9x + 12y = 81\,000}$$

subtracting $\qquad -3y = -9000$

$$y = 3000$$

substitute in ① $x + 3000 = 8000$

$$x = 5000$$

check: The total investment was $8000

$$\$5000 + \$3000 = \$8000$$

The total interest earned was $810

$$0.09(\$5000) + 0.12(\$3000)$$

$$= \$450 + \$360$$

$$= \$810$$

He invested $5000 at 9% and $3000 at 12%.

Put the numbers from 1 to 9 in the spaces to make the statements true.

$$\Box - \Box + \Box = 6$$
$$\Box - \Box - \Box = 6$$
$$\Box \div \Box \times \Box = 6$$

EXAMPLE 2. *A store owner sells peanuts for $4.80/kg and raisins for $2.40/kg. He decides to mix raisins and peanuts and sell the mixture as a T.V. snack for $3.36/kg. He decides to make up 100 kg of the snack. How many kilograms of peanuts and raisins will he need?*

Solution
A table is helpful to solve mixture problems. Expressing money value in cents simplifies the problem.
Let x represent the number of kilograms of peanuts needed.
Let y represent the number of kilograms of raisins needed.

	number of kilograms	cost per kilogram	value in cents
peanuts	x	480	$480x$
raisins	y	240	$240y$
mixture	100	336	33 600

$$x + y = 100 \quad ① \text{ Total mass of mixture—column 1}$$
$$480x + 240y = 33\,600 \quad ② \text{ Total value of mixture—column 3}$$

$$x + y = 100$$

$② \div 240$ $2x + y = 140$

subtracting $-x = -40$

$$x = 40$$

substitute ① $x + y = 100$

$$40 + y = 100$$

$$y = 60$$

> The difference of the squares of two positive whole numbers is 576. Find the numbers.

check: The mass of the mixture is 100 kg.

$$40 \text{ kg} + 60 \text{ kg} = 100 \text{ kg}$$

The value of the ingredients must be the same as the value of the mixture.

$$\text{Ingredients:} \quad \$4.80(40) + \$2.40(60)$$
$$= \$192 + \$144$$
$$= \$336.00$$

$$\text{mixture:} \quad \$3.36(100) = \$336.00$$

He will need 40 kg of peanuts and 60 kg of raisins.

EXAMPLE 3. *A chemistry student was asked to make 100 ℓ of 48% alcohol solution by volume by mixing 40% alcohol solution by volume and 60% alcohol solution by volume. How many litres of each must the student use?*

Solution

Let x represent the number of litres of 40% solution needed.
Let y represent the number of litres of 60% solution needed.

$$x + y = 100 \quad ① \quad \text{solution equation}$$
$$0.4x + 0.6y = (0.48)100 \quad ② \quad \text{alcohol equation}$$

$① \times 4$ $4x + 4y = 400$

$② \times 10$ $4x + 6y = 480$

subtracting $-2y = -80 \qquad y = 40$

substituting in ① $x + y = 100$

$$x + 40 = 100$$
$$x = 60$$

check: $100\,\ell$ of solution are required

$$60\,\ell + 40\,\ell = 100\,\ell$$

There must be $48\,\ell$ of alcohol in the final solution.

$$0.4(60\ell) + 0.6(40\ell)$$
$$= 24\,\ell + 24\,\ell = 48\,\ell$$

EXAMPLE 4. *Jeanne took a trip from Brownsville to Montreal, a distance of 830 km. She travelled part of the way by bus and the rest of the way by plane. The bus averaged 40 km/h and the plane 500 km/h. The whole trip took 3.5 h. How many hours did she spend travelling by bus?*

Solution

Let x represent the time on the bus, in hours.
Let y represent the time flying, in hours.

D ⟋ S ⎮ T	Distance km	Speed (km/h)	Time (h)
Bus	$40x$	40	x
Plane	$500y$	500	y
Totals	830		3.5

$40x + 500y = 830$ ①   Distance equation
$x + y = 3.5$ ②   Time equation

       ① ÷ 10 $4x + 50y = 83$
       ② × 4 $4x + 4y = 14$

subtracting $46y = 69$
                    $y = 1.5$

substitute in ② $x + y = 3.5$

$$x + 1.5 = 3.5$$
$$x = 2$$

check: The total time is 3.5 h.

$$2\,h + 1.5\,h = 3.5\,h.$$

The total distance is 830 km.

$$40(2)\,km + 500(1.5)\,km$$
$$= 80\,km + 750\,km$$
$$= 830\,km$$

Jeanne travelled 2 h by bus.

EXERCISE 8-3

B **1.** Complete the following statements.
(a) The interest, after 1 a, on $2000 at 10% is —— .
(b) The interest, after 1 a, on $300 at 9% is —— .
(c) The interest, after 1 a, on $3000 at 12% is —— .
(d) The interest, after 1 a, on $x at 7% is —— .
(e) The interest, after 1 a, on $y at 11% is —— .
(f) The interest, after 1 a, on $w at 12.5% is —— .

2. Complete the following.
(a) The value of 10 kg of candy at $2.00/kg is —— .
(b) The value of 6 kg of tea at $2.50/kg is —— .
(c) The value of 20 kg of coffee at $3.00/kg is —— .
(d) The value of x kg of peanuts at $3.10/kg is —— .
(e) The value of y kg of soap at $4.50/kg is —— .
(f) The value of m kg of tea at $3.07/kg is —— .

3. Complete the following.
(a) 100 kg of 30% salt solution by mass contains —— kg of salt.
(b) 500 ℓ of 40% alcohol solution by volume contains —— ℓ of alcohol.
(c) 2000 kg of 5% salt solution by mass contains —— kg of salt.
(d) x ℓ of 30% alcohol solution by volume contains —— ℓ of alcohol.
(e) y kg of 35% salt solution by mass contains —— kg of salt.
(f) m kg of 9% silver alloy contains —— kg of silver.

4. (a) The distance travelled in 4 h at 60 km/h is —— km.
(b) The time taken to travel 600 km at 50 km/h is —— h.
(c) If you travel 400 km in 8 h your average speed is —— km/h.
(d) The distance travelled in x h at 40 km/h is —— km.
(e) The time taken to travel y km at 50 km/h is —— h.
(f) The distance travelled in m h at 8 km/h is —— km.
(g) The time taken to travel n km at 30 km/h is —— h.

5. Mary invested $1000, part at 8%/a and the remainder at 9%/a. After one year her total interest from these investments was $84. How much did she invest at each rate?

6. Pierre invested $8000, part at 9%/a and the remainder at 10%/a. After one year his total interest from these investments was $740. How much did he invest at each rate?

7. The student council invested $6000, part at 7.5%/a and the remainder at 8.5%/a. The total interest, after one year, from these investments was $480. How much was invested at each rate?

8. Joe invested two sums of money, part at 8%/a and the remainder at 7%/a. After one year the interest from these investments totalled $380. If he had reversed the investments, his interest would have been $370. What was his total original investment?

9. Jill invested $2000, part at 12%/a and the remainder at 8%/a. At the end of one year the amounts of interest from each investment were equal. How much was invested at each rate?

POP   Addition
POP
_A_
TRAP

word problems   181

10. Fritz invested $3000, part at 8%/a and the remainder at 7%/a. At the end of one year the interest from the 8% investment was $60 more than the interest from the 7% investment. How much was invested at each rate?

11. How would you invest $6400, part at 8%/a and the remainder at 6%/a so that at the end of one year the interest from the 8% investment will be double the interest from the 6% investment?

12. Jelly beans and mints, worth $2.10/kg and $2.70/kg respectively, were mixed to make 500 kg of mixture which sold for $2.52/kg. How many kilograms of mints were used?

13. Coffee that sells for $3.60/kg is mixed with coffee that sells for $2.40/kg to make 1200 kg of coffee that will sell for $2.80/kg. How many kilograms of each type of coffee were used?

14. A hardware store manager mixes nails that sell for $1.10/kg and nails that sell for $1.20/kg to get 100 kg of nails that he puts in 1 kg bags. He sells each bag for $1.14. How many kilograms of each type of nail does he use?

15. A merchant mixes tea that sells for $2.20/kg with tea that sells for $2.40/kg to get 200 kg of mixture that sells for $2.28/kg. How many kilograms of each type of tea did he use?

16. A department store manager decided to mix cashews and pecans to get 400 kg of nuts that sell for $3.36/kg. If cashews sell for $3.20/kg and pecans $3.60/kg, how many kilograms of each type of nut did he use?

17. A store manager mixes tea worth $1.50/kg and tea worth $1.90/kg to make 200 kg of tea that sells for $1.67/kg. How many kilograms of each type of tea does he use?

18. How many kilograms of 30% salt solution by mass and 40% salt solution by mass should be mixed to form 200 kg of 37% salt solution by mass?

19. A lab technician wants to make 500 kg of 28% alcohol solution by mixing 40% alcohol solution and 20% alcohol solution. How many kilograms of each type should be used?

20. A chemist mixes hydrochloric acid solutions of 30% strength and 40% strength to get 100 kg of hydrochloric acid solution of 34% strength. How many kilograms of each should be used?

21. How many kilograms of 9% silver alloy and 12% silver alloy should be combined to make 500 kg of 10.8% silver alloy?

22. How many kilograms of 35% salt solution and 45% salt solution should be mixed to make 500 kg of 43% salt solution?

23. A chemistry student must combine 20% alcohol solution and 40% alcohol solution to make 100 kg of 36% alcohol solution. How many kilograms of each should be used?

24. Jack drove at 50 km/h from Smithville to Dry Gulch. From Dry Gulch to Streetsville he drove at 80 km/h. The whole trip was 550 km and took 8 h. How far is it from Dry Gulch to Streetsville?

25. It took Maria 9 h to drive the 580 km between Devils Basin and Tumbleweed. The first part of the trip was through mountains and she averaged 60 km/h. Once out of the mountains, she averaged 70 km/h the rest of the way. How many hours did she spend driving through the mountains?

26. Fred took 7 h to drive from Cheyenne to Boothill, a total distance of 485 km. He drove most of the way at 80 km/h, but was slowed to 30 km/h for a time by a dust storm during the trip. How many hours did he spend driving through the dust storm?

27. It took the football team 5 h to travel from Titletown to Toronto, a total distance of 1320 km. Part of the trip was by bus and the remainder by plane. The bus averaged 40 km/h and the plane 600 km/h. How many hours were spent travelling by bus?

28. It is 395 km from Ski Valley to Vancouver. Sam made the trip in 6 h, travelling by bus and train. The train averaged 70 km/h and the bus 60 km/h. How much time was spent travelling by train?

29. The distance from the highway to Lake Snow was 160 km and Jacques made the trip in 11 h. For the first part of the journey he used a snowmobile and travelled at 20 km/h. The last part of the trip was made on skis, where he averaged 10 km/h. How far did he travel on skis?

30. Sarah spent 2 h more travelling by train than she did by bus. The train averaged 70 km/h and the bus 50 km/h. The total distance travelled was 740 km. How far did she travel by bus?

C   **31.** The dance committee bought chips for 25¢ a bag and pop for 30¢ a can. The total bill was $155. At the dance, chips sold for 35¢ a bag and pop for 40¢ a can. The dance committee sold all the pop and chips and realized a profit of $55. How many cans of pop did they sell?

32. Flying into the wind, an aircraft made a 360 km trip in 2 h. The return trip with a tail wind took 1.5 h. Find the speed of the wind.

33 It took John 8 h to row 40 km upstream. The return trip, with the aid of the current, took 5 h. Find the speed of the current.

34. The sum of the digits of a 2 digit number is 11. The difference between the number and the number formed by reversing the digits is 27. Find the number.

$83 = 8(10) + 3$

35. An aircraft flying into the wind can make an 1100 km trip in 2 h. The same aircraft can make the same trip in 1 h 50 min if flown with the wind. Find the speed of the wind.

36. Sue left Montreal driving at 30 km/h. Sally left 2 h later and travelled the same road at 40 km/h. At what distance from Montreal will Sally overtake Sue?

37. After robbing the bank, the James boys left Winchester on horseback at 20 km/h. The posse was slow getting organized and didn't start the chase until 1 h had passed. By having fresh horses, they managed to travel at 25 km/h. How far from Winchester did the posse overtake the James boys?

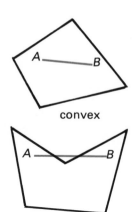

convex

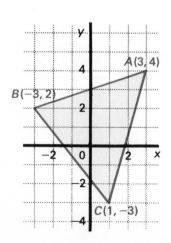

not convex

Figure 8 – 1

38. A secret agent, being a mathematician, transmitted an important 2-digit locker number in the following manner. "The difference in the digits is 4. The sum of the number and the number formed by reversing the digits is 132." Find the locker number.

39. The sum of the digits of a 2-digit number is 9. If the number is doubled and then increased by 18 the result is the number with the digits reversed. Find the number.

8.4 LINEAR PROGRAMMING

Linear programming is a branch of mathematics which uses graphs of linear inequalities and linear equations to solve practical problems.

Linear programming solutions are based on the fact that given (a) a graph of a convex polygonal region, and (b) a linear expression, the maximum or minimum value of the expression over the region occurs at the vertices of the region.

Suppose we are given the convex region as shown in Figure 8-1. The maximum or minimum value of any expression over the region, say $3x + 4y$, will occur at one of the vertices.

At $A(3, 4)$, $\quad\quad\quad\quad\quad 3x + 4y = 3(3) + 4(4)$
$$= 25$$

At $B(-3, 2)$, $\quad\quad\quad\quad 3x + 4y = 3(-3) + 4(2)$
$$= -1$$

At $C(1, -3)$, $\quad\quad\quad\quad 3x + 4y = 3(1) + 4(-3)$
$$= -9$$

The maximum value of $3x + 4y$ over the region is 25 and the minimum value is -9.

The maximum or minimum values may also occur at other points in the region, but all we need test are the vertices in order to determine the maximum and minimum values.

Using the region in Figure 8-1 and the expression $4y - 3x$, we find

At $A(3, 4)$, $\quad\quad\quad\quad\quad 4y - 3x = 4(4) - 3(3)$
$$= 7$$

At $B(-3, 2)$, $\quad\quad\quad\quad 4y - 3x = 4(2) - 3(-3)$
$$= 17$$

At $C(1, -3)$, $\quad\quad\quad\quad 4y - 3x = 4(-3) - 3(1)$
$$= -15$$

The maximum value of $4y - 3x$ over the region occurs at B and the minimum value at C.

EXAMPLE 1. *Sketch the graph of the region defined by*

$$x - 2y \geqq -11, \qquad 4x - y \leqq 12, \qquad x + y \geqq -2$$

and determine the maximum and minimum values of $4x + 2y$ over the region.

Solution

Not only must we graph the region but we must solve the appropriate simultaneous equations in order to determine the vertices of the region.

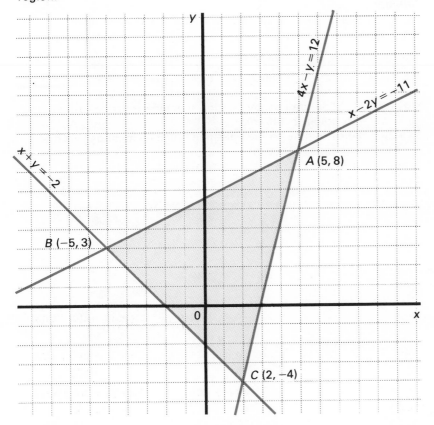

At $A(5, 8)$, $4x + 2y = 4(5) + 2(8)$
$$= 36$$

At $B(-5, 3)$, $4x + 2y = 4(-5) + 2(3)$
$$= -14$$

At $C(2, -4)$, $4x + 2y = 4(2) + 2(-4)$
$$= 0$$

The maximum and minimum values of $4x + 2y$ over the region occur at $A(5, 8)$ and $B(-5, 3)$ respectively. The maximum is 36 and the minimum is -14.

EXAMPLE 2. *The Acme Gem Co. makes two types of artificial gems for rings—a red stone and a blue stone. Each blue stone requires 1 min at the cutting machine and 3 min at the polishing machine. A red stone takes 2 min at the cutting machine and 2 min at the polishing machine. The cutting machine is available for a maximum of 100 min/d and the polishing machine 180 min/d.*

Assuming that the company can sell all the stones they make and that the profit on each blue stone is $2 and on each red $3, how many of each should be made each day in order to maximize the profit?

Solution

Let x represent the number of blue stones made each day.
Let y represent the number of red stones made each day.

The restrictions are as follows.

$x \geq 0$	(the company won't make a negative number of
$y \geq 0$	stones)
$x + 2y \leq 100$	The time on the cutting machine must be less than or equal to 100 min.
$3x + 2y \leq 180$	The time on the polishing machine must be less than or equal to 180 min.

Graph the solution set of the four inequalities.

The profit expression to be maximized is $2x + 3y$

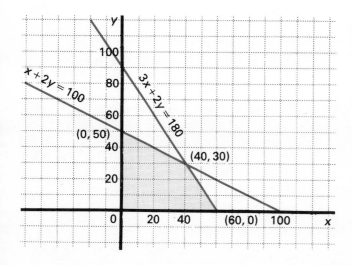

At $(0, 0)$,
$$2x + 3y = 2(0) + 3(0)$$
$$= 0$$

At $(60, 0)$,
$$2x + 3y = 2(60) + 3(0)$$
$$= 120$$

At $(40, 30)$,
$$2x + 3y = 2(40) + 3(30)$$
$$= 170$$

At $(0, 50)$,
$$2x + 3y = 2(0) + 3(50)$$
$$= 150$$

A maximum profit will be realized if 40 blue stones and 30 red stones are made each day.

EXERCISE 8.4

B **1.** Determine the maximum and minimum value of each expression over the given region.

(a)

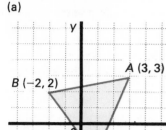

(i) $4x+5y$
(ii) $2x-5y$
(iii) $x+7y$

(b)

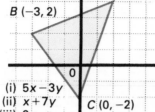

(i) $5x-3y$
(ii) $x+7y$
(iii) $2x-y$

(c)

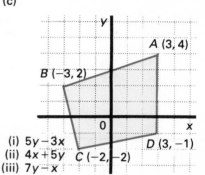

(i) $5y-3x$
(ii) $4x+5y$
(iii) $7y-x$

(d)

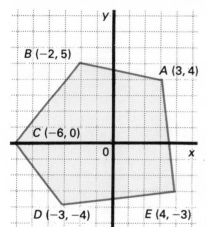

(i) $3x-6y$
(ii) $5y-x$
(iii) $-3x-4y$

(e)

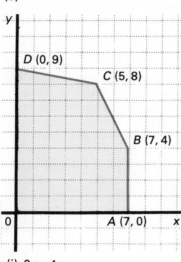

(i) $2x-4y$
(ii) $5x+3y$
(iii) $x-y$

(f)

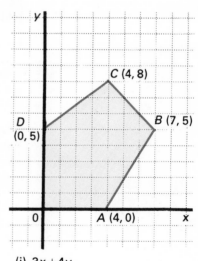

(i) $3x+4y$
(ii) $5x-2y$
(iii) $3y-2x$

2. Sketch the graph of each of the following regions and determine the maximum and minimum value of the given expression over the region.

(a) (i) Region: $5x+4y \leqq 20$, $x \geqq 0$, $y \geqq 0$
    (ii) Expression: $2x+4y$
(b) (i) Region: $x+y \leqq 10$, $x+2y \leqq 16$, $x \geqq 0$, $y \geqq 0$
    (ii) Expression: $5x+7y$
(c) (i) Region: $x+2y \leqq 20$, $2x+y \leqq 16$, $x \geqq 0$, $y \geqq 0$
    (ii) Expression: $7x-y$

(d) (i) Region: $y \leq 2x + 4$, $y \leq -8x + 14$, $y \geq -3x - 1$
   (ii) Expression: $3y - 4x$

(e) (i) Region: $2x + 3y \leq 27$, $2x + y \leq 13$, $x \geq 0$, $y \geq 0$
   (ii) Expression: $5x + 4y$

Find the smallest numbers that satisfy the equation
$$\frac{1}{x^2} + \frac{1}{y^2} = \frac{1}{z^2}$$

3. The All Pro Sports company makes 2 models of footballs—Standard and Championship. Each Standard model requires 2 min at the cutting machine and 1 min at the stitching machine. Each Championship model requires 1 min at the cutting machine and 2 min at the stitching machine. Since both machines are needed for other jobs, the cutting machine is available for a maximum of 180 min/d and the stitching machine 120 min/d.

Assuming that the company can sell all of the footballs made and that the profit on each Standard football is $10 and on each Championship football $12, how many of each type should be made each day in order to maximize the profit?

4. To raise money, the student council decides to make necklaces and bracelets during the lunch hour and then sell them to students. The Grade 12 students will drill holes in the beads and the Grade 11 students will string them. The beads for each bracelet require 4 min to drill and 4 min to string. For each necklace, the drilling time is 5 min and 6 min are required for stringing. The Grade 11 students can provide 132 min/d for stringing and the Grade 12 students 120 min/d for drilling.

Assuming that they sell everything they make and that the profit in each bracelet is $3 and on each necklace $4, how many of each should they make each day in order to maximize their profit?

5. The Ace Electronics Company makes 2 types of radios—portable and table. Both radios must be processed by machine A and machine B. Each portable model requires 6 min at machine A and 10 min at B. Each table model requires 5 min at A and 5 min at B. Machine A is available for 120 min/d and machine B 160 min/d.

Assuming that they sell all the radios they make and that the profit on each portable is $30 and on each table model $20, how many of each should they make a day in order to maximize the profit?

6. The National Instrument Company makes two types of student calculators—Super I and Super II. Each calculator must be processed by three machines—A, B, and C. Super I requires 3 min at A, 3 min at B, and 1 min at C. Super II requires 2 min at A, 4 min at B, and 2 min at C. Machine A is available for 240 min/d, B 300 min/d and C 140 min/d.

Assuming that all the calculators made are sold and that the profit on Super I is $25 and on Super II $30, how many of each should be made each day in order to maximize the profit?

7. The Cuddly Company makes stuffed animals for children. To make a stuffed bear it takes 3 min at the cutting machine, 5 min at the sewing machine, and 3 min at the stuffing machine. Each rabbit requires 4 min at the cutting machine, 6 min at the sewing machine, and 1 min at the stuffing machine. The cutting machine is available for 196 min/d, the sewing machine 300 min/d, and the stuffing machine 141 min/d.

Assuming maximum sales and that the profit on each bear is $4 and on each rabbit $5, how many of each should be made each day in order to maximize the profit?

8. The Wake Up Company makes 2 models of toasters—Standard and Deluxe. The Standard model must be processed for 1 min on machine A, 1 min on B and 3 min on C. The Deluxe model requires 1 min on A, 5 min on B and 1 min on C. Machine A is available for 200 min/d, B 600 min/d and C 480 min/d. If the profit on each Standard model is $15 and on each Deluxe $20, how many of each should be made each day in order to maximize the profit?

REVIEW EXERCISE

1. The sum of two numbers is 377 and their difference is 107. Find the numbers.

2. The sum of 2 numbers is 778 and their difference is 282. Find the numbers.

3. The sum of 2 numbers is 812 and their difference is 42. Find the numbers.

4. Three times the larger of 2 numbers increased by 4 times the smaller is 205. Six times the larger plus 3 times the smaller is 270. Find the numbers.

5. Four times the larger of 2 numbers decreased by 3 times the smaller is 152. Three times the larger increased by 5 times the smaller is 288. Find the numbers.

6 Three times the smaller of 2 numbers increased by 5 times the larger is 229. Four times the smaller decreased by 25 equals 3 times the larger. Find the numbers.

7. A bill of $424 was paid with $5 bills and $2 bills. A total of 128 bills were used. How many of them were fives?

8. After selling a total of 427 adult and student tickets the cashier at a theatre had receipts of $3263.50. If adult tickets sell for $8.50 and student tickets for $6.50, how many student tickets were sold?

9. The length of a rectangle is 19 m longer than the width. If the perimeter is 606 m, what are the dimensions of the rectangle?

10. The sum of Mary's age and Sally's age is 41 years. Five years from now the sum of their ages will be three times Mary's present age. How old is Mary?

11. A coffee machine contained $13.60 made up of dimes and quarters. If there are 97 coins, how many dimes are there?

12. The perimeter of a rectangle is 176 m. The length is equal to 3 times the width decreased by 4. Find the dimensions of the rectangle.

13. Twice Tony's age increased by 6 is 3 times Jim's age. Two years ago the sum of their ages was 23 years. How old is Tony?

14. A parking meter contained 110 coins made up of dimes and nickels. If the value of the coins was $8.60, how many dimes did the meter contain?

15. Adult and student tickets were sold for the school play. The total receipts were $2005. The number of student tickets sold was equal to three times the number of adult tickets sold decreased by 56. If student tickets cost $3.50 and adult tickets cost $5.00, how many adult tickets were sold?

16. John invested $9000, part at 9%/a and the remainder at 8%/a. After one year the total interest from these investments was $750. How much was invested at 9%?

17. A store owner mixed walnuts that sell for $2.50/kg and pecans that sell for $3.50/kg to make 200 kg of mixture that he sells for $2.75/kg. How many kilograms of walnuts did he use?

18. How many kilograms of 40% salt solution by mass and 20% salt solution by mass should be mixed to make 100 kg of 32% salt solution?

19. Sue took a trip of 1900 km, travelling by bus and plane. The bus averaged 60 km/h and the plane 700 km/h. If the total trip took 5 h, how many kilometres did she travel by bus?

20. A lab technician needs to make 400 kg of 51% alcohol solution by combining 60% alcohol solution by mass and 40% alcohol solution by mass. How many kilograms of the 40% solution must be used?

21. Greta invests $5000, part at 7%/a and the remainder at 6%/a. After one year the total interest from these investments was $315. How much was invested at 7%?

22. It took Terry 7 h to drive the 390 km from Cold Bay to Morgan's Cove. He averaged 60 km/h for the first part of the trip, but was forced to complete the trip at 50 km/h due to a thunderstorm. How many hours did he spend driving at 50 km/h?

23. A merchant mixes tea that sells for $3.60/kg and tea that sells for $4.60/kg to make 100 kg of tea that he sells for $4.40/kg. How many kilograms of each type of tea did he mix?

24. The student council invested $4000, part at 8.5%/a and the remainder at 9.5%/a. After one year the interest from the 8.5% investment was $16 more than the interest from the 9.5% investment. How much was invested at 9.5%?

25. A chemist mixes hydrochloric acid solution of 50% strength and 40% strength to get 500 kg of hydrochloric acid solution of 46% strength. How many kilograms of the 50% solution are used?

26. A department store manager has one of his employees mix chocolates that sell for $2.30/kg and chocolates that sell for $3.20/kg to get 150 kg of mixture that sells for $2.72/kg. How many kilograms of each type must be used?

27. John left Cactus Creek driving at 40 km/h. Mary followed 2 h later driving at 50 km/h. How far down the road will Mary overtake John?

C **28.** The sum of the digits of a 2-digit number is 8. When 36 is added to the number the digits are reversed. Find the number.

29. The Summertime Clothing Company makes bikinis and swimming trunks. A bikini requires 2 min at the cutting machine, the trunks 1 min each. Sewing a bikini takes 3 min while the trunks take 4 min each. There is a maximum of 140 min/d available for cutting and 360 min/d for sewing. If the profit on each bikini is $5.00 and on each set of trunks $4.00, how many of each should be made in a day in order to maximize the profit?

30. To raise money for the graduation dance the student council decides to make and sell ice cream sundaes during the lunch period. A Super sundae requires 2 scoops of vanilla, 2 scoops of chocolate and 1 scoop of maple walnut. A Super Duper sundae has 1 scoop of vanilla, 3 scoops of chocolate and 3 scoops of maple walnut. There are 280 scoops of vanilla, 360 scoops of chocolate and 300 scoops of maple walnut available. There is a profit of $0.50 on a Super sundae and $1.00 on a Super Duper. If they can sell all the sundaes they make, how many of each should be made in order to maximize the profit?

REVIEW AND PREVIEW TO CHAPTER 9

ANGLES

Opposite Angle Theorem

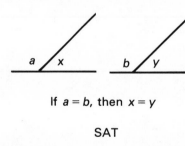

$a = b$

OAT

Complementary Angle Theorem

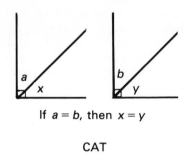

If $a = b$, then $x = y$

CAT

Supplementary Angle Theorem

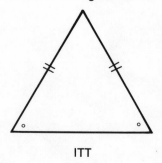

If $a = b$, then $x = y$

SAT

Sum of the Angles of a Triangle Theorem

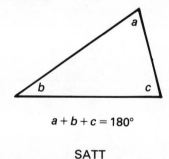

$a + b + c = 180°$

SATT

Isosceles Triangle Theorem

ITT

EXERCISE 1

Compute the measure of the indicated angles in the following.

1.

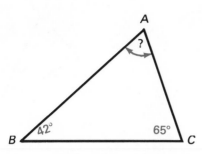

2.

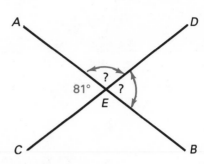

3.

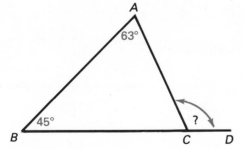

4.

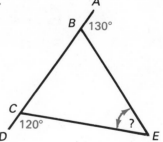

5.

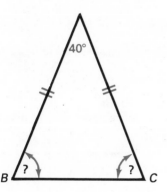

6.

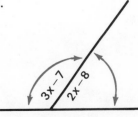

Compute the value of x in the following:

7.

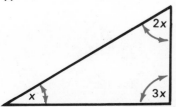

8.

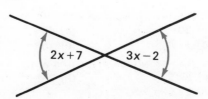

9.

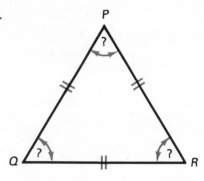

10.

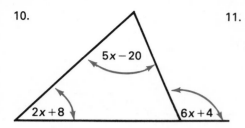

5x − 20

2x + 8   6x + 4

11.

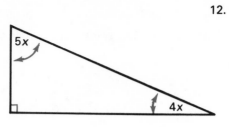

5x

4x

12.

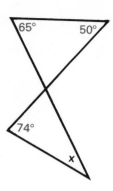

65°   50°

74°

x

EXERCISE 2

CONSTRUCTIONS

Basic constructions

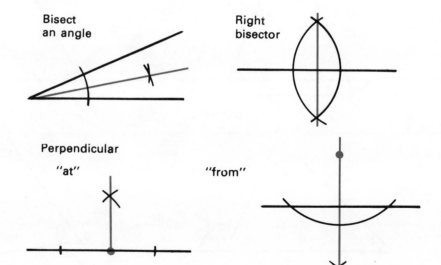

Bisect
an angle

Right
bisector

Perpendicular

"at"   "from"

Construct the following figures using the basic constructions:

1. Angles whose measures are:
(a) 90°   (b) 45°   (c) 22.5°
(d) 120°   (e) 15°   (f) 135°

2. Angles whose measures are:
(a) 67.5°   (b) 75°   (c) 165°
(d) 37.5°

Triangles classified

By angles

acute

right

obtuse

By sides

scalene

isosceles

equilateral

3. (a) Bisect the angles of each of the following types of triangles:
(i) acute   (ii) right   (iii) obtuse
(b) Using the point of intersection as centre, draw a perpendicular to one side, then draw a circle to touch each side once.

4. (a) Bisect the sides of each of the following types of triangles:
(i) acute   (ii) right   (iii) obtuse
(b) Using the point of intersection as centre draw a circle passing through the three vertices.

5. Draw the three altitudes of
(i)   an acute
(ii) a right
(iii) an obtuse triangle.

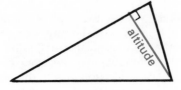

6. Draw the three medians of
(i)   an acute triangle
(ii) a right triangle
(iii) an obtuse triangle.

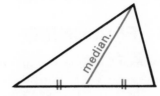

CHAPTER 9

Congruent Triangles

There is no royal road to geometry.

Menaechmus (to Alexander the Great)

Euclid

Very little is known about Euclid other than that he lived about 300 B.C. and founded the great school of mathematics at Alexandria in Egypt. In his monumental work on geometry, the "Elements," Euclid perfected and arranged the geometry of his predecessors (such as Pythagoras and Eudoxus) so that one proposition follows another in strictly logical order. Euclid's "Elements" was the most successful textbook of all time. It has been said that this work has had an influence on the human mind greater than that of any other book except perhaps the Bible.

When we say two figures are *congruent*, we mean that they are equal in all respects—lengths are equal, angles are equal, and areas are equal. Although this definition of congruence holds in both two and three dimensions, the work of this chapter, and Chapter 10, will be restricted to geometry in the plane (*2D*). Three-dimensional geometry is presented later in Chapter 11.

9.1 REASONING

In the past we have accepted many geometrical facts as a result of experimental work. We must now take some of these results and *prove* them. Some ways to prove things follow.

1. Authority:

If two students wish to prove that $a^0 \neq 0$, they can consult an authority, for example "ask the teacher" or look in a textbook. This is not always satisfactory, especially if you are going to use an outdated science text as your authority on nuclear physics.

What 9 letter English word has only 1 vowel?

2. Inspection:

Can you *prove* any of the following by just looking at the situation?

(a) *AB* is longer than *CD*.

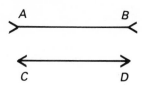

AB ∥ *CD* and both *AB* and *CD* are straight lines.

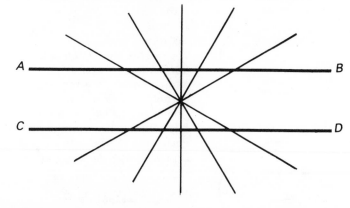

3. Analogy:

If two things agree in at least one respect, can we then reason that there will be agreement in yet another respect? For example, if the product of two natural numbers is always greater than either of the numbers, is it true that the product of two integers is always greater than either number? Since $(-3) \times (4) = -12$ and the product is clearly less than -3 or 4, we see that we cannot always use analogy to prove statements true.

4. Induction:

If you make a general statement following the observation of a significant number of particular cases, you are reasoning *inductively*. For example, you could reason that if you went out in the rain 20 times and got wet every time, you could conclude that when you go out in the rain you will get wet. Can you conclude that a hockey team that has won its first 20 games will also win its twenty-first game? Although inductive reasoning is very useful in discovering new facts, it does not always prove statements true beyond all doubt.

5. Deduction:

Reasoning from a general statement to a particular conclusion is called *deductive reasoning*. One of the goals of studying deductive geometry is to develop the ability to reason. To prove a statement is true, a mathematician will use *logical deduction* to show that the statement follows from other accepted statements. Following is an example of deductive reasoning.

General: If an animal is a bear, then it hibernates.
Particular: Blackie is a bear.
Conclusion: Blackie hibernates.

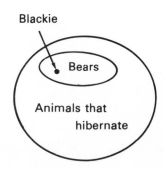

We first have a *general* statement in "If ..., then ...," form and we accept this statement as true. Our *particular* statement must relate to the "If ..." part of the general statement so that we can *conclude* the "then ..." part of the general statement.

EXAMPLE 1. *Use deductive reasoning to arrive at a conclusion for each of the following.*
(a) A parallelogram with a right angle is a rectangle. PQRS is a parallelogram and ∠PQR = 90°.
(b) A triangle with equal sides has equal angles. △ABC has equal sides.

Solution
We rewrite the statements in "If ..., then ..." form.
(a) General: If one angle of a parallelogram is a right angle, then the parallelogram is a rectangle.
Particular: *PQRS* is a parallelogram and ∠PQR = 90°.
Conclusion: *PQRS* is a rectangle.
(b) General: If a triangle has equal sides, then it has equal angles.
Particular: △ABC has equal sides.
Conclusion: △ABC has equal angles.

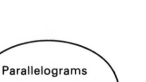

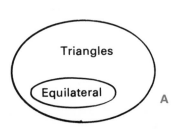

A

EXERCISE 9-1

1. Identify the type of reasoning in the following.
(a) The teacher said the sum of the angles of a triangle is 180°.
(b) △ABC is isosceles because it looks like AB = AC.
(c) In chapter 1 it says that addition of integers is commutative.
(d) Division of integers is not closed under addition, so division of rational numbers is not closed under addition.
(e) Walt will score three touchdowns in the next game because he has scored three touchdowns in every game so far.
(f) In the tables, I found that $\sqrt{2} \doteq 1.414$.
(g) The setting sun is larger than the noonday sun.
(h) John did well in school, so his brother Mark should do well.
(i) None of the people vaccinated got smallpox, so Sheila concluded that she would not get smallpox because she had been vaccinated.
(j) To join the police force, you must be at least 175 cm tall. Sharon is on the police force. Sharon must be at least 175 cm tall.

B   Rewrite one statement from each pair in "If ..., then ...," form, then conclude using deductive reasoning.

2. (i) All cats are animals.
   (ii) Jasper is a cat.

3. (i) All students at Eastdale High take music.
   (ii) Diane attends Eastdale High.

4. (i) A student, in order to take Math 401, must have passed Math 301.
   (ii) Ivan takes Math 401.

5. (i) The sum of the angles of a quadrilateral is 360°.
   (ii) ABCD is a quadrilateral.

6. (i) The opposite angles of a parallelogram are equal.
   (ii) ABCD is a parallelogram.

7. (i) A triangle with two equal sides is isosceles.
   (ii) △STU has two equal sides.

What is the smallest triangle whose sides are consecutive integers and whose area is exactly divisible by 20?

8. (i) The diameter of a circle passes through the centre.
(ii) *AB* is a diameter of a circle.

9. (i) A rhombus is a quadrilateral with four equal sides.
(ii) *ABCD* has four equal sides.

c **10.** (i) A quadrilateral with opposite sides equal is a parallelogram.
(ii) A parallelogram with one right angle is a rectangle.
(iii) All four angles of a rectangle are right angles.
(iv) *ABCD* has *AB* = *DC*, *AD* = *BC*, and ∠*ABC* = 90°.

Starting the Day

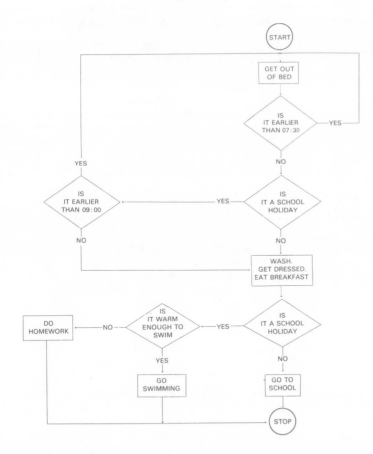

9.2 ANGLES IN POLYGONS

The "follow the dot" puzzles as in Figure 9-1 are examples of *simple polygonal paths*. If a simple polygonal path of three or more non-intersecting sides terminates at the initial point, then the closed figure so formed is called a polygon. A simple polygon can be

(i) convex or   (ii) concave

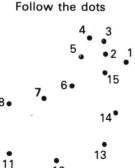

Follow the dots

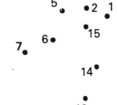

Figure 9-1

Figure 9-2

Polygons are named according to the number of sides they have as in Table 9-1. A polygon with n sides is called an n-gon so that the octagon is also an 8-gon, and Figure 9-2 is a 14-gon.

Polygons	
Number of sides	**Name**
3	Triangle
4	Quadrilateral
5	Pentagon
6	Hexagon
7	Septagon
8	Octagon
9	Nonagon
10	Decagon
. . .	. . .
n	n-gon

Table 9-1

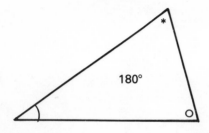

We have seen that the sum of the interior angles of a triangle is 180°, and by dividing a convex quadrilateral into two triangles, we found the sum of the interior angles of a convex quadrilateral to be 360°. This process is continued in the exercise which follows.

EXERCISE 9-2

B 1. (a) Into how many triangles can you divide a quadrilateral, a pentagon, and a hexagon using diagonals drawn from any one vertex?

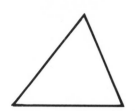 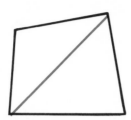 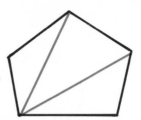 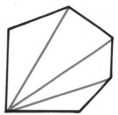

(b) What is the sum of the interior angles of each figure.

(c) Complete the following table in your notebook.

Number of Sides	3	4	5	6	7	8	—	100	—	n
Diagonals drawn from one vertex	0	1								
Triangles formed	1	2								
Interior Angle Sum in Degrees	180°	360°								

(d) State a general formula for the sum of the interior angles of an n-gon.

2. A regular polygon has all angles equal. Calculate the degree measure of one angle of each of the following polygons.

(a) Equilateral triangle
(b) Square
(c) Regular pentagon
(d) Regular hexagon
(e) Regular 40-gon

How many squares are there on a checkerboard?

EXAMPLE 1. *Given: △ABC, with exterior ∠ACD*
Required: to prove ∠ACD = ∠ABC + ∠CAB

Proof

$$\angle ACD + \angle ACB = 180° \text{ (Straight Angle)}$$
$$\angle CAB + \angle ABC + \angle ACB = 180° \text{ (SATT)}$$
$$\angle ACD + \angle ACB = \angle CAB + \angle ABC + \angle ACB$$
$$\angle ACD = \angle CAB + \angle ABC$$

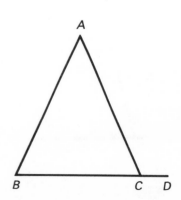

We generalize this result to:

> The degree measure of an exterior angle of a triangle is equal to the sum of the interior and non-adjacent angles.

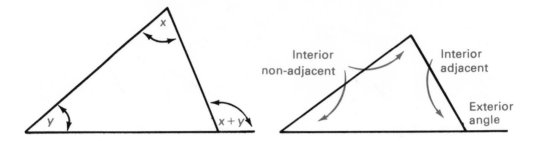

Complete the following deductions showing "Given:, Required:, Proof:," and diagram.

3. Given: Quadrilateral *ABCD*

Required: to prove

$$\angle ABC + \angle BCD + \angle CDA + \angle DAB = 360°$$

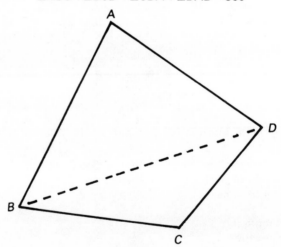

4. Given: Quadrilateral *ABCD*, and exterior angles

$$\angle EAB, \angle FBC, \angle GCD, \text{ and } \angle HDA$$

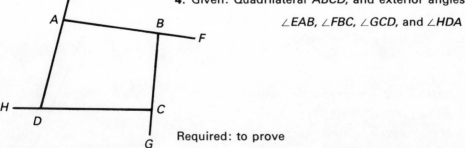

Required: to prove

$$\angle EAB + \angle FBC + \angle DCG + \angle HDA = 360°$$

5. Given: Pentagon *ABCDE* and exterior angles

$$\angle FAB, \angle GBC, \angle HCD, \angle IDE, \text{ and } \angle JEA.$$

Required: to prove

$$\angle FAB, + \angle GBC + \angle HCD + \angle IDE + \angle JEA = 360°$$

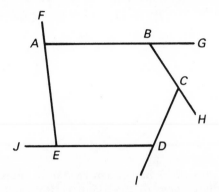

6. Given: an *n*-gon *ABCD...*, *exterior angles of a, b, c, ..., n have been drawn by extending successive sides. Find the sum of the angles:*

$$a + b + c + ... + n$$

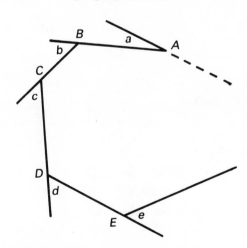

7. If the sum of the interior angles of a *n*-gon is 11 160°, how many sides does it have?

8. Is it possible to have a polygon, the sum of whose interior angles are (a) 990° (b) 1440° (c) 20 180°?

9. Each interior angle of a regular polygon is 108°. How many sides does it have?

10. Is it possible to have a regular polygon having each interior angle equal to 100°? Explain.

9.3 CONGRUENCE

We have stated that two figures are congruent if they are equal in all respects—lengths, angles, areas. Two triangles are congruent if there is a one-to-one correspondence between their vertices so that the corresponding angles and sides are equal. We use the symbol ≅ to indicate that two figures are congruent, and we write

$A \leftrightarrow D$
$B \leftrightarrow E$
$C \leftrightarrow F$

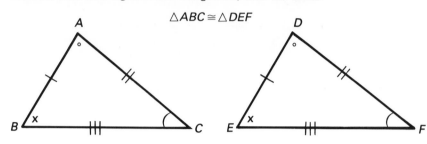

$\triangle ABC \cong \triangle DEF$

Note that $\triangle ABC$ and $\triangle DEF$ have been written to show the correspondence between the vertices of the triangles. Hence, if we write

$$\triangle LMN \cong \triangle XYZ$$

then the correspondence of angles and sides would be

$\angle LMN = \angle XYZ$ $\qquad$ $LM = XY$

$\angle NLM = \angle ZXY$ $\qquad$ $LN = XZ$

$\angle MNL = \angle YZX$ $\qquad$ $MN = YZ$

Use $+$, $-$, $\times$, $\div$, ( ) to make a true statement.

6 6 1 = 5 4 1

EXERCISE 9-3

A   **1.** Given: $\triangle DEF \cong \triangle RST$. Complete the following congruence correspondences.

$\angle DEF \rightarrow$  $\qquad$ $EF \rightarrow$ ▨

$\angle DFE \rightarrow$ ▨ $\qquad$ $DE \rightarrow$ ▨

$\angle EDF \rightarrow$ ▨ $\qquad$ $DF \rightarrow$ ▨

2. Read the equal sides and angles of the two congruent triangles from the congruence correspondence between them:

$$\triangle PQR \cong \triangle STU$$

$PQ =$ ▨ $\qquad$ $\angle PQR =$ ▨

$SU =$ ▨ $\qquad$ $\angle RPQ =$ ▨

$QR =$ ▨ $\qquad$ $\angle QRP =$ ▨

3. Name all pairs of equal angles and sides in the given figures.

(a)

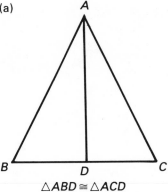

$\triangle ABD \cong \triangle ACD$

(b)

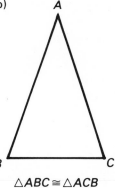

$\triangle ABC \cong \triangle ACB$

(c)

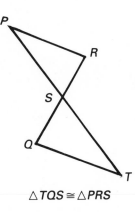

$\triangle TQS \cong \triangle PRS$

B **4.** Given: $\triangle ABC \cong \triangle PQR$, and $\triangle PQR \cong \triangle XYZ$
Required: to prove $\triangle ABC \cong \triangle XYZ$

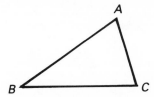 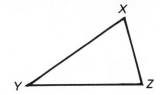

C **5.** Question 4 establishes the transitive property of congruence and can be stated as follows.

Transitive property: If $\triangle_1 \cong \triangle_2$ and $\triangle_2 \cong \triangle_3$, then $\triangle_1 \cong \triangle_3$.

(a) Determine whether the reflexive and symmetric properties hold for congruence by showing

(i) Reflexive property: $\triangle_1 \cong \triangle_1$ for any triangle $\triangle$.

(ii) Symmetric property: If $\triangle_1 \cong \triangle_2$, then $\triangle_2 \cong \triangle_1$.

(b) Is congruence an equivalence relation?

9.4 THE SAS CONGRUENCE POSTULATE

> SAS If two sides and the contained angle of one triangle are respectively equal to two sides and the contained angle of another triangle, the triangles are congruent.

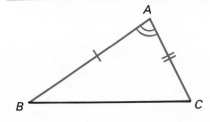 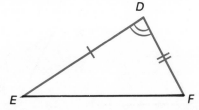

EXAMPLE 1. *Given: AB and CD intersect at E, with AE = DE, CE = BE.*
Required: to prove
(i) △*AEC* ≅ △*DEB*
(ii) AC = DB

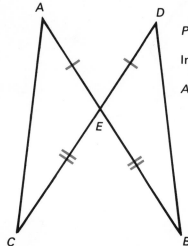

Proof

Statements	Reasons
In △*AEC* and △*DEB*,	
AE = DE	given
AB and DC intersect at E	given
∠AEC = ∠DEB	OAT
EC = EB	given
△AEC ≅ △DEB	SAS
AC = DB	

EXERCISE 9-4

A **1.** Name pairs of triangles congruent by SAS.

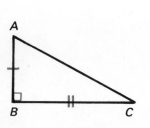

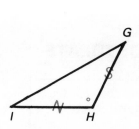

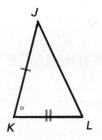

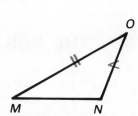

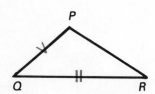

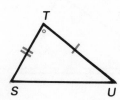

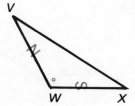

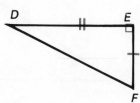

2. Prove that the triangles are congruent by naming the corresponding parts that are equal.

(a)

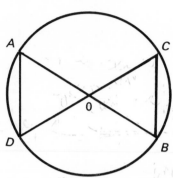

(b)

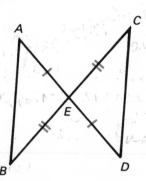

(c)

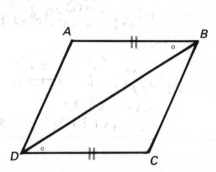

(d)

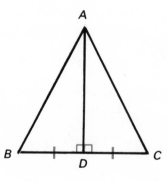

(e)

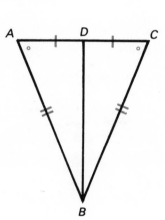

(f)

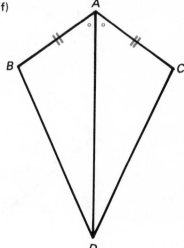

B Prove the following.

3. Given: *AB* and *CD* intersect at *E*,

$$AE = EB \quad \text{and} \quad CE = ED.$$

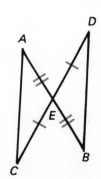

Required: to prove (i) △*ACE* ≅ △*BDE*.
(ii) *AC = BD*

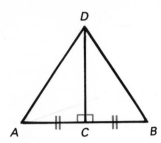

4. Given: $DC \perp AB$, $AC = BC$
Required: to prove (i) $\triangle DAC \cong \triangle DBC$
               (ii) $DA = DB$

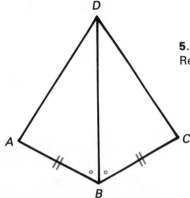

5. Given: BD bisects $\angle ABC$, $AB = CB$
Required: to prove (i) $\triangle ABD \cong \triangle CBD$
               (ii) $AD = CD$
              (iii) $\angle ADB = \angle CDB$

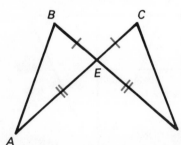

6. Given: AC and BD intersect at E.

        $AE = DE$, $BE = CE$.

Required: to prove $AB = DC$

7. Given: Quadrilateral $ABCD$,

        $\angle ABD = \angle CBD$, $AB = CD$

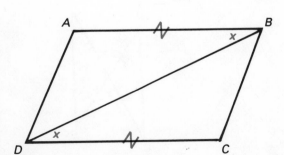

Required: to prove $AD = CB$

C **8.** Given: D is the midpoint of EC,

$$\angle BDE = \angle ADC, \qquad AD = BD,$$
$$ED = CD$$

Required: to prove (i) $\triangle AED \cong \triangle BCD$
(ii) $AE = BC$

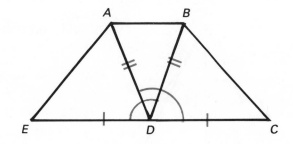

9. Given: $\triangle ABC$, $AB = AC$,

$$\angle ABC = \angle ACB, \qquad DB = BC = CE$$

Required: to prove $AD = AE$

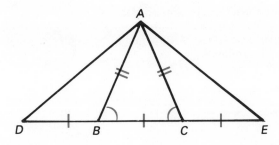

10. AB and CD are diameters of a circle with centre O. Prove $AD = BC$.

9.5 THE SSS CONGRUENCE POSTULATE

> SSS If three sides of one triangle are respectively equal to three sides of another triangle, then the triangles are congruent.

Cross all the dots with four straight lines without lifting your pencil.

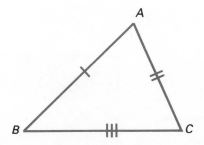

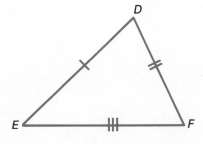

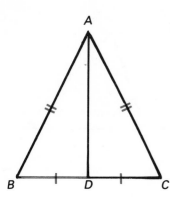

EXAMPLE 1. (*Proving the Isosceles Triangle Theorem—ITT*)
Given: △ABC, with AB = AC

  D is the midpoint of BC

Required: to prove (i) △ABD ≅ △ACD
         (ii) ∠ABC = ∠ACB

Proof

Statements	Reasons
In △ABD and △ACD,	
D is the midpoint of BC	given
BD = CD	definition of midpoint
AB = AC	given
AD = AD	(reflexive property)
△ABD ≅ △ACD	SSS
∠ABC = ∠ACB	

The results of example 1 can be stated as follows

ITT
Part I

> If a triangle has two equal sides, then the angles opposite the equal sides are equal.

EXERCISE 9-5

A **1.** (a) Name pairs of triangles congruent by SSS.
  (b) State the corresponding angles that are equal.

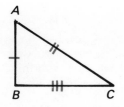
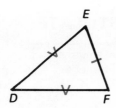
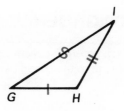
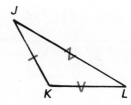

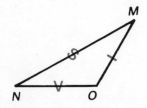
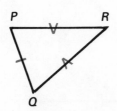
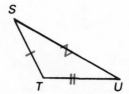
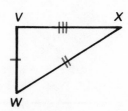

2. Prove that the triangles are congruent by naming the corresponding parts that are equal.

(a)

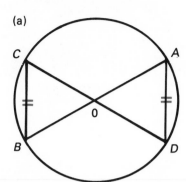

(b)

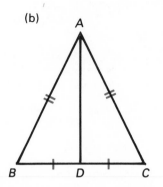

(c)

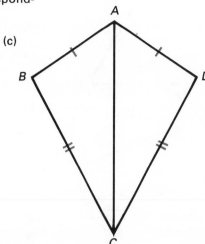

(d)

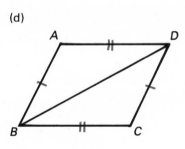

(e)

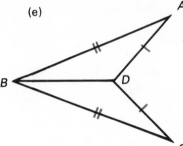

(f)

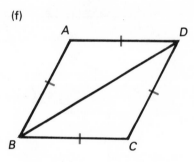

B   Prove the following.

3. Given: $\triangle ABC$, $AB = AC$
Required: to prove (i) $\triangle ABC \cong \triangle ACB$.
(ii) $\angle ABC = \angle ACB$.

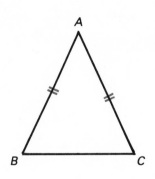

4. Given: Rhombus $ABCD$.
Required: to prove (i) $\angle BAD = \angle DCB$
(ii) $\angle ABD = \angle CDB$

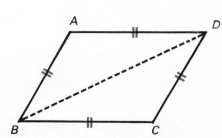

congruent triangles   211

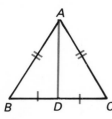

5. Given: $\triangle ABC$, $AB = AC$, $BD = CD$

Required: to prove (i) $\triangle ABD \cong \triangle ACD$
  (ii) $AD \perp BC$

6. Given: AB and CD are chords of a circle centre O. $AB = CD$.

Required: to prove (i) $\triangle AOB \cong \triangle COD$
  (ii) $\angle AOB = \angle COD$

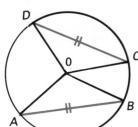

7. Given: Quadrilateral $ABCD$,

  $AB = CD$, $AD = CB$

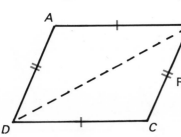

Required: to prove $\angle BAD = \angle DCB$

8. Given: Quadrilateral $ABCD$
  $AB = AD$, $BC = DC$

Required: to prove (i) $BE = DE$
  (ii) $AE \perp BD$

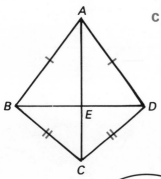

9. Given: Two circles centres A and C intersect at B and D
Required: to prove (i) $\angle DAC = \angle BAC$
  (ii) $\angle DCA = \angle BCA$

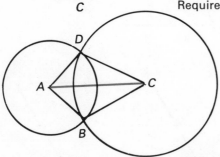

10. In quadrilateral $ABCD$, $AD = BC$ and $AB = DC$. Prove that the opposite interior angles are equal.

9.6 THE ASA CONGRUENCE POSTULATE

> **ASA** If two angles and the contained side of one triangle are respectively equal to two angles and the contained side of another triangle, then the triangles are congruent.

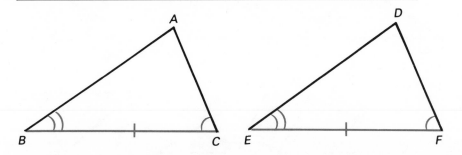

EXAMPLE 1. *Given: AB and CD intersect at E;*

$$AD \perp AB, \quad BC \perp AB, \quad and \quad AE = BE.$$

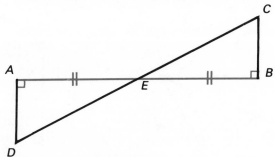

Required: to prove (*i*) $\triangle ADE \cong \triangle BCE$
        (*ii*) $AD = BC$

Proof

Statements	Reasons
In $\triangle ADE$ and $\triangle BCE$,	
$AD \perp AE, \quad BC \perp BE$	given
$\angle DAE = \angle CBE = 90°$	(definition of perpendicular)
$AE = BE$	given
AB and CD intersect at E	given
$\angle AED = \angle BEC$	OAT
$\triangle ADE \cong \triangle BCE$	ASA
$AD = BC$	

Put the numbers from 1 to 9 in the spaces to make the statements true.

$$\square \times \square + \square = 7$$
$$\square \div \square + \square = 7$$
$$\square + \square - \square = 7$$

> **Corollary**
> If any two angles and one side of one triangle are respectively equal to two angles and the corresponding side of another triangle, then the triangles are congruent.

EXERCISE 9-6

A **1.** Name pairs of triangles that are congruent by ASA.

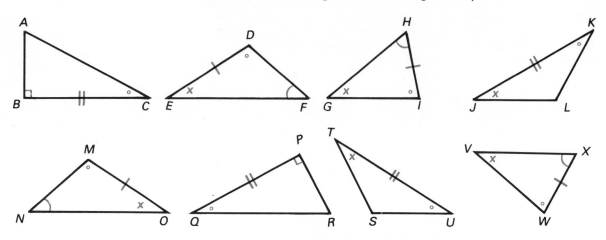

2. Prove that the triangles are congruent by naming the corresponding parts that are equal.

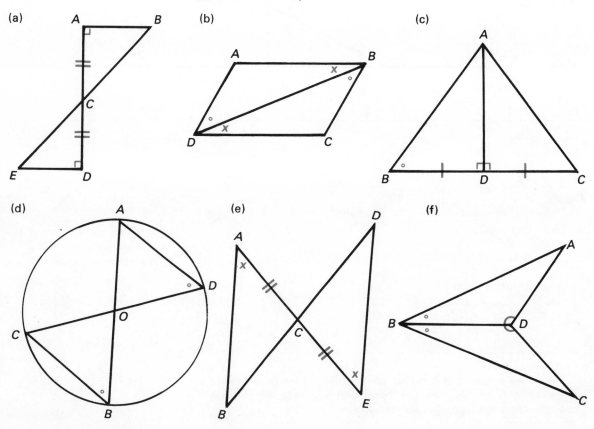

B **3.** Given: $\triangle ABC$, $\angle ABC = \angle ACB$

Required: to prove (i) $\triangle ABC \cong \triangle ACB$
  (ii) $AB = AC$

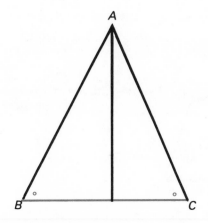

This result is stated as:

> If a triangle has two equal angles, then the sides opposite the equal angles are equal.

ITT
Part II

4. Given: AB and DC intersect at E

  $\angle CAE = \angle BDE$ and $AE = DE$

Required: to prove $AC = DB$

5. Given: Quadrilateral $ABDE$

  C is on BD, $AC = CE$,

  $\angle ACD = \angle ECB$ $\angle BAE = \angle DEA$

Required: to prove (i) $\triangle ABC \cong \triangle EDC$
  (ii) $AB = ED$

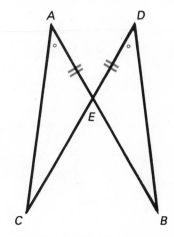

6. Given: Quadrilateral $ABCD$, with

  $\angle ABD = \angle CDB$, $\angle ADB = \angle CBD$

Required: to prove (i) $AD = CB$
  (ii) $AB = CD$

congruent triangles   215

7. Given: Quadrilateral *ABDC*,

∠*BAD* = ∠*CAD*,   ∠*BDA* = ∠*CDA*

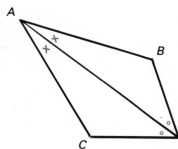

A

B

C   *D*

Required: to prove (i) *BD* = *CD*
(ii) *AB* = *AC*

C   **8.** Given: △*ABC*, ∠*ABC* = ∠*ACB*

CB is extended to *D*.

BC is extended to *E*.

DB = *EC*

Required: to prove *AD* = *AE*

SAS

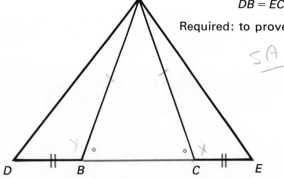

A

D   *B*   *C*   *E*

9. Given: Quadrilateral *ABCD*,

∠*ABC* = ∠*ADC*,   *AC* bisects ∠*BCD*

Required: to prove *BC* = *CD*

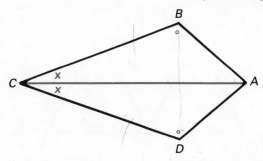

B

C   *A*

D

10. Prove that the bisector of the vertical angle of an isosceles triangle is the right bisector of the base.

9.7 OVERLAPPING TRIANGLES

EXAMPLE 1. *Given:* $\triangle ABC$, and $\triangle DCB$,

$$AB = DC, \qquad \angle ABC = \angle DCB$$

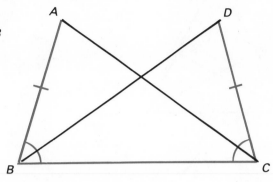

Required: to prove (i) $\triangle ABC \cong \triangle DCB$
(ii) $\angle BAC = \angle CDB$

Proof

Statements	Reasons
In $\triangle ABC$ and $\triangle DCB$,	
$AB = DC$	given
$\angle ABC = \angle DCB$	given
$BC = BC$	reflexive property
$\triangle ABC \cong \triangle DCB$	SAS
$\angle BAC = \angle CDB$	definition of congruence

EXERCISE 9-7

B **1.** Given: $AB = ED$, $BC = DC$
Required: to prove (i) $AD = EB$
(ii) $\angle CAD = \angle CEB$.

2. Given: $AB \perp BC$ and $DC \perp BC$.

$$\angle DBC = \angle ACB$$

Required: to prove $AB = DC$

congruent triangles 217

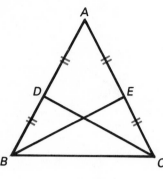

3. Given: In △*ABC*, *AB* = *AC* and *D* and *E* are the midpoints of *AB* and *AC* respectively.

Required: to prove *CD* = *BE*

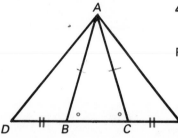

4. Given: △*ABC*, ∠*ABC* = ∠*ACB*
DB = *EC*.

Required: to prove (i) △*ACD* ≅ △*ABE*
(ii) *AD* = *AE*

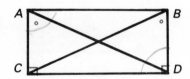

5. Given: In rectangle *ABCD*,
∠*BAC* = ∠*CDB*

Required: to prove △*ABD* ≅ △*DBA*.

6. Given: △*ABC*, *AB* = *AC*, ∠*DBC* = ∠*DCB*

Required: to prove *AD* bisects ∠*BAC*.

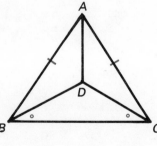

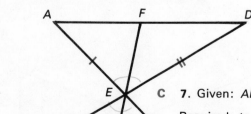

7. Given: *AB* and *CD* bisect each other at *E*. *FG* passes through *E*.

Required: to prove ∠*FED* ≅ △*GEC*

8. Given: △ABE and △ACD, AD = AE, DB = EC

Required: to prove (i) △BDF ≅ △ECF
　　　　　　　 (ii) BF = CF

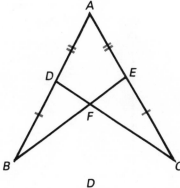

9. Given: △ABC and △DCB, AC = DB,
　　　　　 ∠ACB = ∠DBC

Required: to prove (i) AB = DC
　　　　　　　 (ii) AE = DE

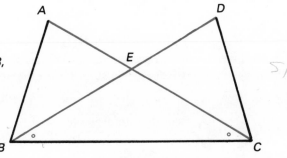

SAS

10. Prove: The diagonals of a rectangle bisect each other.

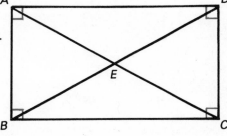

9.8　THE HS RIGHT TRIANGLE
　　　CONGRUENCE POSTULATE

> HS If the hypotenuse and one side of one right triangle are respectively equal to the hypotenuse and one side of another right triangle, then the triangles are congruent.

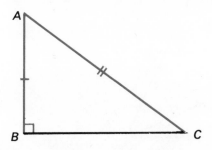

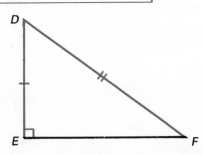

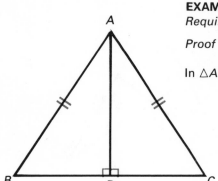

EXAMPLE 1. *Given:* $\triangle ABC$, $AB = AC$, $AD \perp BC$
Required: to prove AD bisects BAC

Proof

Statements	Reasons
In $\triangle ABD$ and $\triangle ACD$,	
$AD \perp BC$	given
$\angle ADB = \angle ADC = 90°$	definition of perpendicular
$AB = AC$	given
$AD = AD$	reflexive property
$\triangle ABD \cong \triangle ACD$	HS
$\angle BAD = \angle CAD$	definition of congruence
AD bisects $\angle BAC$	

EXERCISE 9.8

Prove the following deductions.

B   **1.** Given: $\angle ABC$, $AB = AC$, point D,

$$DA \perp BA, \qquad DC \perp BC$$

Required: to prove (i) $\triangle ABD \cong \triangle CBD$
                   (ii) BD bisects $\angle ABC$

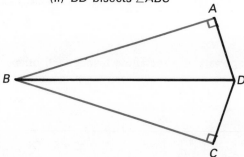

2. Given: $\triangle ABC$, $BE \perp AC$, $CD \perp AB$ and $BD = CE$
Required: to prove (i) $\triangle DBC \cong \triangle ECB$
                    (ii) $\triangle ABC$ is isosceles

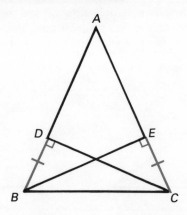

3. Given: Circle centre *O*, and *M* and *N* are midpoints of *AB* and *CD* respectively.

$$OM \perp AB, \qquad ON \perp CD$$
$$OM = ON$$

Required: to prove (i) $AM = DN$
               (ii) $BM = CN$
               (iii) $AB = CD$

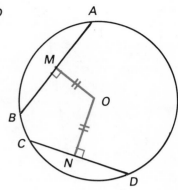

C   **4.** Given: Quadrilateral *ABCD*,

$$AB \perp BC, \qquad DC \perp BC, \qquad AC = DB$$

Required: to prove $AB = DC$

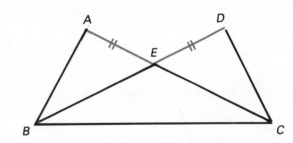

5. Given: $\triangle ABC$, $\triangle DCB$, $AE = ED$

$$\angle BAC = \angle CDB = 90°$$

Required: to prove (i) $\triangle AEB \cong \triangle DEC$
               (ii) $\triangle ABC \cong \triangle DCB$

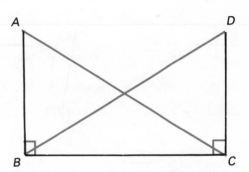

REVIEW EXERCISE

B   **1.** Given: $\triangle ABC$, *AB* extended to *D*, *AC* extended to *E*, $\angle DBC = \angle ECB$
Required: to prove $\triangle ABC$ is isosceles.

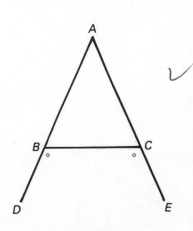

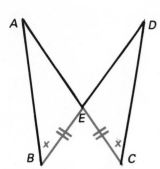

2. Given: *AC* and *BD* intersect at *E*,

   $BE = CE,$ $\angle ABE = \angle DCE$

Required: to prove $AB = DC.$

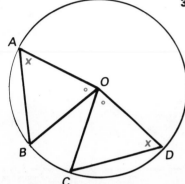

3. Given: *AB* and *CD* are chords of a circle, centre *O*.

   $\angle BAO = \angle CDO,$ $\angle AOB = \angle DOC.$

Required: to prove $AB = CD$

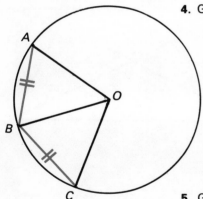

4. Given: Circle with centre *O*, $AB = BC$

Required: to prove $\angle AOB = \angle COB$

5. Given: Quadrilateral *ABCD*, $AB = DC,$ $AD = BC$

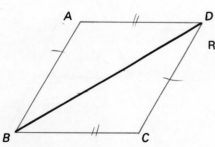

Required: to prove $\angle BAD = \angle DCB.$

6. Given: $\triangle ABC$ and $\triangle DCB$, $AB = DC$
$\angle ABC = \angle DCB$

Required to prove (i) $AC = BD$
(ii) $AE = DE$

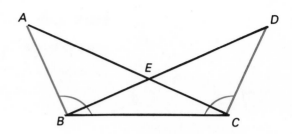

7. Given: BC is a diameter
$BA \perp AC$, $CD \perp BD$, $AB = DC$.

Required: to prove $AC = BD$.

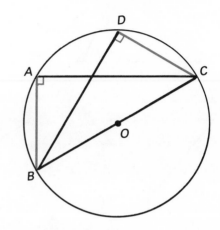

8. Given: $\triangle ABC$, $DF = FE$
$FD \perp AD$, $FE \perp AE$

Required: to prove AF bisects $\angle BAC$.

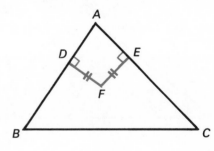

9. Given: CD, the right bisector of AB.

Required: to prove $CA = CB$.

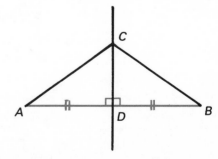

10. Given: Circle centre O, radii OA, OB, OC.
OB bisects $\angle AOC$.

Required: to prove $AB = BC$.

REVIEW AND PREVIEW TO CHAPTER 10

EXERCISE 1

Compute the measure of the unknown angles.

1.
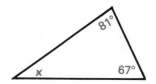

2.
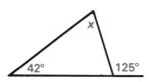

3.
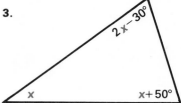

4.
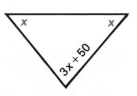

5.
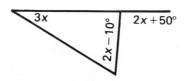

6.
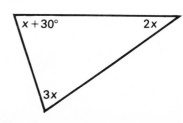

7.
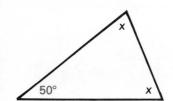

8.
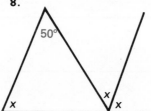

9.
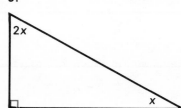

EXERCISE 2

1. If $A = lw$ and $P = 2(l + w)$ for rectangles, find the area and perimeter of each of the following:

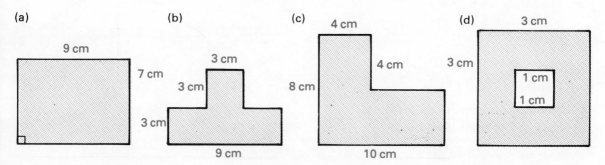

(a) 9 cm, 7 cm

(b) 3 cm, 3 cm, 3 cm, 9 cm

(c) 4 cm, 4 cm, 8 cm, 10 cm

(d) 3 cm, 3 cm, 1 cm, 1 cm

2. For circles, $A = \pi r^2$. Find the area of each of the following ($\pi \doteq 3.14$)

(a)   (b)   (c)   (d)

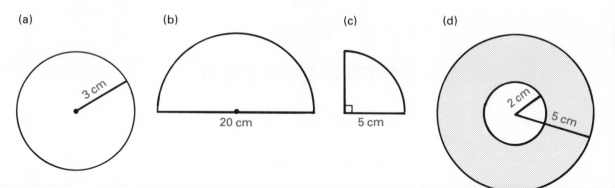

3. For circles, the circumference $C = 2\pi r$ or $C = \pi d$. Find the perimeter of the following figures. ($\pi \doteq 3.14$)

(a)   (b)   (c)   (d)

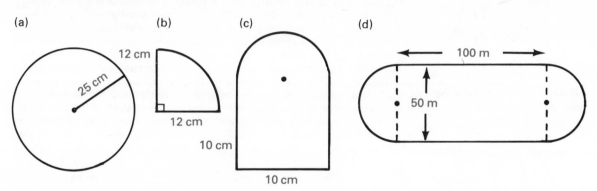

4. The area of a trapezoid is given by $A = \frac{1}{2}(a + b)h$. Find the area of each of the following figures.

(a)   (b)   (c)   (d)

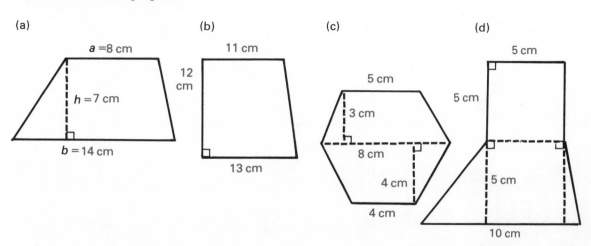

CHAPTER 10

Parallel Lines and The Pythagorean Theorem

Let no one ignorant of geometry enter this door.

Plato

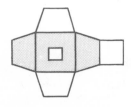

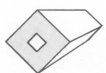

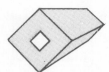

Which of the following figures can you make from the pattern above?

Pythagoras

Pythagoras was both a mystic and a scientist who lived in the sixth century B.C. He started a secret society on the southeastern coast of what is now Italy. The members of this society (The Pythagoreans) were vegetarians whose mystical conception of numbers affected every aspect of their lives. In fact their motto was "All is number." For example they thought of even numbers as being female and odd numbers as being male. Pythagoras travelled to Egypt and Babylon and probably learned of the Pythagorean Theorem from the Babylonians. But the Pythagoreans may have been the first to find a proof for the theorem. Pythagoras is sometimes called the "Father of Mathematics" since he was one of the first to establish mathematics as a rational discipline. In fact he is supposed to have coined the word "mathematics," meaning "that which is learned."

Two lines are parallel if and only if they lie in the same plane and do not intersect. The symbol for "parallel" is $\parallel$, so that when we mean lines l_1 and l_2 are parallel, we can write

$l_1 \parallel l_2$

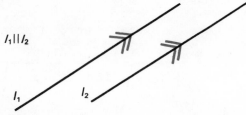

Name five more examples of parallel lines.
1. railroad tracks
2. edges of a sheet of paper
3.
4.
5.
6.
7.

10.1 PARALLEL LINES AND TRANSVERSALS

A transversal is a line, or line segment, that intersects 2 or more distinct lines (or line segments). In figure 10.1, t is a transversal, intersecting the lines l_1 and l_2, making 8 angles (a, b, c, d, e, f, g, h). We relate these angles as follows:

ALTERNATE ANGLES $\begin{cases} \angle c \text{ and } \angle e \\ \angle d \text{ and } \angle f \end{cases}$

CORRESPONDING ANGLES $\begin{cases} \angle a \text{ and } \angle e \\ \angle b \text{ and } \angle f \\ \angle c \text{ and } \angle g \\ \angle d \text{ and } \angle h \end{cases}$

INTERIOR ANGLES on the same side of the transversal $\begin{cases} \angle d \text{ and } \angle e \\ \angle c \text{ and } \angle f \end{cases}$

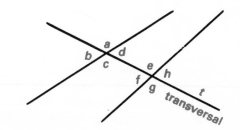

In our earlier study of parallel lines, we found a relationship among the angles formed when a transversal meets two parallel lines. We state this relationship in the first part of the transversal parallel line theorem which follows.

TPT: Transversal Parallel Line Theorem — I
   If a transversal meets two straight parallel lines, then:
(i) the alternate angles are equal
(ii) the corresponding angles are equal
(iii) the interior angles on the same side of the transversal are supplementary.

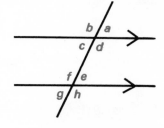

(i) $c = e, d = f$
(ii) $b = f, a = e$
        $c = g, d = h$
(iii) $d + e = 180°$
        $c + f = 180°$

This theorem can be remembered by thinking of the Z, F, C patterns

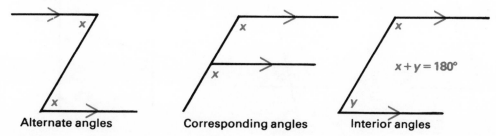

Alternate angles   Corresponding angles   Interior angles

$x + y = 180°$

EXAMPLE 1. *Given: In quadrilateral ABCD,*

AB = CD, and AB ∥ DC.

Required: To prove AD = CB

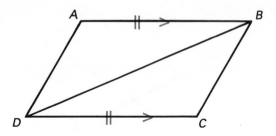

Proof

Statements	Reasons
In △ABD and △CDB,	
AB = CD	given
AB ∥ DC, BD is a transversal	given
∠ABD = ∠CDB	TPT
BD = DB	common
△ABD ≅ △CDB	SAS
AD = CB	

EXERCISE 10-1

A 1. Name the alternate, corresponding, and interior angles in each of the following.

(a)

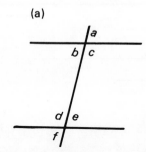

(b)

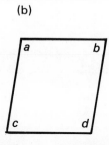

(c)

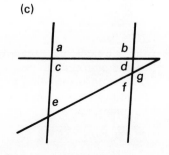

2. Find the values of *a, b,* and *c* in each of the following.

(a)

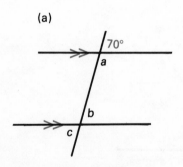

(b)

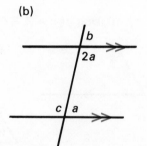

(c)

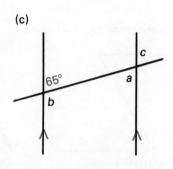

(d)

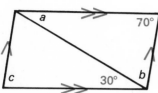

(e)

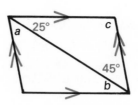

(f)

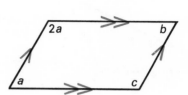

B   3. Find the values of x, y, and z in the following:

(a)

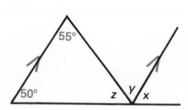

(b)

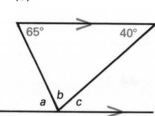

(c)

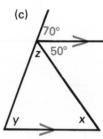

(d)

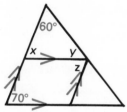

(e)

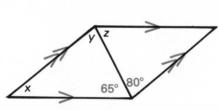

(f)

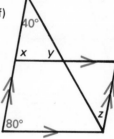

4. Given: AD and BC intersect at E. $AB = CD$, $AB \parallel CD$.

   Required: To prove $\triangle AEB \cong \triangle DEC$.

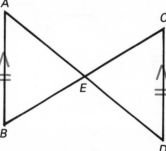

5. Given: Quadrilateral $ABCD$,

$$AB \parallel DC \angle BAD = \angle DCB$$

Required: To prove (i) $\triangle ABD \cong \triangle CDB$
                    (ii) $\angle ADB = \angle CBD$

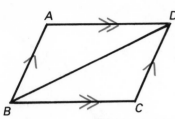

6. Given: Quadrilateral *ABCD*,

$$AB \parallel DC, \qquad AD \parallel BC$$

Required: To prove (i) $AB = CD$
(ii) $CB = AD$

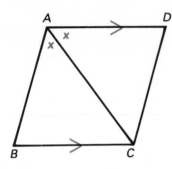

7. Given: Quadrilateral *ABCD*, $AD \parallel BC$,

$$\angle DAC = \angle BAC$$

Required: To prove $AD = CD$

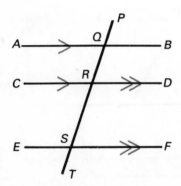

8 Given: $AB \parallel CD$, $CD \parallel EF$

Required: To prove $AB \parallel EF$

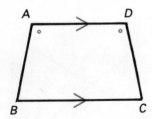

9. Given: Quadrilateral *ABCD*

$$AD \parallel BC, \quad \angle BAD = \angle CDA$$

Required: To prove $AB = DC$

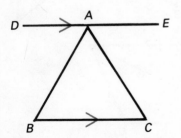

10. Use parallel lines to prove that the sum of the angles of a triangle is 180°.

10.2 PROVING LINES PARALLEL

In section 10.1 we used the first part of the parallel line theorem. We now state the second part (which is the converse of the first part).

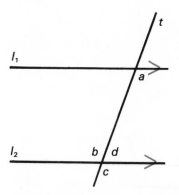

> **TPT Transversal Parallel Line Theorem — II**
>   If a transversal meets two straight lines making
> (i) the alternate angles equal or
> (ii) the corresponding angles equal or
> (iii) the interior angles on the same side supplementary, then
> the lines are parallel.

The following is an example of indirect proof. Given: AB and CD with transversal $PQRS$. $\angle BQR = \angle QRC$

Required: To prove $AB \parallel CD$

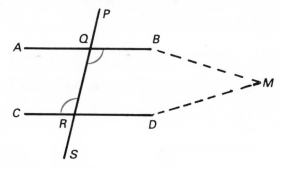

Proof:

Statements	Reasons
Either $AB \parallel CD$ or $AB \nparallel CD$	
We assume $AB \nparallel CD$	
Then AB and CD meet at M	
In $\triangle QRM$,	
$\angle QMR + \angle MQR + \angle QRM = 180°$	ASTT
$\angle MQR = \angle QRC$	given
$\angle MQR + \angle QRM = 180°$	SAT

This contradicts our statement $\angle QRM + \angle MQR + \angle QRM = 180°$
∴ $AB \nparallel CD$ is false
and $AB \parallel CD$ is the only other possibility.

EXAMPLE 1. Given: AB and CD intersect at E,

$$AE = EB, \qquad CE = ED$$

Required: To prove $AD \parallel CB$

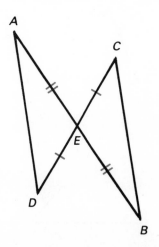

Proof

Statements	Reasons
In $\triangle AED$ and $\triangle BEC$,	
$AE = BE$	given
$\angle AED = \angle BEC$	OAT
$DE = CE$	given
$\triangle AED \cong \triangle BEC$	SAS
$\angle DAE = \angle CBE$	
$AD \parallel CB$	TPT

EXERCISE 10-2

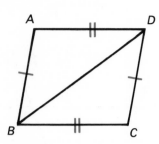

1. Given: Quadrilateral *ABCD*,

$$AB = CD, \qquad AD = CB$$

Required: To prove $AD \parallel BC$

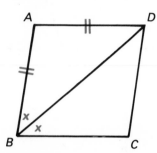

2. Given: Quadrilateral *ABCD*, $AB = AD$,

$$\angle ABD = \angle CBD$$

Required: To prove $AD \parallel BC$

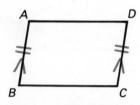

3. Given: Quadrilateral *ABCD*,

$$AB = DC, \qquad AB \parallel CD$$

Required: To prove (i) $AD = BC$

(ii) $AD \parallel BC$

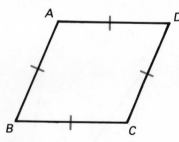

4. Given: Rhombus *ABCD*,

$$AB = BC = CD = DA$$

Required: To prove (i) $AD \parallel BC$

(ii) $AB \parallel DC$

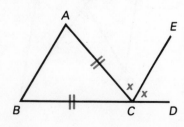

5. Given $\triangle ABC$, $AC = BC$,

CE bisects the exterior $\angle ACD$

Required: To prove $AB \parallel EC$

6. Given: Quadrilateral $ABCD$, $AB = DC$,

        $\angle ABC = \angle DCB$

Required: To prove $AD \parallel BC$

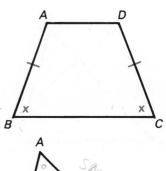

7. Given: $\triangle ABC$, with M and N the midpoints of AB and AC,

       $MN = NO$.

Required: To prove (i) $AB \parallel OC$

                 (ii) $MO \parallel BC$

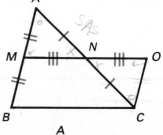

8. Given: $\triangle ABC$ with $AM = AN$, $AB = AC$,

Required: To prove $MN \parallel BC$

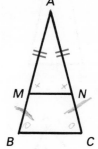

9. Given: $\triangle ABC$, AD bisects $\angle BAC$

       $AE = ED$, $EF \perp AD$

Required: To prove $AB \parallel FD$.

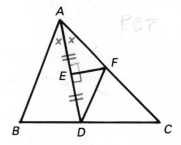

10. Given: $\triangle ABC$, M and N are midpoints of BC and AC respectively.
BN and AB are produced their own lengths to O and P respectively.

Required: To prove (i) $OC \parallel AB$

                 (ii) $PC \parallel AB$

                 (iii) OCP is a straight line

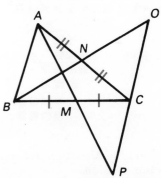

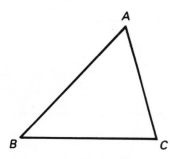

Prove the following deductions using an indirect proof.

11. Given: △ABC, AB ≠ AC

Required: To prove ∠ABC ≠ ∠ACB

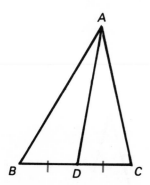

12. Given: △ABC is scalene and AD is a median.

Required: To prove ∠ABC ≠ ∠ACB

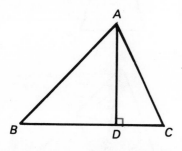

13. Given: △ABC is scalene

AD is the altitude

Required: To prove AD is not the median.

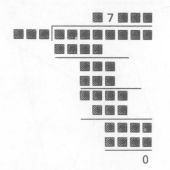

Find the missing digits in this division.

14. Prove that there is only one perpendicular from a point to a line.

15. Prove that the bisector of the vertical angle of an isosceles triangle bisects the base.

10.3 PROPERTIES OF A PARALLELOGRAM

A parallelogram is a quadrilateral with opposite sides parallel. We now state the following theorem for parallelograms.

234   fmt : introduction

> PPT In any parallelogram:
> (i) the opposite angles are equal.
> (ii) the opposite sides are equal.
> (iii) the diagonals bisect each other.

(i)

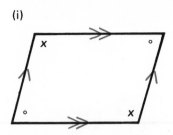

(ii)

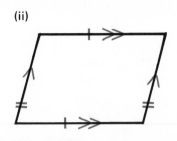

(iii)

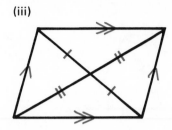

The proofs for the parts of this theorem are given to the student in the exercise which follows.

EXERCISE 10-3

1. The opposite sides of a parallelogram are equal.
Given: $\|^{gm}$ ABCD
Required: To prove $AB = DC$, $AD = BC$

2. The opposite angles of a parallelogram are equal.
Given: $\|^{gm}$ ABCD
Required: To prove (i) $\angle ABC = \angle ADC$
 (ii) $\angle BAC = \angle DCB$

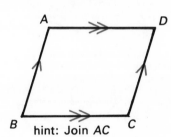

hint: Join AC

3. The diagonals of a parallelogram bisect each other.
Given: $\|^{gm}$ ABCD, with diagonals intersecting at E.

Required: To prove (i) $AE = EC$
 (ii) $BE = ED$

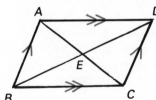

4. If the opposite sides of a quadrilateral are equal, then the figure is a parallelogram.
Given: Quadrilateral ABCD,

$$AD = BC, \qquad AB = DC$$

Required: To prove (i) $AD \parallel BC$
 (ii) $AB \parallel DC$

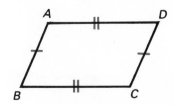

5. If the diagonals of a quadrilateral bisect each other, then the figure is a parallelogram.
Given: Quadrilateral ABCD,

$$AE = EC, \qquad BE = ED.$$

Required: To prove ABCD is a parallelogram.

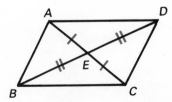

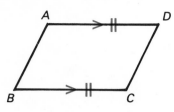

6. Given: Quadrilateral *ABCD*,

$$AD \parallel BC, \qquad AD = BC$$

Required: To prove (i) $AB \parallel DC$

(ii) $AB = CD$

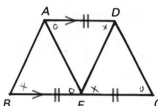

7. Given: Trapezoid *ABCD*,

$$AD \parallel BC, \qquad AD = BE = EC$$

Required: To prove (i) $AE \parallel DC$

(ii) $AE = CD$

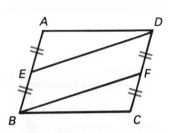

8. Given: $\parallel^{gm}$ *ABCD*, *E* and *F*, midpoints of *AB* and *CD*

Required: To prove *EBFD* is a parallelogram.

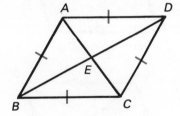

9. Given: Rhombus *ABCD*, with diagonals intersecting at *E*.

Required: To prove (i) $AE = EC$, $BE = ED$

(ii) $AE \perp BE$

Rhombus: a quadrilateral with 4 sides equal.

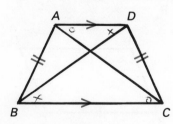

10. Given: Trapezoid *ABCD*,

$$AD \parallel BC, \qquad AB = DC, \qquad AD \neq BC.$$

Required: To prove $AC = DB$.

C Prove each of the following statements, giving "Given, Required, diagram, and Proof".

11. The diagonals of a rectangle are equal.

12. The diagonals of a rhombus bisect each other at right angles.

13. The quadrilateral formed by joining the midpoints of the sides of a parallelogram is also a parallelogram.

14. The midpoint of the hypotenuse of a right triangle is equidistant from the 3 vertices.

15. Given: *D* and *E* are the midpoints of *AB* and *AC* in △*ABC*. *CD* and *BE* intersect at *F*.

$$BH = HF, \qquad CG = GF$$

Required: To prove (i) *DHGE* is a parallelogram

(ii) *HF = FE, GF = FD*

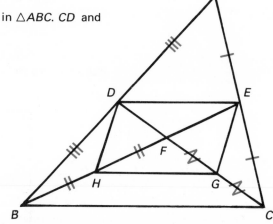

The day before yesterday I was 22 years old. Next year I will turn 25. When is my birthday?

10.4 PROOF OF THE PYTHAGOREAN THEOREM

Long before the time of Pythagoras, Egyptian "harpedonaptae" or rope stretchers used a loop of rope with 12 equally spaced knots to form a right triangle with sides 3, 4, and 5 units. The right angle was used to lay out square corners and boundary markers washed out by the periodic flooding of the Nile. There are many proofs of the theorem in existence; the proof which follows dates from the twelfth century.

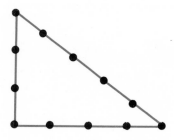

Pythagorean Theorem.

In any right triangle, the square of the length of the hypotenuse is equal to the sum of the squares of the lengths of the other two sides.

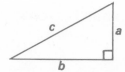

$$a^2 + b^2 = c^2$$

Use $+$, $-$, $\times$, $\div$, ( ) to make a true statement.

2 3 1 = 2 4 2

Given: $CQRS$, a square with sides of length $(a+b)$.
Points A, B, P, D, on CS, QC, RQ, and SR so that
$$CA = QB = RP = SD = b$$
$$SA = CB = QP = RD = a$$
$$AB = c$$

Required: To prove, in $\triangle ABC$, $c^2 = a^2 + b^2$

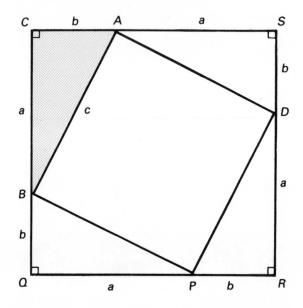

Proof:

Statements	Reasons
In $\triangle ABC$ and $\triangle BPQ$,	
$\quad AC = BQ$	given
$\quad \angle ACB = \angle BQP = 90°$	square
$\quad CB = QP$	given
$\quad \triangle ABC \cong \triangle BPQ$	SAS
Similarly $\triangle ABC \cong \triangle PDR \cong \triangle DAS$	
$\therefore \quad AB = BP = PD = DA = c$	
$\quad \angle CAB = \angle QBP$	
In $\triangle ABC$, $\angle CAB + \angle CBA = 90°$	ASTT
$\quad \angle QBP + \angle CBA = 90°$	
$\therefore \quad \angle ABP = 90°$	
$\because \quad AB = BP = PD = DA$	

then $ABPD$ is a square

$$CQRS = ABPD + \triangle ABC + \triangle BPQ + \triangle PDR + \triangle ADS$$
$$(a+b)^2 = c^2 + \tfrac{1}{2}ab + \tfrac{1}{2}ab + \tfrac{1}{2}ab + \tfrac{1}{2}ab$$
$$a^2 + 2ab + b^2 = c^2 + 2ab$$
and $a^2 + b^2 = c^2$

EXAMPLE 1. *Calculate the value of x in each of the following using the Pythagorean Theorem.*

(*a*)

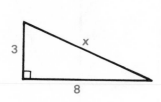

(*b*)

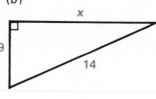

(*c*)

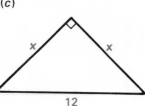

Solution

(a) $x^2 = 3^2 + 8^2$
$= 9 + 64$
$= 73$
$x = \sqrt{73}$
$\doteq 8.54$

(b) $x^2 + 9^2 = 14^2$
$x^2 + 81 = 196$
$x^2 = 115$
$x = \sqrt{115}$
$\doteq 10.7$

(c) $x^2 + x^2 = 12^2$
$2x^2 = 144$
$x^2 = 72$
$x = \sqrt{72}$
$\doteq 8.49$

EXAMPLE 2. *Given: Rectangle ABCD and M in the interior.*

Required: To prove $MA^2 + MC^2 = MB^2 + MD^2$

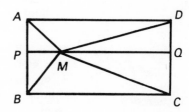

Solution

Statements	Reasons
Draw $PMQ \parallel AD$	
$\angle DAP = \angle APM = \angle MPB = 90°$	
$\angle ADQ = \angle DQM = \angle MQC = 90°$	
In $\triangle APM$, $MA^2 = AP^2 + MP^2$	Pythagorean Theorem
In $\triangle MQC$, $MC^2 = MQ^2 + QC^2$	Pythagorean Theorem
In $\triangle PMB$, $MB^2 = PB^2 + MP^2$	Pythagorean Theorem
In $\triangle DMQ$, $MD^2 = MQ^2 + DQ^2$	Pythagorean Theorem

$$\overbrace{MA^2}^{} + \overbrace{MC^2}^{}$$
$$= \overbrace{AP^2 + MP^2}^{} + \overbrace{MQ^2 + QC^2}^{}$$ Substitution
$$= DQ^2 + MP^2 + MQ^2 + PB^2$$ Opposite sides
$$= \underbrace{PB^2 + MP^2}_{} + \underbrace{MQ^2 + DQ^2}_{}$$ Commutative Property
$$= \quad MB^2 \quad + \quad MD^2$$ Substitution

Put the numbers from 1 to 9 in the spaces to make the statements true.

$\Box + \Box \div \Box = 3$

$\Box - \Box \div \Box = 3$

$\Box - \Box - \Box = 3$

EXERCISE 10-4

B **1.** Find the value of the variable in each of the following.

(a)

(b)

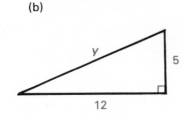

(c)

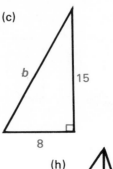

(d)

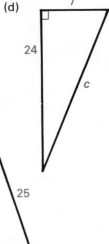

(e)

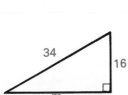

34   16   m

(f)

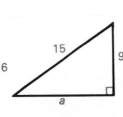

15   9   a

(g)

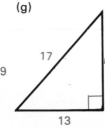

17   r   13

(h)

30   24   25   v   w

2. Find the length of the hypotenuse of a right triangle where the lengths of the other 2 sides are:

(a) 6 cm, 8 cm   (b) 5 m, 12 m

(c) 8 m, 15 m   (d) 14 cm, 48 cm

(e) 30 cm, 40 cm   (f) 10 cm, 24 cm

3. Find the length of the diagonal of a rectangle 2 m by 5 m giving your answer to the nearest centimetre.

$(st)^2 = rst$ Each letter represents a different digit.

4. An isosceles triangle has sides 30 cm, 30 cm, and 20 cm. Find the altitude to the shortest side giving your answer to the nearest millimetre.

5. A rectangular field is 120 m by 300 m. What is the distance from corner to corner?

6. A 2.5 m ladder leans against a wall. How far up the wall will the ladder reach if the foot is 1 m from the base of the wall?

7. A 5 m ladder reaches 4 m up the wall. How far is the foot of the ladder from the wall?

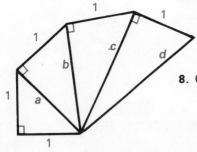

8. Calculate the values of $a, b, c,$ and d in the given diagram.

9. What is the size of the largest square timber that can be cut from a log 30 cm in diameter?

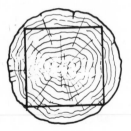

10. Find the length of cable required to secure the sign if 20 cm are required at each end for fastening.

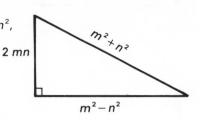

11. Find the value of the variable in each of the following:

(a)

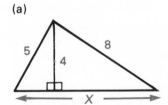

(b)

(c)

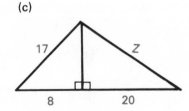

12. If m, $n \in N$ and $m > n$ then the sides of a right triangle are $m^2 + n^2$, $m^2 - n^2$, and 2mn as in the diagram.

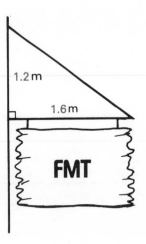

Make a table with the following headings to generate Pythagorean triples.

m	n	$m^2 - n^2$	$2mn$	$m^2 n^2$
2	1	3	4	5
3	1	8	6	10
3	2	5	12	13
—	—	—	—	—

13. The inside dimensions of a crate are $45 \times 60 \times 180$ cm. What is the length of the longest item that can be placed in the crate corner to corner?

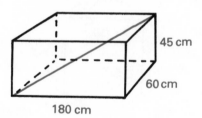

45 cm

60 cm

180 cm

14. Given: Rectangle $ABCD$
Required: To prove

$$AB^2 + BC^2 + CD^2 + DA^2 = AC^2 + BD^2$$

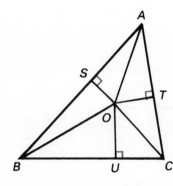

15. Given: $\triangle ABC$ and any point O in the interior.

$$OS \perp AB, \qquad OU \perp BC, \qquad OT \perp AC$$

Required: To prove

$$AS^2 + BU^2 + CT^2 = SB^2 + UC^2 + TA^2$$

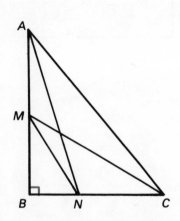

16. Given: $\triangle ABC$, $\angle B = 90°$ M and N are points on AB and BC respectively.
Required: To prove

$$AC^2 + MN^2 = AN^2 + CM^2$$

The theorem has also been stated:

> In any right triangle, the area of the square on the hypotenuse is equal to the sum of the areas of the squares on the other 2 sides.

In the investigation which follows, we shall determine whether the theorem holds for figures other than squares.

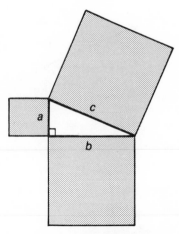

INVESTIGATION 10.4

In each of the following, select a right triangle, then
 (i) test each statement by measurement and calculation and
(ii) prove your conclusion in (i) algebraically.

1. The area of the circle on the hypotenuse of a right triangle is equal to the sum of the areas of the circles on the other 2 sides.

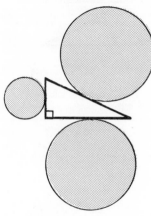

2. The area of the semicircle on the hypotenuse is equal to the sum of the areas of the semicircles on the other 2 sides.

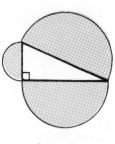

3. The area of the rectangle on the hypotenuse of a right triangle is equal to the sum of the areas of the similar rectangles on the other 2 sides.

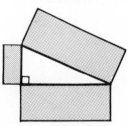

Similar figures have the same shape and the sides are proportional.

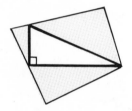

4. The area of the triangle on the hypotenuse of a right triangle is equal to the sum of the areas of the similar triangles on the other 2 sides.

5. (a) How might Pythagoras have stated the theorem in view of the results in 1 to 4?
   (b) Test this statement of the theorem using other figures.

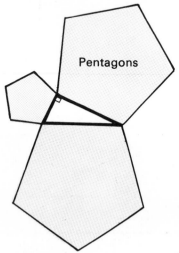

Pentagons

Trapezoids

10.5   CONVERSE OF THE PYTHAGOREAN THEOREM

> If the square of the length of one side of a triangle is equal to the sum of the squares of the lengths of the other two sides, then the angle opposite the longest side is a right angle.

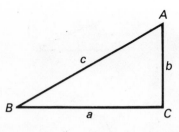

Given: $\triangle ABC$, $c^2 = a^2 + b^2$
Required: To prove $\angle ACB = 90°$
Proof:

Statements	Reasons
We first construct $\triangle XYZ$	
so that $XZ = b$	
$\quad\quad YZ = a$	
$\quad\quad \angle XZY = 90°$	
$\therefore\ XY^2 = XZ^2 + YZ^2$	Pythagorean Theorem
$\because\ XZ = b \quad$ and $\quad YC = a$	By construction
$\quad XY^2 = b^2 + a^2$	Substitution
$\quad\quad\quad = c^2$	given
$\quad XY = c$	

In $\triangle ABC$ and $\triangle XYZ$,

$AB = XY$	above
$BC = YZ$	construction
$AC = XZ$	construction
$\therefore \ \triangle ABC \cong \triangle XYZ$	SSS

$\angle ACB = \angle XYZ = 90°$

$\angle ACB = 90°$

The theorem we have just proved is the converse of the Pythagorean theorem.

Using two of the four digits 1, 2, 3, 4 in the denominator and two in the numerator, form the greatest possible proper fraction

EXERCISE 10-5

1. Determine which of the following are right triangles (the figures may not be drawn to scale).

(a)
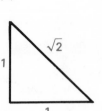

(b)
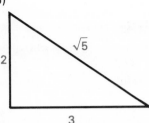

(c)
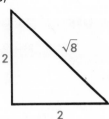

(d)
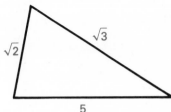

B **2.** Which of the following sets of numbers can be the lengths of the sides of a right triangle?

(a) 5, 8, 10 (b) 1.25, 0.75, 1.00 (c) 30, 34, 16

(d) 24, 10, 26 (e) 1.2, 1.6, 2.0 (f) $\frac{3}{10}, \frac{2}{5}, \frac{1}{2}$

3. Find the area of each triangle with sides whose lengths are:

(a) 3, 4, 5 (b) 5, 12, 13 (c) 8, 15, 17

(d) 7, 24, 25 (e) 10, 6, 8 (f) 3, $\sqrt{34}$, 5

4. Given: Quadrilateral $ABCD$,
$\angle ABC = 90°$, $AB = 12$, $BC = 16$,
$CD = 25$ and $DA = 15$ units.
Required: To prove $\angle CAD = 90°$

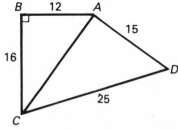

5. Given: $\parallel^{gm} ABCD$, $AC = 10$, $BE = 12$, $AB = 13$
Required: To prove (i) $AE \perp BE$
(ii) $ABCD$ is a rhombus.

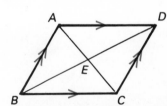

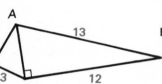

6. Given: Quadrilateral *ABCD*, *AD* = 13, *AB* = 4

$$BC = 3, \qquad CD = 12$$

Required: To prove ∠ *ABC* = 90°

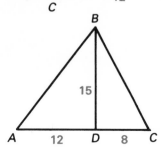

7. Given: △*ABC*, *BD* ⊥ *AC*, and

$$BD = 15, \qquad AD = 12, \qquad DC = 8.$$

Required: To prove ∠ *ABC* = 90°

REVIEW EXERCISE

B **1.** Find the measure of the indicated angle in each of the following.

WRONG   Addition
WRONG
RIGHT

(a)

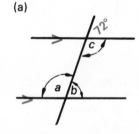

(b)

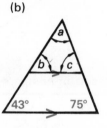

(c)

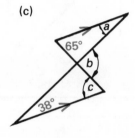

(d)

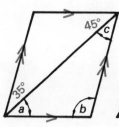

(e)

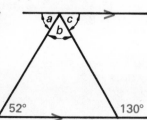

(f)

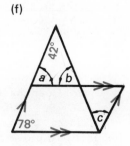

2. Find the measure of the indicated line segment in each of the following.

(a)

(b)

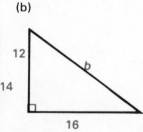

(c)

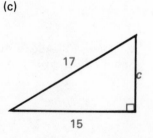

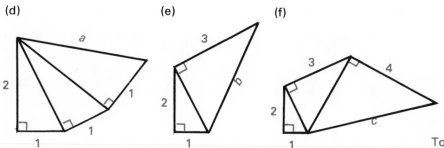

(d) a

2

1

1 1

(e) 3

2

b

1

(f) 3 4

2

c

1

To determine if a triangle with longest side *C* is right angled.

3. Determine which of the following are right triangles. (Figures may not be drawn to scale.)

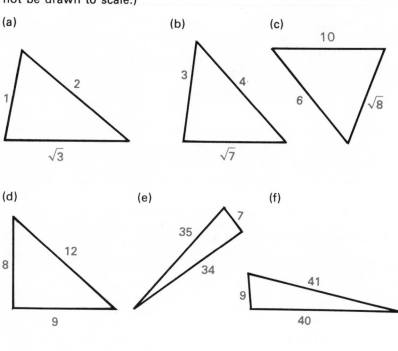

(a)

1

2

$\sqrt{3}$

(b)

3 4

$\sqrt{7}$

(c)

10

6 $\sqrt{8}$

(d)

8

12

9

(e)

35

34

7

(f)

9

41

40

4. Find the area of each of the following:

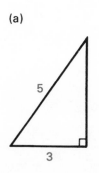

(a)

5

3

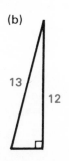

(b)

13

12

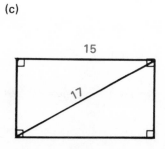

(c)

15

17

Flowchart:

START

Read
A, B, C

Let
$M = A^2 + B^2$

Let $N = C^2$

Is
$M = N$ —YES—

NO

Write
"The triangle is not right angled."

STOP

Write
"The triangle is right angled."

STOP

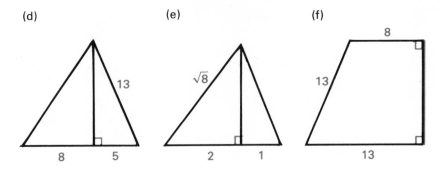

(d)   (e)   (f)

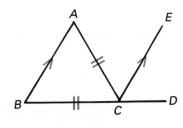

5. Given: $\triangle ABC$, $CE \parallel AB$, $AC = BC$
Required: To prove EC bisects the exterior $\angle ACD$.

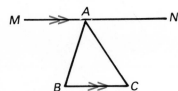

6. Given: $\triangle ABC$, MN passes through A, $MN \parallel BC$.
Required: To prove

$$\angle ABC + \angle BAC + \angle ACB = 180°$$

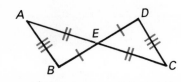

7. Given: AC and BD intersect at E.

$$AE = EC, \qquad BE = ED, \qquad AB = DC$$

Required: To prove $AB \parallel DC$

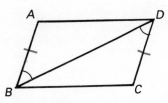

8. Given: Quadrilateral $ABCD$.

$$AB = DC, \angle ABD = \angle CDB$$

Required: To prove $ABCD$ is a parallelogram.

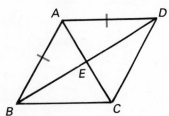

9. Given: $\parallel^{gm} ABCD$, $AB = AD$

Required: To prove $AC \perp BD$

10. Given: $\triangle ABC$, $AB = AC$, $MN \parallel BC$
Required: To prove $\triangle AMN$ is isosceles

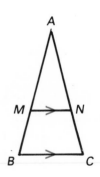

11. Given: $\parallel^{gm} ABCD$, P and Q on AD and BC, $PD = BQ$
Required: To prove $PDQB$ is a parallelogram

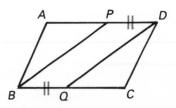

12. Given: $\parallel^{gm} ABCD$, $BF \perp AC$, $DE \perp CA$
Required: To prove $\triangle ABF \cong \triangle DCE$

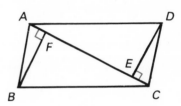

13. Given: $AB \parallel CD$,
MN is a transversal.
MP bisects BMN
NP bisects MND
Required: To prove $\angle MPN = 90°$

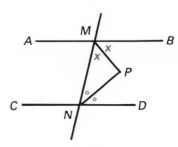

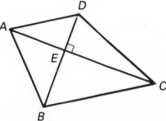

14. Given: Quadrilateral $ABCD$, $AC \perp BD$, AC and BD intersect at E
Required: To prove $AB^2 + CD^2 = BC^2 + DA^2$

15. Prove: The median of an equilateral triangle is also the altitude.

16. Prove: If the altitude of a triangle bisects the angle at the vertex, then the triangle is isosceles.

EXERCISE 1

1. If the volume of a rectangular solid is given by $V = lwh$, find the volume of each of the following.

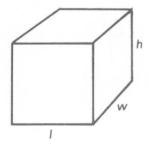

(a)

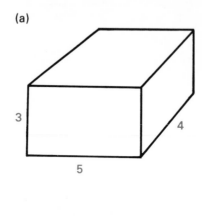

(b)

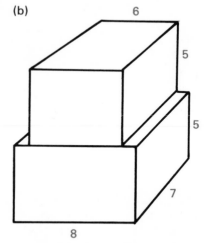

(c)

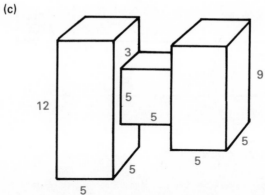

2. If the volume of a cube is given by $V = s^3$, find the volume of each of the following.

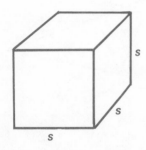

(a)

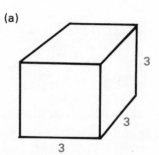

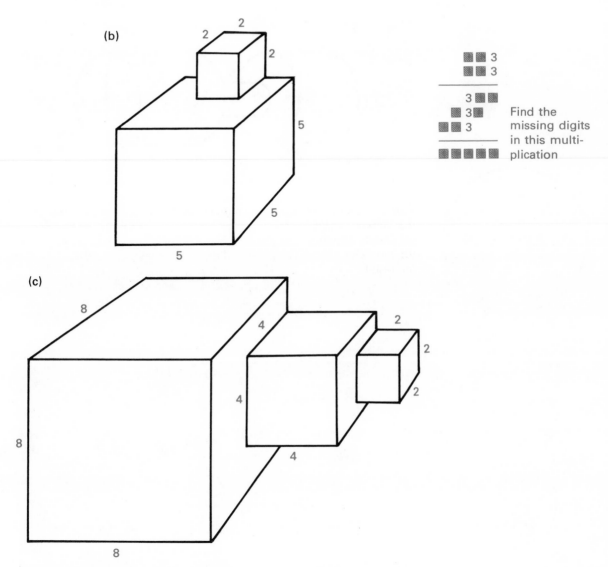

(b)

Find the
missing digits
in this multi-
plication

(c)

3. If the volume of a cylinder is given by $V = \pi r^2 h$, find the volume of each of the following ($\pi = 3.14$).

(a)   (b)

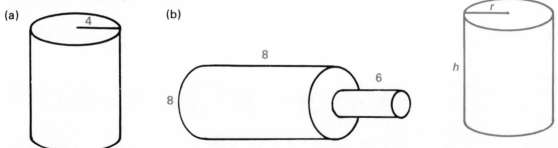

three-dimensional geometry   251

(c)

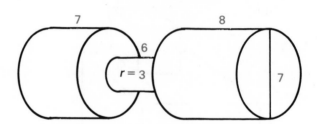

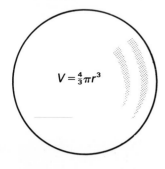

4. If the volume of a sphere is given by $V = \frac{4}{3}\pi r^3$, find the volume of the sphere having
(a) radius 15 cm
(b) diameter 10 cm
(c) radius 7 cm

Three-Dimensional Geometry

It is the glory of geometry that from so few principles, fetched from without, it is able to accomplish so much.

Sir Isaac Newton

Leonard Euler (1707–1783)

Euler, a Swiss mathematician, had an amazing mind. He had a phenomenal memory (for example, he knew whole books of poetry by heart) and a great capacity for mental calculation. On one occasion two of Euler's students had laboriously performed a lengthy calculation but disagreed by one digit in the fiftieth place of the answer. To decide who was correct Euler did the whole calculation *in his head*. Euler produced more mathematics than any other person—over 800 books and papers. His talent for mental calculation helped him during the last seventeen years of his life when he was totally blind but just as productive as ever. One of his accomplishments was proving that no perfect cube is the sum of two perfect cubes.

In our previous work we dealt with plane figures having two dimensions. We shall now study figures with three dimensions in space, where *space is the set of all points*.

11.1 DRAWING THREE-DIMENSIONAL FIGURES

In this section we provide some helpful hints on how to draw three dimensional shapes.

1. Parallel edges in space are represented by parallel lines on the page.

Planes are represented by parallelograms.

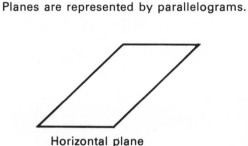

Horizontal plane

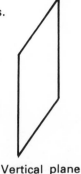

Vertical plane

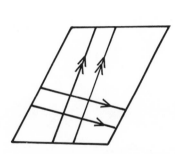

2. Edges that are behind the figure (invisible to us) are either drawn with broken lines, or left out.

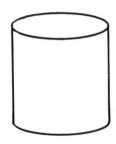 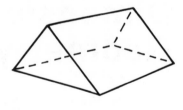

Which of the following figures can you make from the pattern above?

3. Circles in space can be represented by ellipses depending on the view.

Oblique pictorial   Isometric pictorial

4. When drawing scale figures on squared paper, edges which are perpendicular to the plane of the page are represented by lines drawn diagonally through the squares with each diagonal square equalling two units.

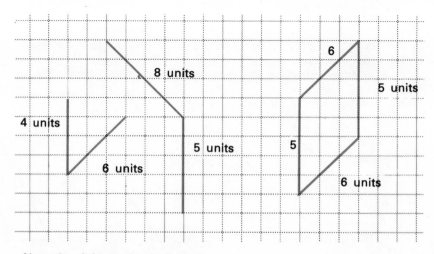

8 units

4 units

6 units

5 units

5

6

5 units

6 units

Note the right angles indicated.

254   fmt : introduction

EXAMPLE 1. *Draw a rectangular solid with edges 5, 12 and 13 units.*

Solution

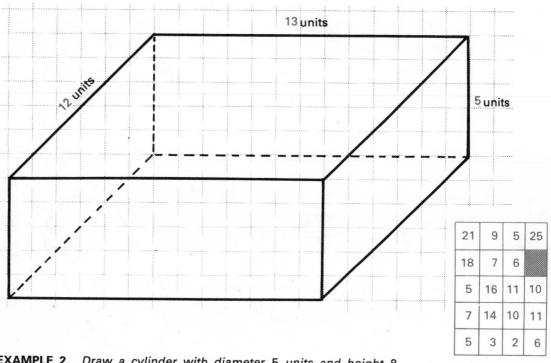

13 units

12 units

5 units

21	9	5	25
18	7	6	
5	16	11	10
7	14	10	11
5	3	2	6

EXAMPLE 2. *Draw a cylinder with diameter 5 units and height 8 units.*

Determine the pattern. Find the missing number.

Solution

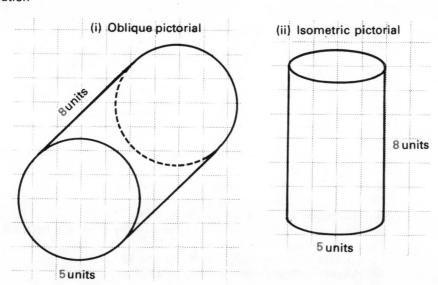

(i) Oblique pictorial

8 units

5 units

(ii) Isometric pictorial

8 units

5 units

EXERCISE 11-1

B **1.** Draw each of the following on squared paper.

(a)

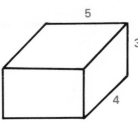

(b)

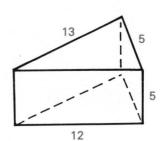

4 ▦▦

1 ▦▦   Find the missing
▦▦ ▦▦   digits in this
multiplication.
▦▦▦▦ 1

(c)

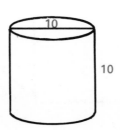

(d)

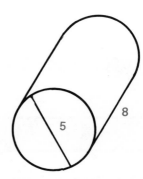

(e)

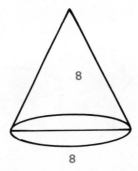

(f)

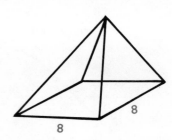

2. Draw each of the following on squared paper.
(a) rectangular solid 3 cm by 6 cm by 8 cm.
(b) rectangular solid 5 cm by 8 cm by 8 cm.
(c) triangular prism with base 3 cm by 4 cm by 5 cm, and height 8 cm
(note that the base is a *right* triangle.)
(d) cylinder with diameter 10 units, height 16 units.
(e) cylinder with diameter 8 units, height 8 units.

D is to *K* as *B* is to ▦.

3. Draw a three-dimensional representation of a figure consisting of a rectangular solid 10 cm by 5 cm by 3 cm and capped with a triangular prism with height 2 cm.

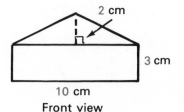

4. Draw a scale diagram of a model rocket having the body a cylinder with diameter 5 cm and length 30 cm. The nose is a cone with base diameter 5 cm and height 3 cm.

11.2 POINTS, LINES AND PLANES

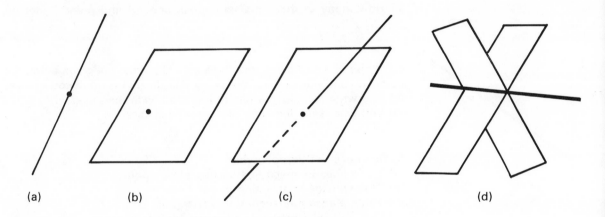

(a)   (b)   (c)   (d)

The above figures show some of the ways points, lines, and planes can be related:
(a) a point is on a line.
(b) a point lies in a plane.
(c) a line intersects a plane in one point.
(d) the intersection of two planes is a line.

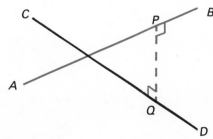

Two lines such as *AB* and *CD* that
(i) do not intersect
(ii) are not parallel are called *skew lines.*
Line segment *PQ* is perpendicular to both *AB* and *CD*, and helps to show that the lines are not in the same plane.

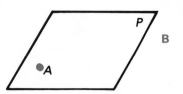

EXERCISE 11-2

B **1** *A* is a point in a plane, *P*.
(a) How many lines can you draw through *A*?
(b) Make a diagram showing four lines passing through the same point in the plane.

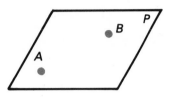

2. *A* and *B* are points in a plane, *P*.
(a) How many lines can you draw through *A* and *B*?
(b) Make a diagram showing all lines passing through *A* and *B*.
(c) Are there any points on the line through *A* and *B* that do not lie in the plane, *P*?

3. *A* and *B* are any two different points in space.
(a) How many lines are there that contain *A* and *B*?
(b) How many planes are there that contain line *AB*?
(c) How many of these planes contain line *AB* and point *C*, not on *AB*?

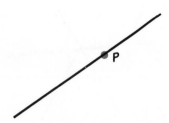

4. A point divides a line into three sets of points: the given point, the points on one side of the given point, and the points on the other side.
(a) Into what sets does a line in a plane divide the plane?
(b) Into what sets does any plane divide space?

5. Draw each of the following.
(a) Three lines in space intersecting at one point.
(b) Three planes intersecting in one line.
(c) Three planes intersecting in a triangular prism.
(d) Two vertical planes intersecting a horizontal plane.
(e) A line perpendicular to a plane.
(f) A line intersecting three parallel planes.
(g) Two lines intersect a plane in one point.
(h) Three points in the same straight line (collinear).
(i) Three noncollinear points in the same plane (coplanar).
(j) A line and a point contained in one plane.
(k) One plane containing two intersecting lines.

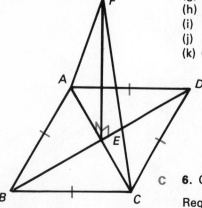

C **6.** Given: *ABCD* is a square *FE* ⊥ *AC*

Required: to prove △*AEF* ≅ △*CEF*

7. Given: AB is a perpendicular to the plane containing CB and BD, $CB = BD$.

Required: To prove $\angle ACB = \angle ADB$

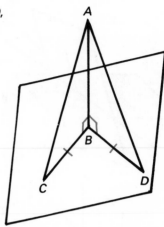

11.3 PARALLEL AND PERPENDICULAR

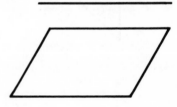

A line and a plane are parallel if they do not intersect.

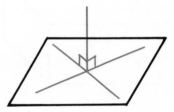

A line and a plane are perpendicular if they intersect and the line is perpendicular to every line in the plane passing through the point of intersection.

Two planes are parallel if they do not intersect.

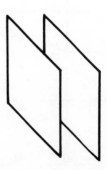

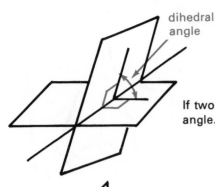

dihedral angle

If two planes intersect, the constant angle formed is called a *dihedral* angle.

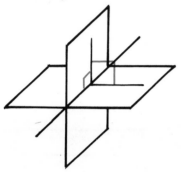

Two planes are perpendicular if the dihedral angle is a right angle.

EXERCISE 11-3

A   **1.** In the accompanying diagram, name:

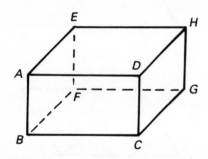

(a) three pairs of parallel faces.
(b) a line parallel to a plane.
(c) a line perpendicular to a plane.
(d) two perpendicular planes.
(e) three planes intersecting at a point.

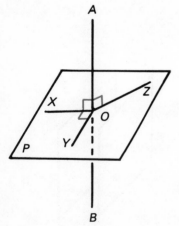

2. In the accompanying diagram, *AB* is perpendicular to plane *P*. Name all right angles in the figure.

3. *P* and *Q* are two points and *A* is a plane.

(a) How would you determine whether *P* and *Q* are on the same side of *A*?

(b) How would you determine whether *P* and *Q* are on opposite sides of *A*?

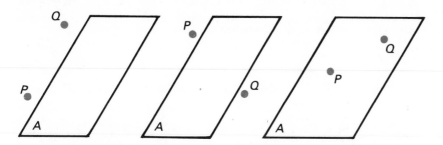

(c) How would you determine whether *P* and *Q* lie in the plane *A*?

4. The accompanying diagram is a drawing of Escher's impossible staircase. In the drawing, capital letters name planes and small letters name lines.

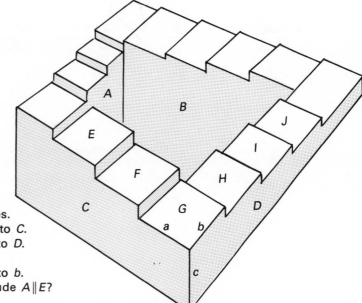

(a) Name four pairs of parallel planes.

(b) Name four planes perpendicular to *C*.

(c) Name five planes perpendicular to *D*.

(d) Name a plane parallel to *C*.

(e) Name two planes perpendicular to *b*.

(f) If $A \perp C$ and $E \perp C$ can you conclude $A \parallel E$?

B   **5.** Determine whether each of the following are (i) always true, (ii) sometimes true (iii) never true, when working in three dimensions. Make a diagram to support your answer.

(a) Two lines perpendicular to the same plane are parallel to each other.

(b) Two lines perpendicular to the same line are parallel to each other.

(c) If a line is perpendicular to one of two parallel planes, then it is also perpendicular to the other.

(d) Two planes parallel to a third plane are parallel to each other.

(e) Two planes perpendicular to a third plane are parallel to each other.

(f) If a line is perpendicular to two different planes, then the planes are parallel.

(g) Two lines that lie in parallel planes are parallel lines.

Use +, −, ×, ÷, ( ) to make a true statement.

3 7 5 = 1 8 2

6. Find the measure of *AB* using information in the diagram.

(a)   (b)

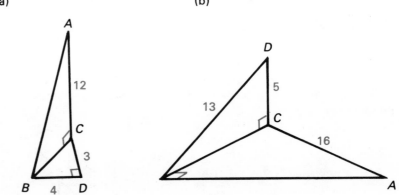

7. Two lines perpendicular to a given plane are parallel to each other.
Given: *AB* and *CD* are perpendicular to plane *P*.
Required: To prove *AB* ∥ *CD*.

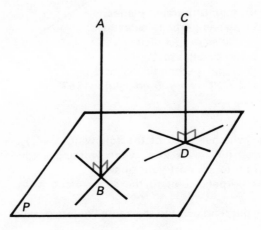

8. Given: *FE* is perpendicular to the plane containing square *ABCD*;
FE = *BE*.
Required: To prove *AB* = *AF*.

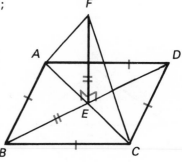

9. Given: *ABCD* is a rectangle.
   FE is perpendicular to the plane containing *ABCD*. *E* is the point of intersection of the diagonals.
Required: To prove *AF* = *CF*.

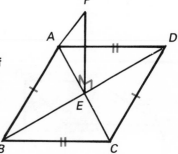

10. Use pieces of cardboard about 10×30 cm to represent planes and a long pencil to represent a line, and illustrate the following:

(a) three planes intersect at a point.
(b) three planes intersect on a line.
(c) two perpendicular planes.
(d) three parallel planes.
(e) a line parallel to a plane.
(f) a line perpendicular to a plane.
(g) the intersection of a line and a plane.

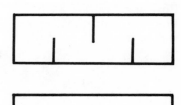

11.4 POLYHEDRA

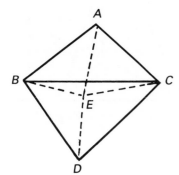

A *polyhedron* is a three-dimensional figure bounded by polygons called *faces*. Two faces meet at an *edge* and 3 or more edges meet at a *vertex*.

A is a vertex.
BC is an edge.
△*ABC* is a face.

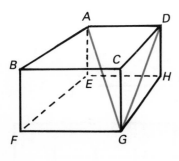

A line segment joining two non-adjacent vertices is called a diagonal.
GD is a *face diagonal*.
GA is a *body diagonal*.

A regular polyhedron is one whose faces are congruent regular polygons. Although the faces could be equilateral triangles, squares, regular pentagons, hexagons, or octagons, it is only possible to construct 5 regular polyhedra. Mathematicians at the time of Plato knew that there were only 5 regular polyhedra. We will discuss this later in the chapter.

How many words can you find that contain the letter sequence UBL?

EXERCISE 11-4

B **1.** *PRISMS.* A *prism* is a polyhedron with one pair of faces that are congruent polygons (bases) and sides that are parallelograms.

(i)

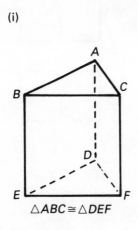

△*ABC* ≅ △*DEF*

(ii)

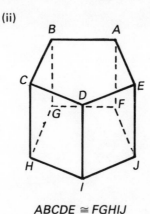

ABCDE ≅ *FGHIJ*

(iii)

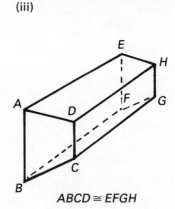

ABCD ≅ *EFGH*

(a) Find the lateral area (*LA*) and total (*TA*) area of a prism with a rectangular base 4 cm by 5 cm and 7 cm in height.
(b) Construct the prism in (a).
(c) Construct a prism 15 cm high, with pentagons having sides 5 cm as bases.

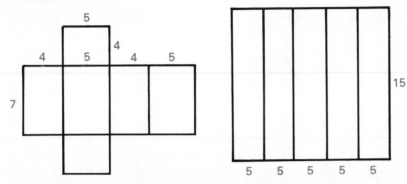

2. *PYRAMIDS*   A pyramid has a polygon as base and the lateral faces are triangles with a common vertex not contained in the base. A regular pyramid has a regular polygon for its base and the lateral faces are congruent isosceles triangles. The vertical height and slant height of a pyramid are not the same.

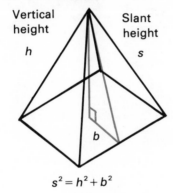

Vertical height h Slant height s

$$s^2 = h^2 + b^2$$

(a) Find the lateral area (*LA*) and total area (*TA*) of the pyramid with square base 6 cm by 6 cm and slant height 5 cm.

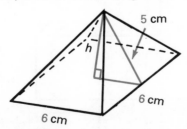

5 cm

h

6 cm

6 cm

(b) Construct the pyramid in part (a).
(c) Construct a pyramid with slant height 6 cm and having a regular hexagon with sides 2 cm as base.

3. THE FIVE REGULAR POLYHEDRA. construct the following polyhedra. The nets show flaps for gluing when the models are made from cardboard. The models can also be built using straws and paperclips.

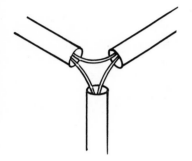

Paper clip
holding straws
at a vertex.

(a) Regular Tetrahedron

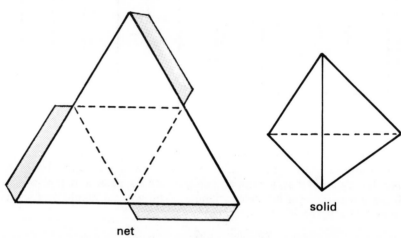

net

solid

(b) Regular Hexahedron

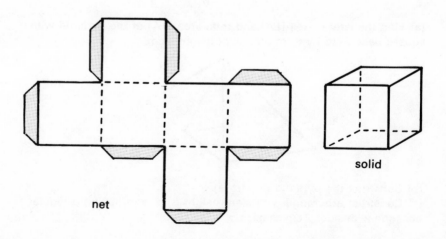

net

solid

(c) Regular Octahedron

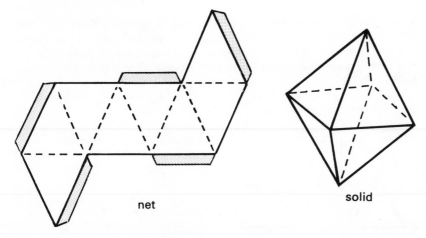

net

solid

(d) Regular Dodecahedron

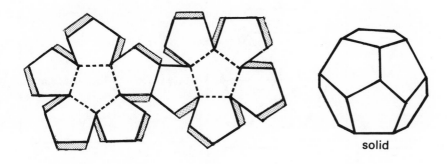

solid

(e) Regular Icosahedron

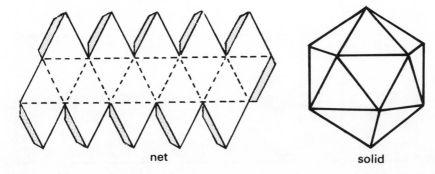

net

solid

$a + b + c + d < 360°$

11.5 EULER'S FORMULA

In section 11.4, we stated that mathematicians in Plato's time knew that only five regular polyhedra exist. In any polyhedron exactly two faces intersect to form an edge, while at least three edges meet to form a vertex. The sum of the face angles at any one vertex must be less than 360° in order to have a solid.

Let us now determine how the following regular *polygons* can form faces of regular polyhedra.

Face	Net Pattern for one vertex	Sum of Angles at one vertex	Regular Polyhedron
Equilateral Triangle		3(60°) = 180°	Tetrahedron
		4(60°) = 240°	Octahedron
		5(60°) = 300°	Icosahedron
Square		3(90°) = 270°	Hexahedron (cube)
Regular pentagon		3(108°) = 324°	Dodecahedron

These are the only 5 possibilities that give the sum of the face angles at one vertex less than 360°.

Euler, a Swiss mathematician, devised a formula that expresses the relationship between the number of faces, vertices, and edges of polyhedra. Work involving the formula follows.

NO   Addition
ROAD
NO
CARS

INVESTIGATION 11.5

1. Using the models of the 5 regular polyhedra, complete the following table in your books.

Polyhedron	Faces F	Vertices V	Edges E	F + V − E
Regular Tetrahedron				
Regular Hexahedron				
Regular Octahedron				
Regular Dodecahedron				
Regular Icosahedron				

From the table we see that for the regular polyhedra

$$F + V - E = 2$$

which is Euler's Formula.

2. Test Euler's formula $F + V - E = 2$ for the following figures:

(a)   (b)   (c)

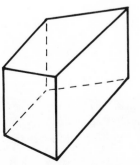
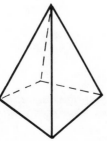
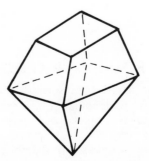

A solid has
1. triangles as faces
2. nine vertices
3. four faces meeting at each of six vertices
4. six faces meeting at each of the other three vertices
How many faces does the figure have?

three-dimensional geometry   269

(d) 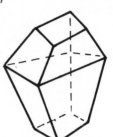 (e) 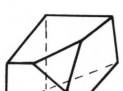 (f)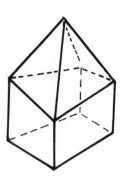

3. Determine whether Euler's theorem holds for cylinders.

$$F = \blacksquare$$
$$V = \blacksquare$$
$$E = \blacksquare$$
$$F + V - E = \blacksquare$$

Is a cylinder a polyhedron?

4. Determine whether Euler's theorem holds for all pyramids by considering one whose base in an *n*-gon.

$$V = \blacksquare$$
$$F = \blacksquare$$
$$E = \blacksquare$$
$$V + F - E = \blacksquare$$

5. Determine whether Euler's theorem holds for all prisms by considering one whose bases are congruent *n*-gons

$$V = \blacksquare$$
$$F = \blacksquare$$
$$E = \blacksquare$$
$$V + F - E = \blacksquare$$

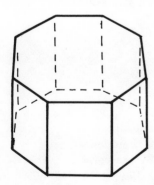

REVIEW EXERCISE

B **1.** Draw each of the following on squared paper:
(a) rectangular solid 6 cm by 5 cm by 10 cm.
(b) triangular prism with base 5 cm by 6 cm by 8 cm, and height 10 cm.
(c) cylinder with diameter 12 cm, and height 12 cm.

2. Draw the following to show the relationships between points, lines, and planes:

(a) two points on opposite sides of a vertical plane.
(b) two lines perpendicular to a horizontal plane.
(c) two planes intersecting in a line.
(d) three lines, each perpendicular to the other two.
(e) three planes intersecting in a line.
(f) three planes intersecting to form a prism.
(g) two planes perpendicular to a third plane.
(h) two points on opposite sides of a plane.

3. Calculate the value of each variable in the following.

(a)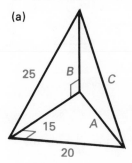

(b)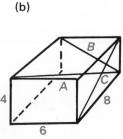

(c)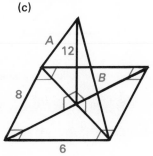

4. (a) State Euler's formula.
(b) Determine which of the following are the nets of solids.

(i)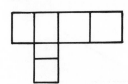

(ii)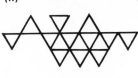

(iii)

5. Calculate the value of

(a)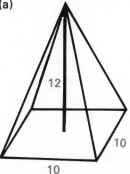

(i) Slant height
(ii) Lateral area

(b)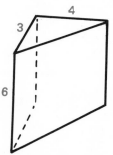

(i) Lateral area
(ii) Total area

(c)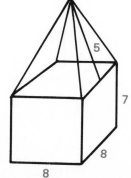

(i) Vertical height
(ii) Total area

Put the numbers from 1 to 9 in the spaces to make the statements true.

$$\square \div \square + \square = 9$$
$$\square \times \square + \square = 9$$
$$\square \times \square - \square = 9$$

REVIEW AND PREVIEW TO CHAPTER 12

EXERCISE 1

1. Calculate the indicated angles.

(a)

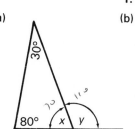

(b)

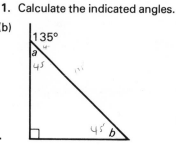

(c)

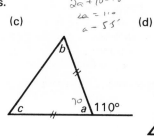

$2a + 70 = 180$
$2a = 110$
$a = 55°$

(d)

$3x + 90 = 180$
$3x = 90$
$x = 30$

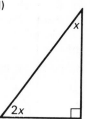

2. Solve the following equations.

(a) $\dfrac{x}{5} = \dfrac{7}{20}$ (b) $\dfrac{y}{3} = \dfrac{9}{20}$ (c) $\dfrac{h}{11} = \dfrac{22}{35}$ (d) $\dfrac{x}{7} = \dfrac{12}{35}$

(e) $\dfrac{a}{35} = \dfrac{2.6}{5.9}$ (f) $\dfrac{h}{7.25} = 1.25$ (g) $\dfrac{h}{5.2} = 0.866$ (h) $\dfrac{a}{320} = 0.707$

3. Use the Pythagorean relation to find the hypotenuse in each of the following.

(a)

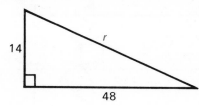

(b)

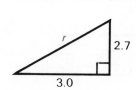

(c)

(d)

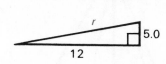

Trigonometry

All nature's structuring, associating, and patterning must be based on triangles.

Buckminster Fuller

Courtesy United States Information Service

The word trigonometry comes from the Greek "trigonon" meaning triangle, and "metrikos" meaning measure. In its earliest forms, this branch of mathematics deals with the measurement of triangles, and is used chiefly in surveying, navigation, astronomy and some scientific applications. In its more advanced forms, trigonometry has little connection with triangle measurement but it finds application in such fields as electronics, wave motion, and business cycles. In this book we will restrict our study of trigonometry to the right triangle.

12.1 RATIOS OF SIDES IN RIGHT TRIANGLES

In geometry we worked with relationships in right triangles for

(i) Angles

$$\angle A + \angle B = \angle C$$

(ii) Sides

$$a^2 + b^2 = c^2 \quad \text{(the Pythagorean Theorem)}$$

In the following investigation we will connect lengths of sides and measures of angles.

INVESTIGATION 12-1

1. Construct the following five triangles with angle measures as indicated and choose your own length for side *BC*.

(a)

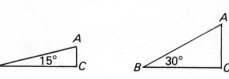

∠ *B* = 15°, ∠ *C* = 90°   ∠ *B* = 30°, ∠ *C* = 90°   ∠ *B* = 45°, ∠ *C* = 90°

(d)

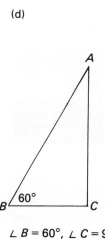

∠ *B* = 60°, ∠ *C* = 90°

(e)

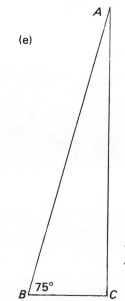

∠ *B* = 75°
∠ *C* = 90°

2. (a) Measure and record the lengths of *AB* and *CA* in each triangle, in the following table

(b) Calculate the ratios $\frac{CA}{AB}$, $\frac{BC}{AB}$ and $\frac{CB}{BC}$ correct to two significant figures.

∠ *B*	*AB*	*BC*	*CA*	$\frac{CA}{AB}$	$\frac{BC}{AB}$	$\frac{CB}{BC}$
15°						
30°						
45°						
60°						
75°						

3. Summarize your class results in the following table.

Angle	$\dfrac{CA}{AB}$	$\dfrac{BC}{AB}$	$\dfrac{CA}{BC}$
$\angle B = 15°$			
$\angle B = 30°$			
$\angle B = 45°$			
$\angle B = 60°$			
$\angle B = 75°$			

4. Do the lengths of the sides affect the ratios of the givern angle?

5. Write a conclusion in general terms.

12.2   SINE, COSINE, AND TANGENT

In the given right triangle, the side opposite the right angle is called the hypotenuse. If we *designate* an acute angle, *A*, of the triangle, then we can name the remaining sides of the triangle as in the diagram. Naming the sides of the right triangle in this manner, we now define the primary trigonometric ratios.

$$\text{sine of } A = \frac{\text{opposite side to } A}{\text{hypotenuse}}$$

$$\text{cosine of } A = \frac{\text{adjacent side to } A}{\text{hypotenuse}}$$

$$\text{tangent of } A = \frac{\text{opposite side to } A}{\text{adjacent side to } A}$$

These definitions are abbreviated to

$$\sin A = \frac{\text{opp}}{\text{hyp}} \qquad \cos A = \frac{\text{adj}}{\text{hyp}} \qquad \tan A = \frac{\text{opp}}{\text{adj}}$$

In figure **12**-1, $\triangle ABC$ is a right triangle with $\angle C = 90°$. We label the triangle so that the small letter *a* represents the length of the side opposite $\angle A$, *b* represents the length of the side opposite $\angle B$, and *c* represents the

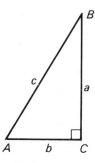

Figure 12-1

length of the side opposite $\angle C$. Applying the above definitions to $\triangle ABC$, we have

$$\sin A = \frac{a}{c} \qquad \cos A = \frac{b}{c} \qquad \tan A = \frac{a}{b}$$

$$\sin B = \frac{b}{c} \qquad \cos B = \frac{a}{c} \qquad \tan B = \frac{b}{a}$$

Note that when $\angle A$ is the designated angle, the opposite side is a, and b is the adjacent side. When $\angle B$ is the designated angle, b is opposite side and a is the adjacent side.

EXAMPLE 1. State the primary trigonometric ratios of the acute angles of the given triangle.

Solution From the diagram,

$$\sin A = \frac{4}{5} \qquad \cos A = \frac{3}{5} \qquad \tan A = \frac{4}{3}$$

$$\sin B = \frac{3}{5} \qquad \cos B = \frac{4}{5} \qquad \tan B = \frac{3}{4}$$

EXAMPLE 2. In $\triangle ABC$, $\sin A = \frac{5}{13}$, find $\cos A$ and $\tan C$.

Solution We label the triangle as shown. Then

$$c^2 = b^2 - a^2$$
$$c^2 = 13^2 - 5^2$$
$$= 169 - 25$$
$$= 144$$
$$c = 12$$

$$\cos A = \frac{12}{13} \text{ and } \tan C = \frac{12}{5}.$$

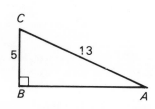

EXERCISE 12-2

A **1.** State the primary trigonometric ratios for $\angle A$ in each of the following.

(a)   (b)

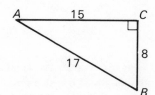

(c)

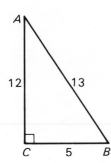

(d)

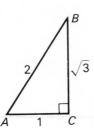

Put the numbers from 1 to
9 in the spaces to make
the statements true.

□×□--□=2
□+□÷□=2
□-□+□=2

(e)

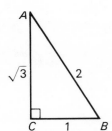

(f)

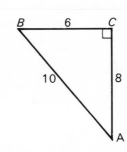

2. State a primary trigonometric ratio for ∠B in each of the following.

(a)

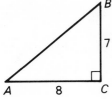

(b)

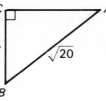

(c)

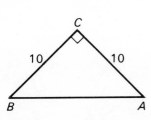

(d)

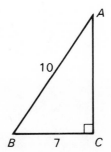

B **3.** Without simplifying, find the primary trigonometric ratios for the acute angles of the following triangles.
(a) $\triangle ABC$, $\angle A = 90°$, $a = 5$, $b = 4$
(b) $\triangle ABC$, $\angle B = 90°$, $a = 6$, $c = 8$
(c) $\triangle ABC$, $\angle C = 90°$, $b = 12$, $c = 13$

4. In $\triangle ABC$, $\tan B = 0.75$ and $\angle C = 90°$. Find (a) $\sin A$
(b) $\sin B$ (c) $\cos B$

5. in $\triangle PQR$, $\angle Q = 90°$ and $\tan R = 1$. Find
(a) $\sin P$ (b) $\cos P$ (c) $\sin R$ (d) $\tan P$

C **6.** In $\triangle ABC$, $\angle C = 90°$, $a = 1$, $b = 1$
(a) Find c, the hypotenuse.
(b) Use $\angle A$ or $\angle B$ to find $\sin 45°$, $\cos 45°$ and $\tan 45°$.

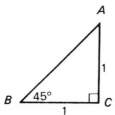

The sum of 3 consecutive integers is 222. Find the integers.

7. In $\triangle ABC$, $AB = BC = CA = 2$. $AD \perp BC$.
(a) Find the length of BD and AD.
(b) State the measure of $\angle ABD$ and $\angle BAD$.
(c) Use $\triangle ABD$ to find the primary trigonometric ratios of   (i) $60°$ (ii) $30°$.

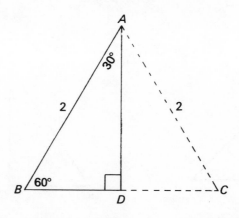

12.3 COSECANT, SECANT, AND COTANGENT.

In the previous section, we defined the primary trigonometric ratios in terms of the sides of a right triangle. We can also define three additional ratios, by taking the reciprocals.

$$\text{cosecant of } A = \frac{\text{hypotenuse}}{\text{opposite side to } A}$$

$$\text{secant of } A = \frac{\text{hypotenuse}}{\text{adjacent side to } A}$$

$$\text{cotangent of } A = \frac{\text{adjacent side to } A}{\text{opposite side to } A}$$

The definitions of the reciprocal ratios are abbreviated to:

$$\csc A = \frac{\text{hyp}}{\text{opp}} \qquad \sec A = \frac{\text{hyp}}{\text{adj}} \qquad \cot A = \frac{\text{adj}}{\text{opp}}$$

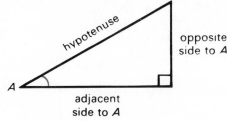

$$\csc \theta = \frac{1}{\sin \theta}$$

$$\sec \theta = \frac{1}{\cos \theta}$$

$$\cot \theta = \frac{1}{\tan \theta}$$

EXAMPLE 1. State the reciprocal trigonometric ratios of the acute angles of the given triangle.

Solution

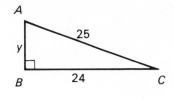

Applying the Pythagorean Theorem

$$y^2 + 24^2 = 25^2$$
$$y^2 + 576 = 625$$
$$y^2 = 49$$
$$y = 7$$

$$\csc A = \frac{25}{24} \qquad \sec A = \frac{25}{7} \qquad \cot A = \frac{7}{24}$$

$$\csc B = \frac{25}{7} \qquad \sec B = \frac{25}{24} \qquad \cot B = \frac{24}{7}$$

EXAMPLE 2. In $\triangle ABC$, $\cot C = \frac{12}{5}$ and $\angle B = 90°$.

Find   (a) $\csc C$ (b) $\cos C$

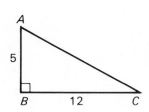

Solution

We label the triangle as shown.

$$b^2 = a^2 + c^2$$
$$= 12^2 + 5^2$$
$$= 144 + 25$$
$$= 169$$
$$b = 13$$

$$\csc C = \frac{13}{5} \text{ and } \cos C = \frac{12}{13}.$$

EXERCISE 12-3

A　**1.** State the value of csc θ, sec θ, and tan θ in each of the following.

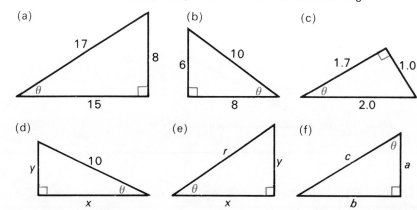

(a)　　　　　　　(b)　　　　　　　(c)

(d)　　　　　　　(e)　　　　　　　(f)

B　**2.** Without simplifying, find the six trigonometric ratios for the acute angles of the following triangles.

(a) $\triangle ABC$, $\angle A = 90°$, $a = 10$, $b = 6$

(b) $\triangle ABC$, $\angle B = 90°$, $a = 3$, $c = 4$

(c) $\triangle ABC$, $\angle C = 90°$, $b = 5$, $c = 13$

3. In $\triangle ABC$, csc $B = 1.25$ and $\angle C = 90°$. Find the other five trigonometric ratios of $\angle B$.

4. In $\triangle STU$, $\angle T = 90°$, and cot $U = 1$. Find

(a) sin S　　　　(b) csc U　　　　(c) sec S　　　　(d) tan U

C　**5.** In $\triangle ABC$, $a = 12$, $c = 13$, $\angle C = 90°$.

(a) Find the six trigonometric ratios of $\angle B$.

(b) Use your answers to (a) to show
　　(i) $\sin^2 B + \cos^2 B = 1$
　　(ii) $1 + \tan^2 B = \sec^2 B$
　　(iii) $1 + \cot^2 B = \csc^2 B$
　　Where $\sin^2 B$ means $(\sin B)^2$

12.4 SOLVING RIGHT TRIANGLES

We have defined the trigonometric ratios in terms of the sides of a right triangle. In order to organize our work in this section we agree to label triangles so that the small letter represents the length of the side opposite the vertex with the corresponding capital letter.

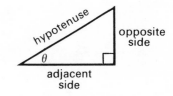

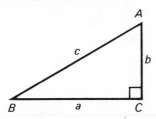

A triangle is said to be solved when we are able to state the lengths of the three sides and the measures of the three angles. For convenience, tables of values of the trigonometric ratios have been provided in the appendix.

EXAMPLE 1. Find the length of the indicated sides in the given triangle.

Solution

$$\frac{x}{10} = \sin 28° \qquad \frac{y}{10} = \cos 28°$$
$$x = 10 \sin 28° \qquad y = 10 \cos 28°$$
$$= 10(0.4695) \qquad = 10(0.8829)$$
$$\doteq 4.70 \qquad \doteq 8.83$$

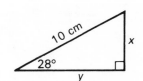

We can find the length of a side using the relationship

$$\frac{\text{unknown}}{\text{known}} = \text{trigonometric ratio}$$

EXAMPLE 2. Find the measure of the indicated angle.

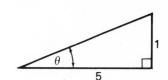

Solution

$$\tan \theta = \frac{1}{5} = 0.4$$
$$\theta = 22°$$

EXAMPLE 3. Solve the given triangle.

Solution

$$\tan B = \frac{35}{45}$$
$$= 0.7778$$

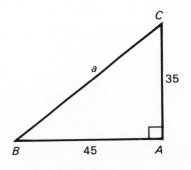

trigonometry   281

$$\angle B = 38°$$

$$\angle C = 90° - \angle B$$

$$= 90° - 38°$$

$$= 52°$$

$$\frac{a}{45} = \sec 38°$$

$$a = 45 \sec 38°$$

$$\doteq 45(1.269)$$

$$\doteq 57.1$$

$$\therefore a = 57.1, \angle B = 38°, \angle C = 52°$$

and we say that the triangle is solved.

EXERCISE 12-4

A **1.** Read the following values from tables.

(a) $\sin 35°$ (b) $\tan 51°$ (c) $\csc 46°$ (d) $\cos 62°$

(e) $\cos 17°$ (f) $\sin 28°$ (g) $\tan 84°$ (h) $\sec 75^b$

2. State the measure of the angle in each of the following.

(a) $\sin A = 0.4282$ (b) $\tan C = 2.745$ (c) $\cos B = 0.1192$

(d) $\tan M = 0.6522$ (e) $\sec A = 1.752$ (f) $\cot B = 1.881$
(g) $\csc C = 1.051$ (h) $\sec Q = 2.669$

3. Examine the tables on pages 418 and 419 then complete the following statement: ''As the angle θ increases from 0° to 90°,

(a) $\sin \theta$ increases from ▇ to ▇ .

(b) $\cos \theta$ decreases from ▇ to ▇ .

(c) $\tan \theta$ increases from ▇ to ▇ .

(d) $\csc \theta$ decreases from ▇ to ▇ .

(e) $\sec \theta$ increases from ▇ to ▇ .

(f) $\cot \theta$ decreases from ▇ to ▇ .

B **4.** Use a trigonometric ratio to find the length of the indicated side.

(a)

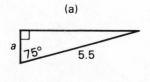

(b)

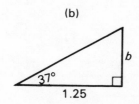

(c)

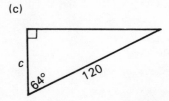

(d)

(e)

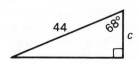

(f)

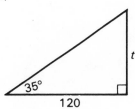

5. Find the angle θ in each of the following.

(a)

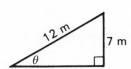

(b)

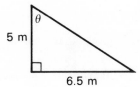

(c)

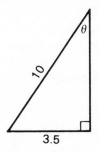

(d)

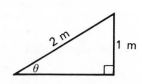

C **6.** Solve the following triangles.

(a)

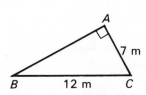

(b)

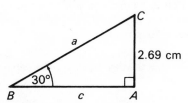

(c)

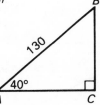

(d) △ABC, ∠A = 90°, ∠C = 35°, c = 15

(e) △ABC, ∠C = 90°, ∠B = 71°, a = 24

(f) △ABC, ∠B = 90°,   a = 20, c = 30

12.5 APPLICATIONS OF TRIGONOMETRY

Problems that can be represented in a diagram involving triangles can often be solved using trigonometry. In this section we will see that it is possible to find the height of an object such as a flagpole without actually climbing the pole to measure. The following figure shows some of the terminology that will be used in the work which follows.

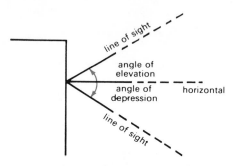

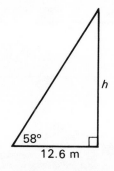

When measuring angles, a surveyor uses an instrument such as a transit or theodolite. A simple measuring device for angles can be constructed using a blackboard protractor with two nails for sighting, and a plumb bob for the vertical.

EXAMPLE 1. The angle of elevation of the top of a building is 58° from a point 12.6 m from the foot of the building. Find the height of the building.

Solution: Let the height of the building in metres be represented by h.

$$\frac{h}{12.6} = \tan 58°$$

$$h = 12.6 \times \tan 58°$$

$$\doteq 12.6 \times 1.6003 \doteq 20.2$$

The height of the building is approximately 20.2 m.

EXAMPLE 2. From the top of a fire tower, the angle of depression of a cabin is observed to be 27°. Find the distance from the cabin to the tower if the tower is 75 m high.

Solution: Let the distance from the cabin to the tower in metres be d.

$$\angle BAC = 90° - 27° = 63°$$

$$\frac{d}{75} = \tan 63°$$

$$d = 75 \tan 63°$$

$$\doteq 75(1.963)$$

$$\doteq 147$$

∴ the cabin is 147 m from the tower.

EXERCISE 12-5

B **1.** How high up a wall will a 7 m ladder reach, if the ladder must make an angle of 65° with the ground?

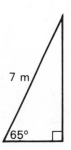

2. The Empire State Building casts a shadow 257 m long when the angle of elevation of the sun is 55°. How high is the building?

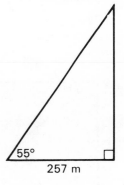

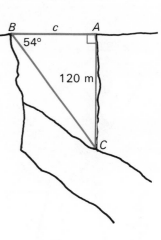

3. Find the distance across a gorge, *AB,* if the angle of depression from *B* to the base of the opposite side is 54°, and the depth *AC* is 120 m.

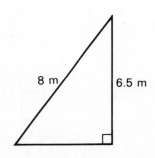

4. An 8 m ladder reaches 6.5 m up a wall.

(a) Find the angle the ladder makes with the wall.

(b) How far is the foot of the ladder from the wall?

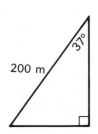

5. How far is it to the foot of a 200 m tower if the angle of elevation of the top is 15°?

6. A 200 m guy wire makes an angle of 37° at the top of a radio tower. Calculate the height of the tower.

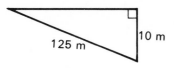

7. A road drops 10 m for every 125 m of road surface. Calculate the angle of inclination of the road.

8. A ramp at a football stadium rises 1 m for every 5 m of run. Calculate the angle of inclination of the ramp.

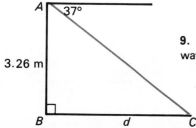

9. From the top of a low building 3.26 m high, the angle of depression of a water valve is observed to be 37°. How far is the valve from the building?

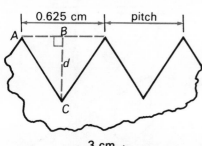

10. Calculate the dimension *d* in the given diagram.

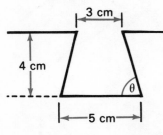

11. Find the measure of the indicated angle in the given diagram.

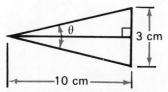

12. Find the angle of the wedge in the diagram using a right triangle.

13. From a point 100 m from the foot of a building, the angles of elevation of the top and bottom of the building's flagpole are 42° and 39° respectively. Calculate the height of

(a) the building

(b) the tip of the flagpole.

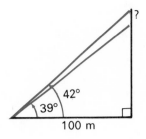

14. From the top of a cliff 70 m high the angles of depression of two small boats on the water are 8° and 13°. Calculate the distance:

(a) from the bottom of the cliff to the closer boat

(b) between the boats.

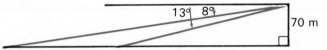

15. A surveyor wishes to find the height *BC* of an inaccessible cliff. To do this, he sets up his transit at *A*, measures ∠*CAB*, lays off a base line *AD* perpendicular to *AB*, and measures ∠*D*. From such a procedure, he records the following data: ∠*CAB* = 66°, ∠*ADB* = 42°, *AD* = 34.5 m. Calculate the height of the cliff.

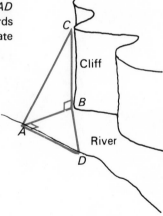

16. Mont Blanc, the highest of the Alps, is 4.8 km high. If the angles of elevation from points *A* and *B* on opposite sides are 43° and 54° as in the diagram, calculate the length of the tunnel *AB*.

17. A bridge is 130 m above the water. From the ends of the bridge, the angles of depression of a boat in the water directly between the points are 46° and 68°. Find the width of the bridge.

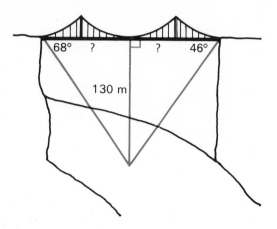

TWEET   Addition
TWEET
LI T TLE
BI RDIE

REVIEW EXERCISE

1. Find the length of the side labelled *x* in each of the following.

(a)   (b)   (c)

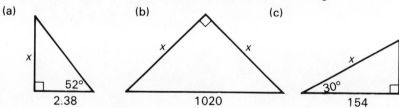

2. Find the measure of the indicated angle in each of the following.

(a)   (b)   (c)

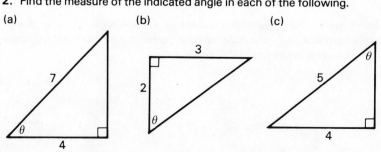

3. Solve the following triangles.

(a)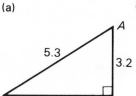

(b)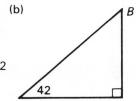

(c)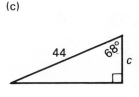

(d) $\triangle ABC$, $\angle A = 90°$, $b = 15$, $c = 10$

(e) $\triangle KLM$, $\angle L = 90°$, $\angle K = 36°$, $m = 24$

(f) $\triangle PQR$, $\angle R = 90°$, $p = 18$, $\angle Q = 68°$

---

4. Find the height of the tree in the given diagram.

5. From the top of a cliff 300 m high, the angle of depression of a sailboat on the water is 22°. How far is the boat from the cliff?

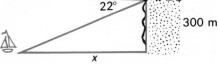

6. A tree casts a shadow 25 m long when the elevation of the sun is 36°. Calculate (a) the height of the tree (b) the length of the shadow when the elevation of the sun is 63°.

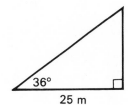

7. From the top of a cliff 100 m high the angles of depression of two channel markers on the water are 15° and 22°. How far apart are the markers?

8. From two points A and B on opposite sides of a small bay, the distances to a point C were measured and found to be 1500 m and 2100 m respectively. If $\angle A = 30°$ and $\angle B = 26°$, calculate the distance across the bay.

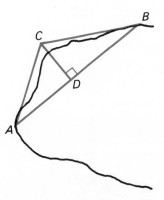

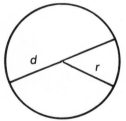

$C = \pi d$
$C = 2\pi r$
$A = \pi r^2$

EXERCISE 1
THE CIRCLE

Find the perimeter and area of each of the following figures.

1.

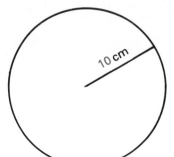

10 cm

2.

10 cm

3.

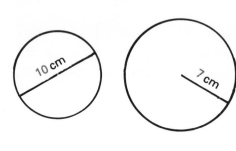

7 cm

4.

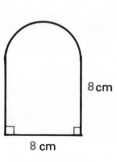

8 cm

8 cm

5.

10 cm

15 cm

6.

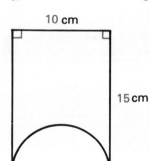

100 m

50 m

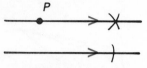

P

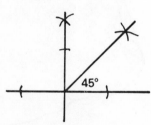

45°

EXERCISE 2
CONSTRUCTING PARALLELOGRAMS

Construct the following parallelograms using only ruler and compass.

1. $\|^{gm}$ *ABCD, AB* = 3 cm, *BC* = 5 cm, $\angle ABC$ = 45°
2. $\|^{gm}$ *PQRS PQ* = 2.5 cm, *QR* = 7 cm, $\angle QRS$ = 135°
3. $\|^{gm}$ *STUV, ST* = 4 cm, *TU* = 10 cm, $\angle UVS$ = 45°

4. ‖ᵍᵐ *JKLM, JK = AB, KL = PQ, ∠JKL = ∠XYZ*

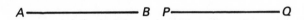

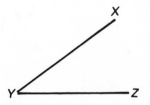

5 ‖ᵍᵐ *EFGH, EF = ST, EH = XY, ∠EFG = ∠ABC*

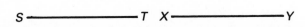

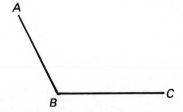

CHAPTER 13

Vectors

Algebra is generous, she often gives more than is asked of her.

D'Alembert

You have studied mathematical objects such as numbers, geometric figures, and systems. In this chapter you will study mathematical objects that can be represented by either an ordered pair, or a line segment with direction indicated. We shall call these objects *vectors.*

13.1 DIRECTED LINE SEGMENTS

A *displacement* 3 units to the right and 4 units up can be represented by the directed line segment $\overline{AB}$ as in Figure 13-1. The length of the line segment, *AB*, is 5 units (using the Pythagorean Theorem). This displacement can also be represented by the ordered pair [3,4]. Note that we shall use square brackets to signify a displacement and the round brackets to locate a point.

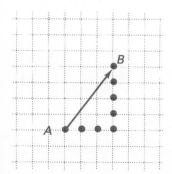

Figure 13-1

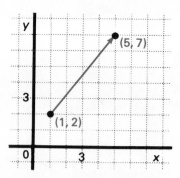

In a coordinate system, a displacement from (1, 2) to (5, 7) is represented by [4, 5]. [5, −2] represents a directed line segment which causes a displacement "five units to the right and down two." In Figure 13-2, the displacement is shown with the initial points *O*(0, 0), *A*(5, 2), *B*(3, 5), and *C*(−2, −1). The displacement [5, −2] originates from four different initial points to produce four different terminal points.

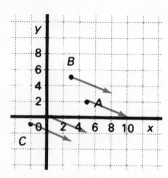

Figure 13-2

Displacements can be represented *geometrically* by directed line segments and *algebraically* by ordered pairs with square brackets, [a, b], where a and b are the *components* of the displacement.

Initial point

[a, b]

Terminal point

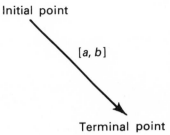

EXERCISE 13-1

A **1.** Express each of the following displacements in the form [a, b]

(a) $\overrightarrow{AB}$ (b) $\overrightarrow{CD}$ (c) $\overrightarrow{EF}$ (d) $\overrightarrow{GH}$

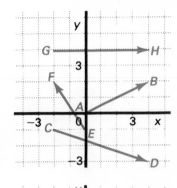

2. Find the terminal points determined by the displacement [2, 5] for each of the initial points.

(a) $O(0,0)$ (b) $A(0,6)$ (c) $B(1,-2)$ (d) $C(-3,-2)$

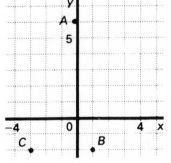

3. Find the displacement determined by the initial point (3, 2) for each of the terminal points.

(a) $O(0,0)$ (b) $A(2,7)$ (c) $B(8,5)$ (d) $C(3,-3)$

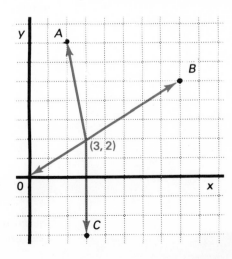

Place each of the digits from 0 to 9 in the spaces to make the addition correct.

B **4.** Make a diagram to show each of the following displacements as a *directed line segment* and label (i) initial point, (ii) terminal point, (iii) the displacement as an ordered pair, $[a, b]$. From:
(a) $O(0,0)$ to $A(3, 6)$ (b) $B(-2, 5)$ to $C(10, 8)$
(c) $D(-4, 0)$ to $E(6, -3)$ (d) $F(2, 1)$ to $G(5, -4)$
(e) $G(5, -4)$ to $H(2, 1)$

5. Find the terminal points of the directed line segments representing the displacements $[4, 3]$ for each of the initial points.
(a) $A(2, 5)$ (b) $B(-4, -3)$ (c) $C(0, -2)$ (d) $D(3, 8)$ (e) $E(-5, -2)$

6. Each of the following pairs of points describes a displacement. Make a diagram and determine which are the same displacement.
(a) from $(0, 0)$ to $(3, 4)$ (b) from $(-3, 4)$ to $(1, 7)$
(c) from $(7, 0)$ to $(11, 3)$ (d) from $(6, 3)$ to $(10, 5)$
(e) from $(5, 1)$ to $(1, -2)$ (f) from $(-4, 3)$ to $(0, 0)$

C **7.** Choosing any initial point, plot the following displacements on squared paper and find a single displacement equivalent to each.
(a) $[3, 2]$ followed by $[2, 7]$ [b] $[5, 4]$ followed by $[-2, 3]$
(c) $[6, 4]$ followed by $[-2, -5]$ [d] $[4, 3]$ followed by $[4, 3]$

8 Find the lengths of the directed line segments indicated by the following displacements.
(a) $[-4, 3]$ (b) $[5, 12]$ [c] $[-5, -12]$
(d) $[8, -15]$ (e) $[-7, 24]$ (f) $[-15, -8]$
(g) $[-6, 8]$ (h) $[-3, -4]$

13.2 VECTORS

Mathematical objects that have both *magnitude and direction*, and can be represented by ordered pairs or by directed line segments, are called *vectors*. The vector from A to B shown in Figure 13-3 can be represented geometrically by the directed line segment $\overrightarrow{AB}$ or algebraically by the ordered pair $[4, 5]$. The geometric vector $\overrightarrow{AB}$ can also be represented simply by $\vec{v}$.

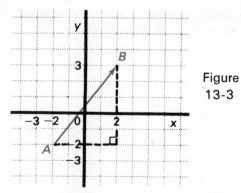

Figure 13-3

Figure 13-4 shows the vector $[4, 5]$ represented geometrically by selecting several initial points. While each geometric vector in the figure has a different initial point, each can be represented by the same ordered pair [4, 5]. The *magnitude* or length of each vector is

$$\sqrt{4^2 + 5^2} = \sqrt{41}$$

and each has the same slope, $\frac{5}{4}$.

If $\vec{v} = [a, b]$, then the magnitude of $\vec{v}$ is $|\vec{v}| = \sqrt{a^2 + b^2}$

Vectors with the same magnitude and direction can be represented by the same pair and are called *equal vectors*.

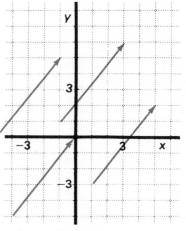

Figure 13-4

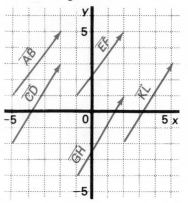

EXERCISE 13-2

A **1.** (a) State the algebraic vectors represented by each of the following $\vec{AB}$, $\vec{CD}$, $\vec{EF}$, $\vec{GH}$, $\vec{KL}$.

(b) Name the vectors in (a) that are equal vectors.

B **2.** Draw 3 geometric vectors representing each of the algebraic vectors
(a) [3, 6]   (b) [4, −3]   (c) [0, −4]   (d) [2, 2]   (e) [−3, −5]

3. Plot the points $A(2, 4)$, $B(7, 2)$, $C(-3, -6)$, $D(5, -1)$ and find the algebraic vectors represented by $\vec{AB}$, $\vec{BA}$, $\vec{BC}$, $\vec{CD}$, $\vec{DA}$, $\vec{AC}$, $\vec{DB}$.

4 (a) Plot the points $P(-1, 3)$, $Q(-3, -5)$, $R(8, 1)$, $S(10, 9)$ and draw the vectors represented by $\vec{PQ}$, $\vec{QR}$, $\vec{SR}$, $\vec{PS}$. Identify figure $PQRS$.
 b) Find the algebraic vectors represented by $\vec{PQ}$, $\vec{QR}$, $\vec{SR}$, $\vec{PS}$.

5. If $A(-2, 5)$ $B(3, 2)$, and $C(1, 6)$ are 3 points in the plane, make a diagram and find the coordinates of point D so that $\vec{AB}$ and $\vec{CD}$ are equal vectors.

6 Given points $A(2, 7)$, $B(3, 1)$ and $C(-2, 0)$, find the following.
(a) The coordinates of D so that $\vec{AB}$ and $\vec{CD}$ are equal vectors.
(b) The coordinates of point E so that $\vec{AC} = \vec{BE}$.

7 (a) Given points $P(-5, 5)$, $Q(9, 2)$, and $R(4, -7)$, find the coordinates of point S so that $PQRS$ is a parallelogram.
(b) Verify that $PQRS$ is a parallelogram by showing that $\vec{PQ} = \vec{SR}$.
 c) Verify that $PQRS$ is a parallelogram by showing that $\vec{RQ} = \vec{SP}$.
(d) Is it necessary to show both $\vec{PQ} = \vec{SR}$ and $\vec{RQ} = \vec{SP}$ in order to verify that $PQRS$ is a parallelogram?

8	20	24	44
4	10	12	22
2	5	6	

Determine the pattern. Find the missing number.

8. (a) Complete the following table

Initial point	Terminal point	Algebraic vector [a, b]	Magnitude $\sqrt{a^2+b^2}$	Slope $\dfrac{b}{a}$
A(2, 4)	B(3, 6)			
C(2, 7)	D(5, 3)			
E(−2, 1)	F(0, 5)			
G(3, −2)	H(6, −6)			
I(−4, −3)	J(−3, −1)			
K(0, −5)	L(1, −3)			
M(0, 2)	N(3, −2)			
P(5, 3)	Q(4, 1)			

An apartment building has 6 stories. How many times as long is the climb to the sixth floor as the climb to the third?

(b) Name vectors from part (a) which are equal vectors. Note: When 2 vectors have the same magnitude and the same slope they are not equal unless they can be represented by the same ordered pair.

9. (a) If [5, 3], [5, b], and [a, 3] are equal vectors, state the numerical values of a and b.
(b) If [a, b] = [c, d], how are the numbers a, b, c and d related?
(c) If a = c and b = d, how are [a, b] and [c, d] related?
In general:

Two vectors [a, b] and [c, d] are equal if and only if a = c and b = d.

C **10.** Three aircraft are flying northeast at 125, 150, and 200 kn respectively. Using a suitable scale, draw vectors to show the flight paths of the aircraft.
(a) How are the 3 vectors related?
(b) How do they differ?
(c) How would you change the vector of the first aircraft so that it has the same vector as the second aircraft?

11. (a) Using a suitable scale, draw vectors to represent a flight path 200 nautical miles north followed by 400 nautical miles west.
(b) Draw the vector to show the resulting displacement from the starting point to the terminal point of the flight.
(c) Measure the length of this new vector and the angle it makes with the horizontal vector.

12. A man rows a boat at the rate of 5 kn in a direction directly across a river. The river has a current of 12 kn.

(a) Using a suitable scale, make a vector diagram to show the actual direction of his travel.

(b) Find his actual speed:

(i) by measurement   (ii) by calculation

13. Express the following as vectors in the form [*a, b*].

(a) 500 km north.

(b) 100 km east.

(c) 200 km in a direction 120° west of north.

14. (a) Draw a geometric vector $\overrightarrow{PQ}$ with magnitude 10 units at an angle of 30° to the horizontal measured counterclockwise. Draw $\overrightarrow{QR}$ with magnitude 5 units and direction 90° to the horizontal measured clockwise.

(b) Find the direction of $\overrightarrow{PR}$ and the approximate magnitude.

13-3 ADDITION OF VECTORS

When we add 2 vectors, the result is another vector. In this section, we will add vectors—algebraic and geometric.

Algebraic Solution

Geometric Solution

EXAMPLE 1. *An aircraft flies* 200 km *east from A to B, then continues another* 400 km *to C.*

$$\overrightarrow{AB} = [200, 0]$$
$$\overrightarrow{BC} = [400, 0]$$
$$\overrightarrow{AB} + \overrightarrow{BC} = [200, 0] + [400, 0]$$
$$= [600, 0]$$
$$\overrightarrow{AB} + \overrightarrow{BC} = \overrightarrow{AC}$$
$\overrightarrow{AC}$ is the resultant of $\overrightarrow{AB} + \overrightarrow{BC}$

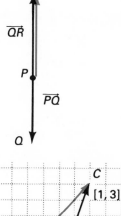

EXAMPLE 2. *A man walks* 200 m *south from P to Q, then north* 500 m *to R.*

$$\overrightarrow{PQ} = [0, -200]$$
$$\overrightarrow{QR} = [0, 500]$$
$$\overrightarrow{PQ} + \overrightarrow{QR} = [0, -200] + [0, 500]$$
$$= [0, 300]$$
$$\overrightarrow{PQ} + \overrightarrow{QR} = \overrightarrow{PR}$$
$\overrightarrow{PR}$ is the resultant of $\overrightarrow{PQ} + \overrightarrow{QR}$.

EXAMPLE 3. *A ship sails according to the vector* $\overrightarrow{AB} = [4, 2]$ *followed by the vector* $\overrightarrow{BC} = [1, 3]$.

$$\overrightarrow{AB} = [4, 2]$$
$$\overrightarrow{BC} = [1, 3]$$
$$\overrightarrow{AB} + \overrightarrow{BC} = [4, 2] + [1, 3]$$
$$= [5, 5]$$
$$\overrightarrow{AC} = [5, 5]$$
$\overrightarrow{AC}$ is the resultant of $\overrightarrow{AB} + \overrightarrow{BC}$.

In general, vectors can be added	
(i) Algebraically	(ii) Geometrically
$$[a, b] + [c, d]$$ $$= [a+c, b+d]$$ by adding the respective first components and second components.	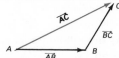 by arranging the vectors so that we can join the *initial* point of the second vector to the *terminal* point of the first vector.

EXAMPLE 4. *If* $\overrightarrow{AB} = [4, 1]$, $\overrightarrow{BC} = [1, 3]$ *and* $\overrightarrow{CD} = [-3, 4]$, *find the resultant of* $\overrightarrow{AB} + \overrightarrow{BC} + \overrightarrow{CD}$.

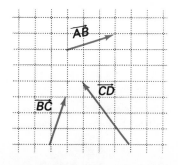

Solution

(i) Algebraic

$\overrightarrow{AB} + \overrightarrow{BC} + \overrightarrow{CD} = [4, 1] + [1, 3] + [-3, 4]$
$= [4+1-3, 1+3+4]$
$= [2, 8]$

The resultant is $\overrightarrow{AD} = [2, 8]$

(ii) Geometric

We first arrange the vectors joining initial point of one vector to the terminal point of another.

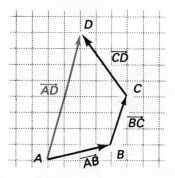

EXERCISE 13.3

A **1.** Add the following vectors algebraically:

(a) $[2, 3] + [5, 7]$

(b) $[-5, 4] + [6, 3]$

(c) $[-2, -5] + [5, 4]$

(d) $[3, -5] + [4, 2]$

(e) $[-3, -4] + [-2, -3]$

(f) $[4, 7] + [3, 6]$

(g) $[5, 2] + [-5, -2]$

(h) $[10, 3] + [-10, -3]$

(i) $[0, 0] + [3, 6]$

(j) $[2, 5] + [3, 12] + [-5, -8]$

2 Find $[x, y]$ for each of the following:

(a) $[x, y] + [2, -5] = [0, 0]$ (b) $[3, -4] + [x, y] = [3, 4]$

(c) $[x, y] + [-2, 5] = [-2, 5]$ (d) $[4, 7] + [-2, 3] = [x, y]$

(e) $[5, -2] + [x, y] = [4, -3]$ (f) $[x, y] + [x, y] = [4, 10]$

Use $+, -, \times, \div, (\ )$ to make a true statement.

$7\ 5\ 6\ 1 = 4\ 3\ 3\ 1$

B   **3.** Using a suitable scale, add the following vectors geometrically:

(a) 5 km east followed by 12 km north

(b) 30 km north followed by 15 km west

(c) 10 km northwest followed by 3 km west

(d) 10 km east, 5 km north, 7 km north

4. Find the following sums geometrically, using a vector diagram.

(a) $[2, 3] + [5, 2]$ (b) $[5, 1] + [4, 3]$

(c) $[3, -4] + [2, 6]$ (d) $[-5, 3] + [4, -2]$

(e) $[3, 6] + [-2, -6]$ (f) $[-2, -3] + [-4, 4]$

(g) $[3, -2] + [2, -3] + [-4, 8]$

(h) $[4, -5] + [0, 4] + [-4, 5] + [3, 0]$

5 (a) Find $[3, 7] + [-1, -4]$ and identify the result of adding two vectors.

(b) Find $[a, b] + [c, d]$ and identify the result of adding any two vectors.

(c) Is the sum of two vectors always a vector? Name the property.

In questions 6 and 7, simplify the left side and right side separately and insert the proper sign, $=$ or $\neq$.

6. (a) $[-5, 4] + [3, -6] \blacksquare [3, -6] + [-5, 4]$

(b) $[a, b] + [c, d] \blacksquare [c, d] + [a, b]$

7. (a) $([3, 5] + [4, -2]) + [-5, 6] \blacksquare [3, 5] + ([4, -2] + [-5, 6])$

(b) $([a, b] + [c, d]) + [e, f] \blacksquare [a, b] + ([c, d] + [e, f])$

8. (a) Find the sums:

(i) $[3, 2] + [0, 0]$ (ii) $[0, 0] + [-2, -6]$

(iii) $[-4, 3] + [0, 0]$ (iv) $[0, 0] + [-2, -4]$

(b) Add

(i) $[a, b] + [0, 0]$ (ii) $[0, 0] + [a, b]$

(c) Find values of x and y so that

(i) $[a, b] + [x, y] = [a, b]$

(ii) $[x, y] + [a, b] = [a, b]$

(d) What is the zero vector?

> The zero vector is $\vec{0} = [0, 0]$

SANTA
<u>CLAUS</u> subtraction
XMAS

9. Find values of x and y so that

(a) $[3, 4] + [x, y] = [0, 0]$ (b) $[x, y] + [3, 11] = [0, 0]$

(c) $[-5, 3] + [x, y] = [0, 0]$ (d) $[-4, -7] + [x, y] = [0, 0]$

(e) $[a, b] + [x, y] = [0, 0]$ (f) $[x, y] + [a, b] = [0, 0]$

> The inverse or negative of $[a, b]$ is $[-a, -b]$
> $[a, b] + [-a, -b] = [0, 0]$

10. (a) Make a diagram to show $\vec{a} = [3, 4]$ and its negative, both having the same initial point.

(b) Repeat part (a) for $\vec{b} = [0, 5]$, $\vec{c} = [-3, 5]$.

(c) From your diagrams in (a) and (b) state how a vector and its negative are

(i) similar   (ii) different

13.4   TRIANGLE AND PARALLELOGRAM LAWS OF ADDITION

In the previous section, we added vectors algebraically and geometrically. When we add the geometric vectors $\vec{AB}$ and $\vec{BC}$, by joining the initial point of $\vec{BC}$ to the terminal point of $\vec{AB}$, we form $\triangle ABC$ with the resultant $\vec{AC}$.

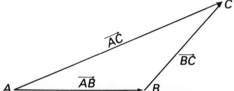

This method of adding 2 vectors permits us to state the triangle law.

The Triangle Law:
$\vec{AB} + \vec{BC} = \vec{AC}$ if the three vectors can be arranged to form the sides of a triangle, $\triangle ABC$.

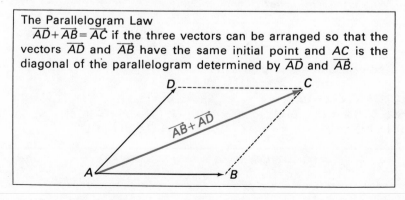

Equivalent to the triangle law, we can also add vectors geometrically using the parallelogram law, by arranging the 2 given vectors so that they have the same initial point.

The Parallelogram Law
$\vec{AD} + \vec{AB} = \vec{AC}$ if the three vectors can be arranged so that the vectors $\vec{AD}$ and $\vec{AB}$ have the same initial point and AC is the diagonal of the parallelogram determined by $\vec{AD}$ and $\vec{AB}$.

EXAMPLE 1. *Add the following pairs of vectors using the (i) triangle law, (ii) the parallelogram law.*

(a)

$\vec{w}$

$\vec{v}$

(b)

$\vec{a}$

$\vec{b}$

Solution: (i) Using the triangle law.

(a)

$\vec{v}$ $\vec{w}$

$\vec{v}$ $\vec{w}$
$\vec{v} + \vec{w}$

We first arrange the vectors with initial point of the second on the terminal point of the first.

Then we draw the resultant from the initial point of the first vector to the terminal point of the second vector.

(b)

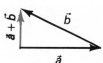

(ii) Using the parallelogram law.

(a)

$\vec{v}$

$\vec{w}$

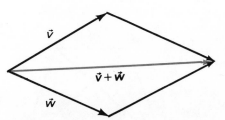

$\vec{v}$
$\vec{v} + \vec{w}$
$\vec{w}$

We first arrange the vectors to have the same initial point.

The resultant is found by completing the parallelogram and drawing the appropriate diagonal

(b)

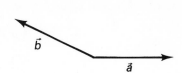

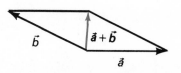

Note that both the triangle law and the parallelogram law produced the same resultant vectors in each case.

EXERCISE 13-4

A **1.** Express $\vec{v}$ as the sum of two other vectors.

(a)   (b)   (c)

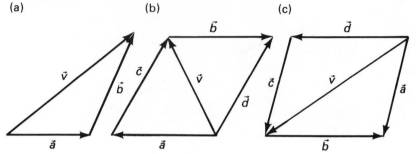

2. Name a single vector equal to $\vec{a} + \vec{b}$ in the following parallelograms.

(a)   (b)   (c)

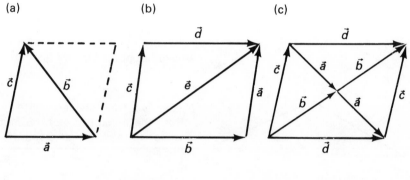

(d)   (e)   (f)

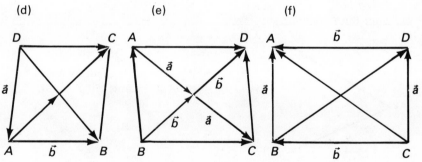

3. Name a single vector equal to
(a) $\overrightarrow{AB} + \overrightarrow{BC}$
(b) $\overrightarrow{BC} + \overrightarrow{CD}$
(c) $\overrightarrow{AB} + \overrightarrow{BC} + \overrightarrow{CD}$

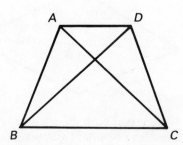

4. Use a vector diagram to find the sum of the following:

(a)   (b)   (c)   (d)

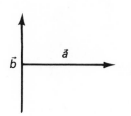
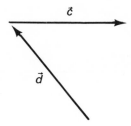
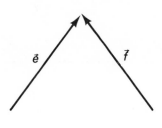
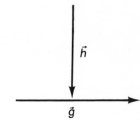

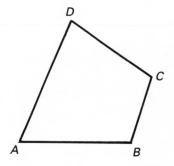

5. In quadrilateral $ABCD$ show that $\vec{AB}+\vec{BC}=\vec{AD}+\vec{DC}$.

6. In $\parallel^{gm}$ $ABCD$, E is the midpoint of AC. Redraw the diagram inserting arrowheads then express each of the following as a single vector.

(a) $\vec{AB}+\vec{BE}$
(b) $\vec{CE}+\vec{EA}$
(c) $\vec{DA}+\vec{CD}$
(d) $\vec{BC}+\vec{EB}$
(e) $\vec{BC}+\vec{AB}$
(f) $\vec{CE}+\vec{EB}$

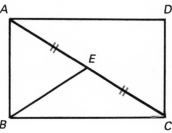

7. $ABCDE$ is a pentagon. Redraw the figure inserting appropriate arrowheads and diagonals to express each of the following as a single vector.

(a) $\vec{AB}+\vec{BC}$
(b) $(\vec{AB}+\vec{BC})+\vec{CD}$
(c) $\vec{CD}+\vec{DE}$
 d) $\vec{BC}+(\vec{CD}+\vec{DE})$
(e) $(\vec{AB}+\vec{BC})+(\vec{CD}+\vec{DE})$

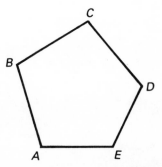

8. Add the following vectors using scale diagrams.

(a)

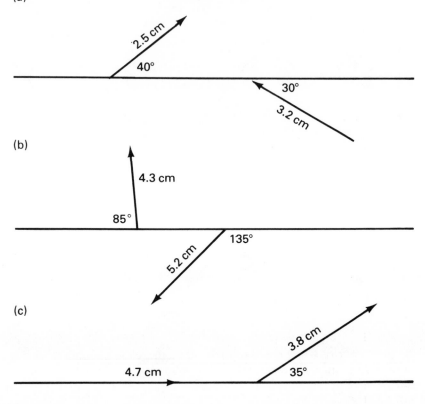

(b)

(c)

13.5 MULTIPLICATION OF A VECTOR BY A SCALAR

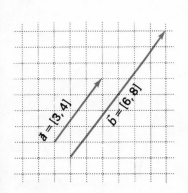

We have represented vectors as directed line segments or as ordered pairs with square brackets, [a, b]. When working with vectors, we also use real numbers which we shall call *scalars*. While a vector has both magnitude and direction, a scalar has only magnitude.

Consider two vectors $\vec{a} = [3, 4]$ and $\vec{b} = [6, 8]$. Both $\vec{a}$ and $\vec{b}$ have the same direction, but $|\vec{a}| = 5$ and $|\vec{b}| = 10$, so that the magnitude of $\vec{b}$ is twice the magnitude of $\vec{a}$. We can express this as

$$\vec{b} = 2\vec{a}$$

When we write

$$\vec{c} = 5\vec{a}$$

we mean that $\vec{c}$ has the same direction but five times the magnitude of $\vec{a}$.

Using $\vec{a}$ and $\vec{b}$, above, we can also find a meaning for multiplication of an algebraic vector by a scalar.

$$2\vec{a} = \vec{a} + \vec{a} \qquad\qquad \vec{b} = [6, 8]$$
$$= [3, 4] + [3, 4]$$
$$= [6, 8]$$

$2[3, 4]$
$= [6, 8]$

We get the same result by the following method:

$$2[3, 4] = [2 \times 3, 2 \times 4]$$
$$= [6, 8]$$

which suggests the following rule.

> If $\vec{v} = [a, b]$, then
> $k\vec{v} = k[a, b] = [ka, kb]$

Note that while the vectors $[3, 4]$ and $[-3, -4]$ have the same magnitude, 5, and the same slope, $\frac{4}{3}$, they are not equal vectors because they have opposite direction.

EXERCISE 13-5

A 1. State each of the following in the form $[a, b]$
(a) $3[2, 5]$ (b) $3[6, -2]$ (c) $\frac{1}{2}[4, 8]$
(d) $-3[-2, -3]$ (e) $\frac{2}{3}[-3, 6]$ (f) $2[0, 0]$
(g) $3[0, -2]$ (h) $-\frac{1}{2}[4, -16]$ (i) $5[2, 4]$

B 2. Simplify and express your answer in the form $[a, b]$
(a) $2[2, 3] + 3[2, 1]$ (b) $2[-1, 5] + [4, -3]$
(c) $\frac{1}{2}[0, 6] + \frac{2}{3}[3, 6]$ (d) $\frac{1}{4}[0, 4] + \frac{1}{3}[3, 9]$
(e) $(-2)[2, 5] + (-3)[2, -1]$ (f) $3([2, 3] + [4, -2])$
(g) $5([2, 3] + 2[1, -2])$ (h) $5([3, 2] + (-3)[1, 2])$

3. If $\vec{a} = [2x, 3y]$ and $\vec{b} = [3x, -2y]$, find
(a) $4\vec{a} + 2\vec{b}$ (b) $3\vec{a} + \vec{b}$
(c) $4(\vec{a} + \vec{b})$ (d) $3(\vec{a} + 2\vec{b})$

4. Make a diagram to verify that
(a) $3\vec{a} + 2\vec{a} = (3 + 2)\vec{a}$, for $\vec{a} = [3, -2]$
(b) $-2(\vec{a} + \vec{b}) = (-2)\vec{a} + (-2)\vec{b}$ for $\vec{a} = [-3, 5]$ and $\vec{b} = [-2, -3]$

$$\dfrac{1}{1 + \dfrac{2}{2 + \dfrac{3}{3+4}}}$$ Simplify

13.6 SUBTRACTION OF VECTORS

In working with real numbers, we subtract by adding the *negative*.
For example, $8 - (-3) = 8 + (+3) = 11$

$$9 - (+11) = 9 + (-11) = -2$$

We also subtract a vector by adding its negative. For example, we subtract $[4, -7]$ by adding $[-4, 7]$. Recall that the negative of a vector has the same magnitude as the original vector but opposite direction.

EXAMPLE 1.   *Simplify* $[7, 5] - [4, -3]$

Solution

$$[7, 5] - [4, -3] = [7, 5] + [-4, 3]$$
$$= [3, 8]$$

This result may be generalized to

$$[a, b] - [c, d] = [a, b] + [-c, -d]$$
$$= [a - c, b - d]$$

EXAMPLE 2.   *Given* $\vec{a} = [3, -5]$ *and* $\vec{b} = [-2, -6]$, *find* $\vec{a} - \vec{b}$
(*a*) *algebraically*   (*b*) *geometrically*

Solution
(a) $\vec{a} - \vec{b} = [3, -5] - [-2, -6]$
$\qquad\quad = [3, -5] + [2, 6]$
$\qquad\quad = [3 + 2, -5 + 6]$
$\qquad\quad = [5, 1]$

(b)
Step 1: Draw $\vec{a} = [3, -5]$
$\qquad\qquad \vec{b} = [-2, -6]$

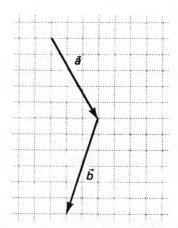

Step 2: Draw $-\vec{b} = [2, 6]$

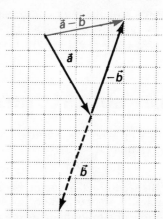

Step 3: Draw the resultant
$\qquad \vec{a} - \vec{b} = [5, 1]$

EXERCISE 13-6

A **1.** Simplify and express your answers in the form $[a, b]$.

(a) $[5, 2] - [4, 0]$ (b) $[7, -5] - [-2, -4]$

(c) $[-3, -4] - [-5, -6]$ (d) $[6, 9] - [-6, -9]$

(e) $[4, 5] - [4, 5]$ (f) $[0, 0] - [4, -7]$

(g) $[3x, 2b] - [x, b]$ (h) $[5a, -2b] - [3a, 2b]$

(i) $[4a, 3b] - [7a, -3b]$ (j) $[p, q] - [m, n]$

2. Express $\vec{a} - \vec{b}$ as a single vector in the following parallelograms.

(a)   (b)   (c)

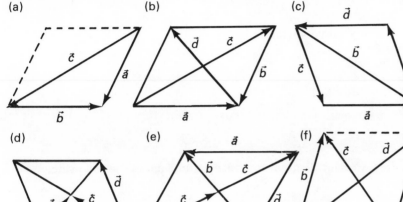

(d)   (e)   (f)

3. Express each vector in terms of the other two.

(a)   (b)   (c)

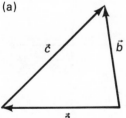 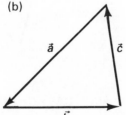 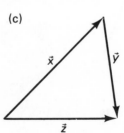

B **4.** Simplify and express your answer in the form $[a, b]$.

(a) $3[5, -2] - 7[1, -1]$ (b) $4[6, -3] - 2[5, 4]$

(c) $\frac{1}{2}[-6, 4] - \frac{1}{4}[-4, 8]$ (d $5[\frac{3}{5}, \frac{1}{5}] - 4[6, -1]$

(e) $-2[4, -1] - 3[1, -2]$ (f) $-5([6, -3] - [-2, 5])$

(g) $3(-2[1, 5] - 4[-1, -1])$ (h) $4[2, 7] - [2, 7]$

5. If $\vec{v} = [x, y]$, find $\vec{v} - \vec{v}$.

6. Express in the form $[a, b]$.

(a) $[5, 7] - [2, 4]$ (b) $[-3, 12] - [2, -7]$

(c) $3[4, -7] - 2[1, 5]$ (d) $4[3, 6] - [7, 4]$

(e) $[2, 7] - 3[-1, 4]$ (f) $[3, -7] - 4[0, 2]$

(g) $3[2, -5] - 3[-5, 2]$ (h) $[7, -2] - [2, 5] - [-3, -3]$

(i) $2[4, 1] - 3[1, -2] + 4[2, 7]$

(j) $3[-7, -1] - 2[-1, -7] - \frac{1}{2}[4, -6]$

How many words can you find that contain the letter sequence DIA?

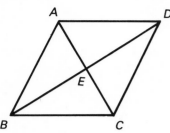

7. Given ∥^{gm} *ABCD*, redraw the figure inserting arrowheads and find the following.
(a) $\overrightarrow{AB} - \overrightarrow{BC}$
(b) $\overrightarrow{AB} - \overrightarrow{AE}$
(c) $\overrightarrow{BC} - \overrightarrow{EC}$
d) $\overrightarrow{AE} - \overrightarrow{EB}$
(e) $\overrightarrow{AE} - \overrightarrow{AE}$
(f) $\overrightarrow{BE} - \overrightarrow{EB}$

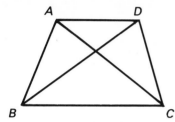

8. Name a single vector equal to
(a) $\overrightarrow{AB} - \overrightarrow{CB}$
(b) $\overrightarrow{BC} - \overrightarrow{DC}$
(c) $(\overrightarrow{AB} + \overrightarrow{BC}) - \overrightarrow{DC}$
(d) $\overrightarrow{BA} - (\overrightarrow{BC} + \overrightarrow{CD})$

9. Use a vector diagram to find $\vec{a} - \vec{b}$ in each of the following.

(a)　　　　　　(b)　　　　　　(c)　　　　　　(d)

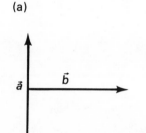

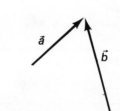

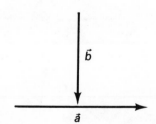

10. Show that in Figure *ABCD* $\overrightarrow{BA} - \overrightarrow{BC} = \overrightarrow{CD} - \overrightarrow{AD}$

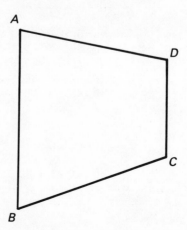

13.7 GEOMETRY WITH VECTORS

In this section we shall apply some of the vector properties we have studied to geometrical problems.

Which of the following nets can you draw without lifting your pencil or retracing any lines?

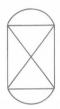

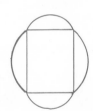

Summary of Geometric Properties of Vectors	
1. Equality: $\overrightarrow{AB} = \overrightarrow{CD}$ 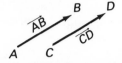	$\overrightarrow{AB}$ and $\overrightarrow{CD}$ have the same magnitude and direction.
2. Multiplication by Scalar 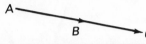	If $\overrightarrow{AB} = \overrightarrow{BC}$, then $\overrightarrow{AC} = 2\overrightarrow{AB} = 2\overrightarrow{BC}$ and $\overrightarrow{AB} = \overrightarrow{BC} = \frac{1}{2}\overrightarrow{AC}$.
3. Negative: 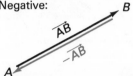	The negative of a vector is a vector with the same magnitude as, but opposite direction to, a given vector.
4. Addition: 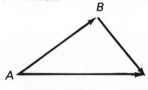	$\overrightarrow{AC} = \overrightarrow{AB} + \overrightarrow{BC}$ $\overrightarrow{AC}$ is the resultant of $\overrightarrow{AB} + \overrightarrow{BC}$ when the initial point of $\overrightarrow{BC}$ coincides with the terminal point of $\overrightarrow{AB}$.
5. Subtraction: 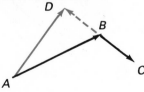	$\overrightarrow{AB} - \overrightarrow{BC} = \overrightarrow{AB} + (-\overrightarrow{BC})$ $\qquad\qquad = \overrightarrow{AB} + \overrightarrow{BD}$ $\qquad\qquad = \overrightarrow{AD}$ where $\overrightarrow{BD} = -\overrightarrow{BC}$ To subtract a vector, we add its negative.

EXAMPLE 1. *M and N are the midpoints of AD and BC respectively in* ‖^{gm} *ABCD. Show that AN is equal to and parallel to MC (i.e. show that* $\overrightarrow{AN} = \overrightarrow{MC}$).

Solution

$$\vec{AN} = \vec{AB} + \vec{BN}$$
$$= \vec{DC} + \tfrac{1}{2}\vec{BC}$$
$$= \vec{DC} + \tfrac{1}{2}\vec{AD}$$
$$= \vec{DC} + \vec{MD}$$
$$= \vec{MC}$$
$$\therefore \ AN = MC \text{ and } AM\|MC$$

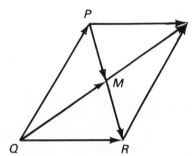

EXAMPLE 2. *Point M is the midpoint of the diagonal PR of parallelogram PQRS.*
Prove that QM = MS.

Solution
In $\|^{gm}$ *PQRS,* $\vec{QP} = \vec{RS}$, $\vec{PS} = \vec{QR}$.
$$\vec{PM} = \vec{MR} = \tfrac{1}{2}\vec{PR} \text{ (midpoint)}$$
$$\vec{QM} = \vec{QP} + \vec{PM}$$
$$= \vec{RS} + \vec{MR}$$
$$= \vec{MS}$$
$$\therefore \ QM = MS$$

EXERCISE 13-7

A **1.** Express each vector in terms of the other two.

(a)

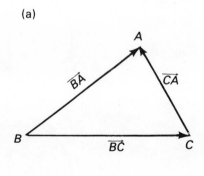

(b)

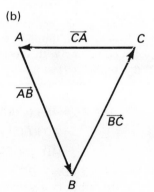

(c)

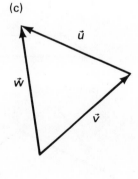

B **2.** In $\|^{gm}$ *PQRS,*
$\vec{PQ} = \vec{x}$, $\vec{QR} = \vec{y}$, and $\vec{PR} = \vec{z}$.

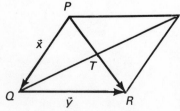

Express each of the following
in terms of $\vec{x}$, $\vec{y}$, and $\vec{z}$.
(a) $\vec{SR}$ (b) $\vec{PS}$ (c) $\vec{QP}$
(d) $\vec{PR}$ (e) $\vec{RS}$ (f) $\vec{QS}$

(g) $\overrightarrow{SQ}$ (h) $\overrightarrow{PT}+\overrightarrow{TR}$ (i) $\overrightarrow{PT}$

(j) $\overrightarrow{PQ}+\overrightarrow{QR}$ (k) $\overrightarrow{QT}+\overrightarrow{TS}$ (l) $\overrightarrow{QT}$

(m) $\overrightarrow{TS}$ (n) $\overrightarrow{ST}$

3. D is the midpoint of BC in $\triangle ABC$. Make a vector diagram and find $\overrightarrow{AD}$ in terms of $\overrightarrow{AB}$ and $\overrightarrow{BC}$.

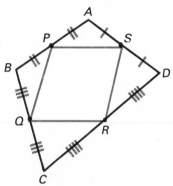

4. $ABCD$ is any quadrilateral with P, Q, R, and S the midpoints of AB, BC, CD, and DA respectively. Using vectors:

(a) Prove $\overrightarrow{PQ}=\overrightarrow{SR}$

(b) Identify $PQRS$.

(c) Check your answer to (b) using PS and QR.

(d) Identify the figure formed by joining the midpoints of a quadrilateral.

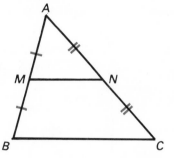

5. M and N are the midpoints of the sides AB and AC in $\triangle ABC$ as shown.

(a) Prove $\overrightarrow{MN}=\frac{1}{2}\overrightarrow{BC}$.

(b) Make a general statement concerning the line joining midpoints of two sides of a triangle and the third side.

(c) Check this statement using P, the midpoint of BC, and either M and N.

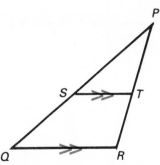

6. In $\triangle PQR$, S and T are points on PQ and PR such that $ST=\frac{1}{2}QR$ and ST is parallel to QR (i.e. $\overrightarrow{ST}=\frac{1}{2}\overrightarrow{QR}$).

(a) Use vectors to show that $PS=SQ$.

(b) Show that $PT=TR$.

(c) How does a line segment parallel to and equal to one-half of the base of a triangle divide the other two sides?

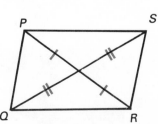

7. X is the midpoint of PR and QS in quadrilateral $PQRS$.

(a) Show that $PS=QR$ and that $PQ=SR$.

(b) Prove $PQRS$ is a parallelogram.

(c) Make a general statement concerning the above.

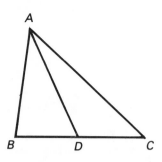

8. In $\triangle ABC$, D is the midpoint of BC. Make a vector diagram and prove that $\vec{AD} = \frac{1}{2}\vec{AB} + \vec{AC}$.

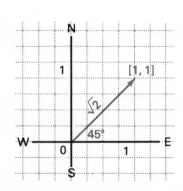

9. In $\triangle ABC$, $AM = \frac{1}{3}AB$ and $AN = \frac{1}{3}AC$. Make a vector diagram and prove that $MN = \frac{1}{3}BC$ and $MN \parallel BC$.

13.8 APPLICATIONS OF VECTORS

Since vectors have both *magnitude and direction*, they are used to represent such items as displacements, forces, and velocities.

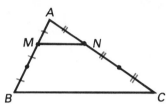

The vector [1, 1] can also be described in terms of its direction and magnitude. The length of the line segment is $\sqrt{2}$, and its angle with the vertical is 45°. If we use compass directions, then the vector [1, 1] can be represented by (45°, $\sqrt{2}$). We shall call this a *polar* representation of a vector, where the first number is the *bearing* (or direction) and the second number is the magnitude.

In this section, we shall solve problems using vectors with *scale drawings*. It is often convenient to choose a scale relating the given magnitudes to centimetres.

EXAMPLE 1. *Using a suitable scale, make a vector diagram for each of the following.*

(*a*) 30 m/s *west*   (*b*) 620 N force downwards
(*c*) 125 km *south-west*   (*d*) 35 m *east*

Solution
(a) Scale: 10 m/s → 1 cm

$$1 \text{ m/s} \rightarrow 0.1 \text{ cm}$$
$$30 \text{ m/s} \rightarrow 3 \text{ cm}$$

Direction: west requires arrowhead pointing left.
(b) Scale: **500** N → 1 cm

$$1 \text{ N} \rightarrow \tfrac{1}{500} \text{ cm}$$
$$620 \text{ N} \rightarrow 620 \times \tfrac{1}{500} = 1.24 \text{ cm}$$

Direction: arrowhead pointing down

30 m/s

(270°, 30)

620 N

(c) Scale:100 km → 1 cm

　　　　1 km → 0.01 cm

　　　　125 cm → $125 \times 0.01 = \textbf{1.25 cm}$

125 m

(225°, 125)

Direction: south-west requires arrowhead pointing downwards to the left.

(d) Scale: 25 m → 2 cm

　　　　1 m → $\frac{2}{25}$ cm

　　　　35 m → $35 \times \frac{2}{25} = 2.8$ cm

35 m

(90°, 35)

Direction: east requires arrowhead pointing right.

EXAMPLE 2. *A ship sails* 300 km *north and* 125 km *west, then develops engine trouble. Find the distance and direction in which a rescue ship must sail to go directly to the first ship if both ships leave from the same point.*

Solution

We solve the problem using an accurate construction. Let $\overrightarrow{R}$ represent the course of the rescue ship.

Scale:　30 km → 1 cm

　　　　125 km → 4.2 cm

　　　　300 km → 10 cm

125 km

300 km

The length of the resultant in the drawing is 10.8 cm (by measurement) so that the real magnitude of $\overrightarrow{R}$ is 325 km and using a protractor the angle is measured and found to be approximately 23°. Hence,

$$\overrightarrow{R} = (337°, 325)$$

EXAMPLE 3. *A pilot wishes to fly his aircraft, according to the vector* (90°, 350), *where the velocity,* 350, *is in knots. A* 65 kn *north wind causes the pilot to alter his course. Make a vector diagram and find the course the pilot must set.*

Solution

　The pilot must set a course $\vec{c}$ which is the sum of the two vectors (90°, 350) and the opposition to the wind.

　Note that a north wind blows *from* the north, and the vector representing opposition to this wind has the same magnitude but opposite direction.

Scale:　30 kn → 1 cm

　　　　350 kn → 11.7 cm

　　　　65 kn → 2.2 cm

65 kn

350 km

65 kn

The length of the resultant in the drawing is 11.9 cm (by measurement) so that the real magnitude of $\vec{C}$ is 356 kn and using a protractor the angle is measured and found to be approximately 11°. Hence,

$$\vec{C} = (79°, 356)$$

EXAMPLE 4. *The bearing from Winnipeg to Prince Albert is 302°. If there is a 35 kn west wind and the cruising speed of the aircraft is 180 kn find (i) the course that must be set to fly from Winnipeg to Prince Albert (ii) the ground speed.*

Solution

Scale: 18 kn → 1 cm

180 kn → 10 cm

35 kn → 1.94 cm

$\overrightarrow{WE}$ represents the wind. The line *WA* gives the direction to Prince Albert.

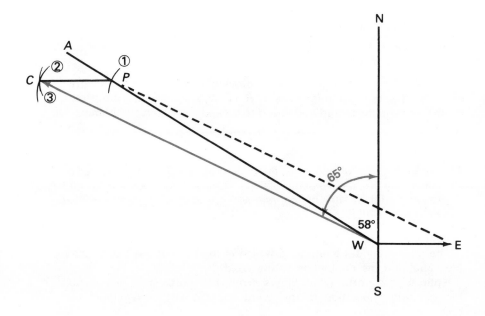

With compasses, radius 10 cm (180 kn) and centres *E* and *W* draw arcs ① and ② respectively. Arc ① cuts *WA* at *P*.

With centre *P* and radius *WE*, draw arc ② to cut arc 3 at *C*. *WC* represents the required course. Using a protractor, ∠ *EWC* is measured and found to be 65°. Hence the required course is (295°, 180). The length of *WP* is 8.1 cm (by measurement) so that the real magnitude of $\overrightarrow{WP}$ is 145 kn. Hence the ground speed is 145 kn.

EXERCISE 13-8

A **1.** Name the following vectors in polar form:

(a)

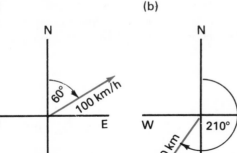

(b)

(c)

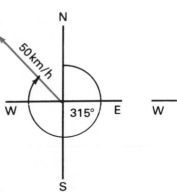

(d)

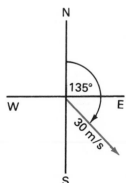

2. What is the length of the line segment representing the following quantities using the scale: 5 km = 2 cm?
(a) 10 km east
(b) 15 km left
(c) 7.5 km south
(d) 12.5 km north
(e) 4 km south-east
(f) 9 km north-west

B **3.** Using a suitable scale, draw each of the following vectors.
(a) (180°, 20)
(b) (110°, 75)
(c) (285°, 150)
(d) (135°, 300)
(e) (315°, 450)

4. A ship sails 300 km north, then 500 km east. Make a vector diagram to find the direct course that will reach the same position.

5. A ship sails 500 km north then 1200 km west and develops engine trouble. Make a vector diagram and find the course that a rescue ship would sail.

6. A small motorboat with a speed of 20 kn in still water is driven across a river with a current of 5 kn. Find the actual direction and velocity of the boat if the captain does not compensate for the current.

7. A plane travels north with an air speed of 400 kn. Find the ground speed and direction if there is a 40 kn east wind.

8. An airliner is heading east at 600 kn and encounters a 75 kn north wind. Find the resultant velocity and the true direction.

9. A pleasure craft is speeding across a river at 25 kn. Find the actual speed and direction if the current is 5 kn.

10. A pilot sets his course according to the vector (270°, 400), relative to the ground. Find the true ground velocity and direction if the flight is affected by a 45 kn south wind.

11. A plane flies 300 km east then 200 km north. In what direction and how far should the aircraft fly to return to its home field?

12. In what direction should a pilot set his course if he wants to fly south at 300 kn and there is a 50 kn west wind?

13. A pilot wishes to fly at 400 kn towards the west and there is a 35 kn south wind. Find the course he must set and the air speed.

14. What course must a pilot set to fly north if his air speed is 350 kn and there is a 50 kn west wind? What is the ground speed?

15. A pilot wishes to fly his aircraft directly east. What course must he set and what is his ground speed if there is a 50 kn north wind and the aircraft cruises at 300 kn?

REVIEW EXERCISE

B **1.** Find the terminal point determined by the vector $[2, -3]$ if the initial point is

(a) $(5, 2)$ (b) $(2, -3)$ (c) $(0, 0)$ (d) $(-3, 2)$

2. Simplify:

(a) $3[2, 5] + 2[3, -1]$ (b) $2[-4, 3] + 3[4, -5]$
(c) $4[1, -2] - [3, -2]$ (d) $3[-2, 5] - 2[4, 3]$

3. Find the magnitude of the following vectors.

(a) $[4, 3]$ (b) $[3, -4]$ (c) $[5, -12]$ (d) $[-8, 15]$
(e) $[11, -7]$ (f) $[-5, -7]$ (g) $[-15, 8]$ h) $[m, n]$

4 Express the following vectors in polar form (bearing, magnitude).

(a) $[200, 0]$ (b) $[0, -100]$ (c) $[-150, 0]$ (d) $[0, 200]$
(e) $[10, 10]$ (f) $[5, -5]$ (g) $[-3, -3]$ (h) $[-7, 7]$

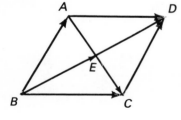

5. Name equal vectors if $ABCD$ is a parallelogram.

6. Name a single vector equal to $\vec{v} + \vec{w}$.

(a)   (b)   (c)

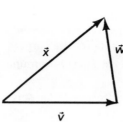
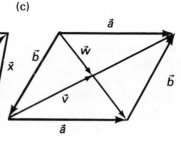

In how many ways is it possible to make change for a quarter?

7. If $\vec{x} = [4, 2]$, $\vec{y} = [-1, 5]$, $\vec{z} = [4, -3]$, find:

(a) $3\vec{x}$ (b) $\vec{x} + \vec{z}$ (c) $4\vec{x} + 3\vec{y}$
(d) $\vec{x} - \vec{y}$ (e) $|\vec{x}|$ (f) $|\vec{x} + \vec{y}|$
(g) $|\vec{x}| + |\vec{y}|$ (h) $-(3\vec{x} + 2\vec{y} - \vec{z})$

8. If $\vec{x} = [4, 7]$, $\vec{y} = [-2, 6]$, $\vec{z} = [0, -3]$, find

(a) $\vec{x} + \vec{y} + \vec{z}$ (b) $3\vec{x} + 2\vec{z}$
(c) $\vec{x} - (\vec{y} + \vec{z})$ (d) $\vec{x} - \vec{y} + \vec{z}$
(e) $|\vec{x}| + |\vec{y}| + |\vec{z}|$ (f) $|\vec{x} + \vec{y} + \vec{z}|$

9. (a) Plot the points $O(0,0)$, $A(4,2)$, $B(7,5)$, $C(2,0)$, $D(-6,1)$ and show $\overrightarrow{OA}$, $\overrightarrow{AB}$, $\overrightarrow{BC}$, $\overrightarrow{CD}$, $\overrightarrow{OD}$.

(b) Express $\overrightarrow{OA}$, $\overrightarrow{AB}$, $\overrightarrow{BC}$, $\overrightarrow{CD}$, $\overrightarrow{OD}$ in the form $[a, b]$.

10. (a) Given: $\overrightarrow{TP} = [4,2]$, $\overrightarrow{PQ} = [4,2]$, $\overrightarrow{QR} = [7,5]$, $\overrightarrow{RS} = [2,0]$, $\overrightarrow{ST} = [-6,1]$, show the addition $\overrightarrow{TP} + \overrightarrow{PQ} + \overrightarrow{QR} + \overrightarrow{RS} + \overrightarrow{ST}$ on squared paper.

(b) State the coordinates of P, Q, R and S if the coordinates of T are $(-2, 4)$

11 Given the points $A(4,2)$, $B(7,3)$, $C(-3,0)$, $D(0,1)$ determine which of $\overrightarrow{AB}$, $\overrightarrow{CD}$, $\overrightarrow{BA}$ and $\overrightarrow{DC}$ are equal vectors.

12. Use a scale drawing to find the direction and magnitude of

$$\overrightarrow{AB} + \overrightarrow{BC}$$

if $\overrightarrow{AB} = (30°, 25)$ and $\overrightarrow{BC} = (300°, 6)$.

13. Given three points $A(-2,-2)$, $B(0,3)$, $C(8,5)$:

(a) Find the coordinates of point D by means of a diagram so that $\overrightarrow{AB} = \overrightarrow{DC}$.

(b) Express $\overrightarrow{AB}$, $\overrightarrow{BC}$, $\overrightarrow{AD}$, $\overrightarrow{DC}$, in the form $[a, b]$.

(c) Identify figure $ABCD$.

14. (a) Make a diagram to show $(-3)[4, -2] = [-12, 6]$.

(b) Find x and y so that $[4, -2] = 2[x, y]$.

15. An aircraft flies east at 250 kn relative to the ground and encounters a north wind of 40 kn. Make vector diagrams and find:

(a) the ground speed and direction if the pilot does not adjust his course to account for the wind.

(b) the course the pilot should set to maintain his heading at 250 kn east.

16 In quadrilateral $ABCD$, $\overrightarrow{AB} = \overrightarrow{DC}$

(a) Show that $\overrightarrow{AD} = \overrightarrow{BC}$ and make a general conclusion.

(b) Identify figure $ABCD$.

17 P and Q are the midpoints of AD and BC respectively in parallelogram $ABCD$.

(a) Make a vector diagram.

(b) Show that

(i) $ABQP$ (ii) $PQCD$ (iii) $AQCP$ (iv) $PBDQ$

are parallelograms.

PARALLEL LINES
EXERCISE 1

Find the values of the variables.

1.

2.

3.

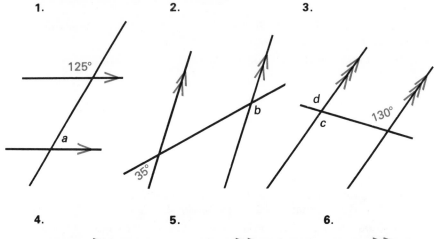

4.

5.

6.

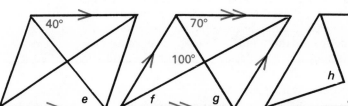

SIMILAR TRIANGLES

If $\triangle ABC \sim \triangle DEF$, then

$$\frac{AB}{DE} = \frac{BC}{EF} = \frac{CA}{FD}$$

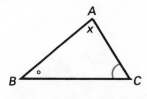

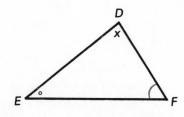

EXERCISE 2

Find the values of the variables.

1.

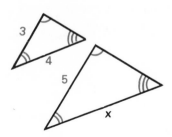

2.

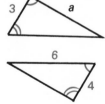

3.

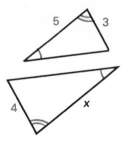

4.

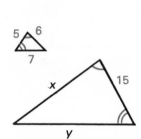

5.

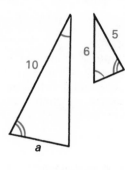

6.

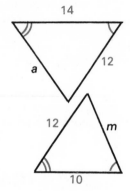

7.

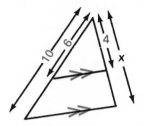

8.

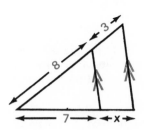

9.

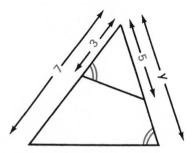

CHAPTER 14

Transformations

Symmetry, as wide or as narrow as you may define its meaning, is one idea by which man through the ages has tried to comprehend and create order, beauty, and perfection.

Hermann Weyl

A *transformation* is a 1:1 mapping which maps the points of a plane onto the points of the same plane. If a point P is mapped into a point P', then we write

$$P \to P'$$

and we call P' the *image* of P under the transformation.

In this chapter we shall study certain kinds of transformations, namely translations, reflections, rotations, and dilatations, which have been found to be useful in such fields as geometry, chemistry, physics, painting, and music.

14.1 TRANSLATIONS

Suppose that we add 5 to the x-component and 8 to the y-component of every point (x, y) in the plane. This describes a transformation which maps the point $P(x, y)$ into the point $P'(x+5, y+8)$. This transformation is called a translation and we can represent it by the notation

$$(x, y) \to (x+5, y+8).$$

Notice that every point in the plane is displaced "five units to the right and eight up" by this translation, and so we can think of the translation as having been defined by the vector [5, 8].

In general:

> Any vector $[a, b]$ defines a translation which maps the point $P(x, y)$ into the image point $P'(x+a, y+b)$, i.e., $(x, y) \to (x+a, y+b)$.

EXAMPLE 1. *Find the images P', Q' of the points $P(1, 1)$ and $Q(4, 2)$ under the translation defined by the vector $[2, -3]$. Compare the slopes and lengths of the line segments PQ and $P'Q'$.*

Solution

The vector $[2, -3]$ gives the translation

$$(x, y) \rightarrow (x+2, y-3).$$

Therefore $(1, 1) \rightarrow (3, -2)$ and $(4, 2) \rightarrow (6, -1)$.

The slope of PQ is $\dfrac{1-2}{1-4} = \dfrac{1}{3}$ and the slope of $P'Q'$ is $\dfrac{-2-(-1)}{3-6} = \dfrac{1}{3}$.

The distance $PQ = \sqrt{(1-2)^2 + (1-4)^2}$

$$= \sqrt{1+9}$$
$$= \sqrt{10},$$

and the distance $P'Q' = \sqrt{(-2+1)^2 + (3-6)^2}$

$$= \sqrt{1+9}$$
$$= \sqrt{10}.$$

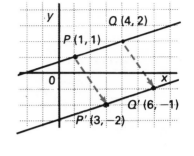

Notice that both the slope and the distance were unchanged under the translation. You will see from the following exercise that, in general, translations preserve distances and slopes (and therefore angles). A mapping which preserves distances and angles is called a *rigid motion*; it maps any geometric figure into a congruent figure.

EXERCISE 14-1

A **1.** Find the images of the following points under the translation

$$(x, y) \rightarrow (x-5, y+3)$$

(a) $(7, 7)$ (b) $(3, -1)$ (c) $(0, 0)$ (d) $(5, -3)$
(e) $(3, 5)$ (f) $(2, -7)$ (g) $(-3, -5)$ (h) $0, -5)$

2. Find the images of the single point $(1, -2)$ under the translation defined by the following vectors.
(a) $[6, 4]$ (b) $[-1, -1]$ (c) $[0, 5]$ (d) $[3, -2]$
(e) $[-2, 3]$ (f) $[5, -3]$ (g) $[4, 7]$ (h) $[0, -3]$

3. State the vector that defines the following translations.
(a) $(3, 5) \rightarrow (7, 8)$ (b) $(1, 1) \rightarrow (11, 9)$
(c) $(-1, 4) \rightarrow (4, 3)$ (d) $(-2, -3) \rightarrow (5, 6)$
(e) $(-4, -5) \rightarrow (-1, 4)$ (f) $(-7, -2) \rightarrow (-5, -8)$
(g) $(0, -6) \rightarrow (5, 0)$ (h) $(-4, 0) \rightarrow (0, 0)$
(i) $(0, 0) \rightarrow (-3, \frac{1}{2})$

15	5	7	17
22	12	13	23
21	11	4	

Determine the pattern. Find the missing number.

B **4.** A translation maps $P(1, -3) \rightarrow P'(3, 4)$.
(a) Find the vector that defines the above translation.
(b) Find the images of the points $A(3, 0)$, $B(-1, 1)$ and $O(0, 0)$ under this translation.

5. Given the three points $A(2, 1)$, $B(1, 6)$, $C(3, 5)$ and the translation $(x, y) \rightarrow (x+4, y+2)$.
(a) Graph $\triangle ABC$.
(b) Find the images A', B', C' of A, B, C under this translation.
(c) Draw $\triangle A'B'C'$ using the same axes as in part (a).
(d) Find the lengths AB, BC, CA, $A'B'$, $B'C'$, $C'A'$.
(e) Show that $\triangle ABC \cong \triangle A'B'C'$.
(f) Find and compare the slopes of the lines AB, BC, CA, $A'B'$, $B'C'$, $C'A'$.

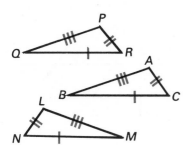

6. Repeat question 5 using the 3 points $A(0,0)$, $B(5,1)$ and $C(2,4)$ and the translation given by the vector $[-2, 1]$.

7. For the triangles illustrated, is there a translation which maps $\triangle ABC \rightarrow \triangle PQR$? Is there a translation which maps $\triangle ABC \rightarrow \triangle LMN$?

8. Draw a circle with centre the origin and radius 5. Pick any four points on the circle and find their images under the translation

$$(x, y) \rightarrow (x, y - 5).$$

Draw the image of the circle under this translation.

C **9.** Points $P(x_1, y_1)$ and $Q(x_2, y_2)$ are mapped into the points P' and Q' under the translation

$$(x, y) \rightarrow (x + a, y + b).$$

Prove that the lines PQ and $P'Q'$ are parallel, and that the line segments PQ and $P'Q'$ have the same length.

10. Find the equation of the image of the line $2x + y = 5$ under the translation

$$(x, y) \rightarrow (x - 1, y + 3).$$

14.2 REFLECTIONS

We see examples of the transformation known as reflection any time we look in a mirror, or in any other shiny surface, even a calm lake.

If you look in a mirror it appears as if the mirror-image of any object is located on the other side of the mirror at an equal distance from the mirror. It also appears as if an imaginary line joining an object to its image intersects the mirror at right angles. In other words, it appears as if the mirror is the perpendicular bisector of the line joining the object to its image.

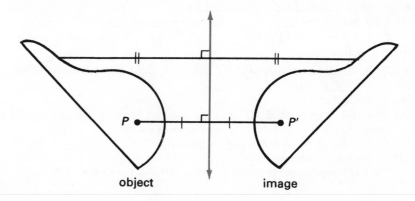

object   image

We use this as the defining property of a reflection:

> Reflection in a line m is the transformation that maps any point P into a point P' such that m is the perpendicular bisector of PP'.

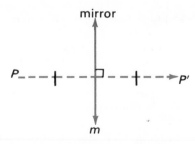

mirror

P ---+---□---+--→ P'

m

The line m is often called the mirror line because it acts like a mirror. We shall indicate mirror lines by double-ended arrows.

EXAMPLE 1. *Find the image of the triangle ABC after reflection in the line m.*

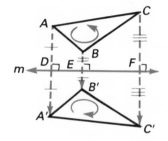

Solution
Draw the line through A perpendicular to m and mark the point A' on this line such that $AD = DA'$. Similarly, draw the lines through B and C perpendicular to m and mark the points B' and C' on them such that $BE = EB'$ and $CF = FC'$. Then the image of the triangle ABC after reflection in the mirror-line m is the triangle $A'B'C'$.

Notice that in Example 1 if ABC is traversed counterclockwise then its image triangle $A'B'C'$ is traversed clockwise. Reflection reverses the sense of direction of a figure.

EXAMPLE 2. *Find the image of the point P(3, 2) under reflection in the x-axis.*

Solution
Here the mirror-line is the x-axis. If $P \rightarrow P'$ under reflection, then the x-axis is perpendicular to PP' and so PP' is parallel to the y-axis. This means that the points P and P' are the same distance from the y-axis. Therefore P' has the same x-coordinate as P, namely 3. Also P and P' must be the same distance from the x-axis but on opposite sides. Since the y-coordinate of P is 2, the y-coordinate of P' must be -2. Thus the image of $P(3, 2)$ is $P'(3, -2)$ after reflection in the x-axis, that is $(3, 2) \rightarrow (3, -2)$.
In general:

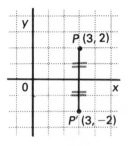

> Reflection in the x-axis maps the point $P(x, y)$ into its mirror-image $P'(x, -y)$, i.e.,
> $$(x, y) \rightarrow (x, -y).$$

EXAMPLE 3. *Find the image of the point P(3, 2) under reflection in the y-axis.*

Solution

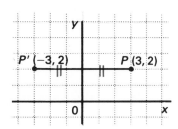

Here the mirror-line is the *y*-axis which is the perpendicular to *P'P*. By reasoning as in Example 2, we see that *P* and *P'* have the same *y*-coordinate, namely 2. *P'* and *P* are the same distance from the *y*-axis but on opposite sides. The *x* coordinate of *P* is 3, and so the *x* coordinate of *P'* must be −3. Thus P(3, 2) → P'(−3, 2).
In general:

> Reflection in the *y*-axis maps the point *P(x, y)* into its mirror-image *P'(−x, y)*, i.e.,
>
> $$(x, y) \to (-x, y).$$

You will see from the following exercise that reflections preserve distances and angles. Therefore reflections, like translations, are rigid motions. Any figure is congruent to its mirror-image.

EXERCISE 14-2

A **1.** Suppose you are standing two metres in front of a mirror.
(a) Where does your reflection appear to be?
(b) If you raise your right hand, which hand of your reflection appears to be raised?
(c) If you part your hair on the left, on which side of your reflection does the hair seem to be parted?

2. State the images of the following points after reflection in the *x*-axis.
(a) (4, 7)   (b) (−2, 9)   (c) (6, 0)   (d) (0, −5)
(e) (−1, −1)   (f) (6, −3)   (g) (8, 1)   (h) (0, 0)

Use +, −, ×, ÷, ( ) to make a true statement.

10 6 1 = 5 3 10

3. State the images of the following points under reflection in the *y*-axis.
(a) (2, 5)   (b) (4, 3)   (c) (−8, 6)   (d) (−1, 2)
(e) (7, 11)   (f) (0, −4)   (g) (6, 0)   (h) (−1, −1)

4. Under a reflection are there any points or lines which are left unchanged?

B **5.** Copy the following figures and draw the reflection of each figure in the given mirror-line.
(a)   (b)   (c)

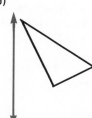

324   fmt : introduction

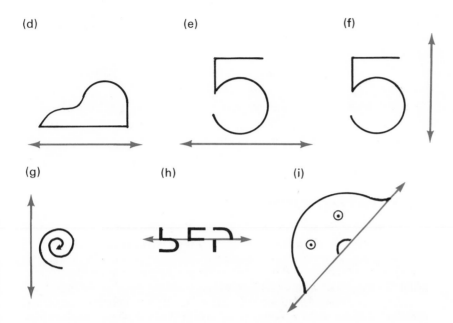

(d)

(e)

(f)

(g)

(h)

(i)

6. Print your initials in capital letters and draw the images in the two mirror lines as shown.

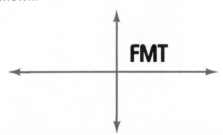

FMT

7. The points $P(-2, -4)$ and $Q(3, 8)$ are reflected in the x-axis.
(a) Find the images P', Q' of P and Q.
(b) Calculate and compare the lengths PQ and $P'Q'$.

8. The points $A(-1, -3)$ and $B(-3, 2)$ are reflected in the y-axis.
(a) Find the images A', B' of A and B.
(b) Calculate and compare the lengths AB and $A'B'$.

9. Given the points $A(-1, 1)$, $B(5, 2)$, $C(3, 4)$.
(a) Graph $\triangle ABC$.
(b) Find the images A', B', C' of A, B, C under reflection in the x-axis.
(c) Draw $\triangle A'B'C'$ using the same axes as in part (a).
(d) Find the lengths AB, BC, CA, $A'B'$, $B'C'$, $C'A'$.
(e) Show that $\triangle ABC \cong \triangle A'B'C'$.
(f) Repeat parts (b), (c), (d), (e) for reflection in the y-axis.

10. The triangle with vertices $A(-1, -1)$, $B(6, -1)$, $C(6, 5)$ is reflected in the x-axis.
(a) Find the vertices of the image of this triangle.
(b) Find and compare the areas of the triangle and its image.

11. Using a graph, find the image of the point $(7, 2)$ after reflection in the following lines.

(a) $x = 4$ (b) $y = 4$

C **12.** Find the image of the point $(7, 2)$ after reflection in the lines

(a) $y = x$ (b) $x + y = 0$

13. Find the image of the point (a, b) after reflection in the line $y = x$.

14. The points $P(a, b)$ and $Q(c, d)$ are reflected in the x-axis giving the images P', Q'. Prove that the lengths PQ and $P'Q'$ are the same.

15. The points $P(a, b)$ and $Q(c, d)$ are reflected in the y-axis giving the images P', Q'. Prove that $P'Q' = PQ$.

14.3 ROTATIONS

The word *rotation* has the same meaning in mathematics as it does in everyday life. We see examples of it any time we look at the wheels of a moving car or the hands of a clock.

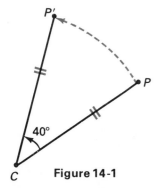

Figure 14-1

In Figure 14-1 a point P has been rotated counterclockwise about the point C through an angle of 40° to a new position P'. P' is the image of P under the rotation. Notice that $CP = CP'$. C is called the *centre of rotation*. The angle of rotation is 40°. Note that the same result could have been achieved by a clockwise rotation of 320°. Then we would say that the angle of rotation is −320°. The convention is that a *counterclockwise rotation is positive* and a *clockwise rotation is negative*.

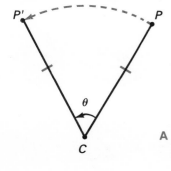

> A rotation about a point C through an angle θ is the transformation that maps any point P into a point P' such that
>
> $$\angle PCP' = \theta \quad \text{and} \quad CP = CP'.$$

If $\theta = 90°$, then the rotation is called a *quarter-turn*, and if $\theta = 180°$, the rotation is called a *half-turn*.

EXERCISE 13-3

A **1.** In the following diagrams P' is the image of P under a rotation about C. In each case name two angles of rotation (counterclockwise and clockwise).

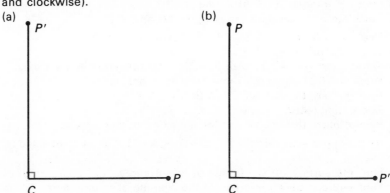

(a)   (b)

What time will the clock show 547 h after 17:00?

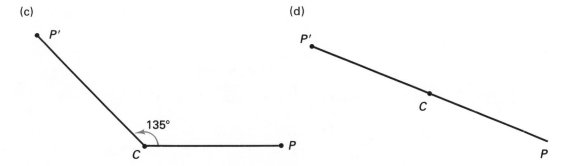

(c)

P'

135°

C   P

(d)

P'

C

P

2. Name rotations which have the same effect as rotations through the following angles.

(a) 60°   (b) 10°   (c) −30°
(d) −270°   (e) 400°   (f) 100°

3. Under a rotation are there any points which are left unchanged?

4. What angles of rotation will cause the following figures to map onto themselves if *C* is the centre of rotation?

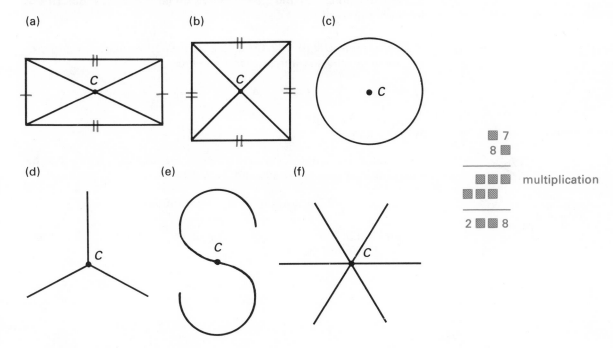

(a)

(b)

(c)

(d)

(e)

(f)

■ 7
8 ■

■ ■ ■   multiplication
■ ■ ■

2 ■ ■ 8

B   **5.** Construct △*ABC* so that ∠*BCA* = 30°, ∠*BAC* = 60°, and *AC* = 4 cm. On the same diagram draw the images of this triangle under rotation about *C* through angles of 90°, 180°, and 270°.

6. Draw an equilateral triangle *ABC*, and on the same diagram draw the images of △*ABC* after rotation about *C* through angles of 60°, 120°, 180°, 240°, and 300°.

7. Complete Table 14-1 in your notebook by finding the image of each given point after rotation about the origin through the given angle.

Point	Angle of Rotation		
	90°	180°	270°
$A(1, 0)$			
$B(2, 1)$			
$C(3, 4)$			
$D(-1, 3)$			
$P(x, y)$			

Table 14-1

8. Find the image of the point $P(5, 7)$ under rotation about $C(3, 4)$ through angles of
(a) 90°   (b) 180°   (c) 270°

9. The triangle $O(0,0)$, $P(2, 0)$, $Q(2, 2)$ is rotated through an angle of 45° about 0. Find the image triangle $O'P'Q'$.

10. In Figure 14-2, $P \rightarrow P'$ and $Q \rightarrow Q'$ under a rotation about C of θ. Prove that
(a) $\triangle CPQ \cong \triangle CP'Q'$
(b) $PQ = P'Q'$

This shows that lengths are preserved under rotations. It can also be shown that angles are preserved. It follows that

> Any rotation is a rigid motion.

C **11.** Prove that if $P \rightarrow P'$ under a rotation about C, then C lies on the perpendicular bisector of PP'.

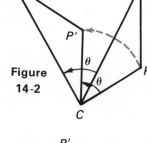

Figure 14-2

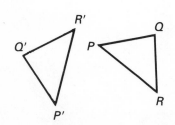

Figure 14-3

12. In Figure 14-3, $\triangle PQR$ is mapped onto $\triangle P'Q'R'$ by a rotation about a point C. Use question 11 to find C.

14.4 COMPOSITION OF TRANSFORMA-TIONS

So far we have only looked at images of figures under single transfor-mations. In this section we apply two or more transformations succes-sively. For example, Figure 14-4 shows the result of first reflecting a point P in a mirror line m and then rotating the image point P' through 90° giving a new point P''. The reflection is described by $P \rightarrow P'$ and the rotation is written as $P' \rightarrow P''$. The new transformation obtained by first reflecting and then rotating is written as $P \rightarrow P''$. It is called the *composition* of the two transformations. Let us call the reflection F and the rotation R. Then the composition is denoted by $R \circ F$. Note that F is performed first and then R is performed.

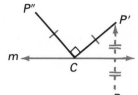

Figure 14-4

Does the order of F and R matter? Let us see by reversing the order and finding the transformation $F \circ R$. This means that we first rotate and then reflect. In Figure 14-5 we first rotate P through 90° about C and then reflect in m. P' obviously has different locations in Figures 14-4 and 14-5, and so $F \circ R$ and $R \circ F$ and different transformations.

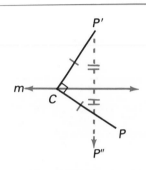

Figure 14-5

> If a transformation T_1 maps $P \rightarrow P'$ and a transformation T_2 maps $P' \rightarrow P''$, then the transformation $T_2 \circ T_1$ obtained by apply-ing first T_1, then T_2, is called the composition of T_1 and T_2 and maps $P \rightarrow P''$.

EXAMPLE 1. *If T is the translation $(x, y) \rightarrow (x+5, y-3)$ and F is reflection in the y-axis, find the image of the point $P(1, 1)$ under the transformations*
(a) $F \circ T$ (b) $T \circ F$ (c) $T \circ T$

Solution
(a) Under T, $(1, 1) \rightarrow (6, -2)$ and under F, $(6, -2) \rightarrow (-6, -2)$. Therefore under $F \circ T$, $(1, 1) \rightarrow (-6, -2)$.
(b) Under F, $(1, 1) \rightarrow (-1, 1)$ and under T, $(-1, 1) \rightarrow (4, -2)$. Therefore under $T \circ F$, $(1, 1) \rightarrow (4, -2)$.
(c) Under T, $(1, 1) \rightarrow (6, -2)$ and under T, $(6, -2) \rightarrow (11, -5)$. So under $T \circ T$, $(1, 1) \rightarrow (11, 5)$.

In example 1 the transformations $T \circ F$ and $F \circ T$ had different effects on P. This reminds us to be careful of the order in applying transfor-mations.

EXERCISE 14-4

B **1.** Copy the following figures. If *L* is reflection in *l* and *M* is reflection in *m*, draw the images of these figures under *L* ∘ *M* and *M* ∘ *L*.

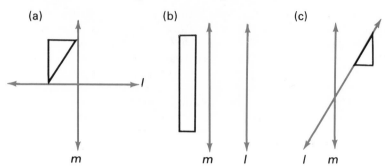

(a)   (b)   (c)

2. Given that *R* is rotation about *C* of 90°

     M is reflection in *m*, copy Figure 14-6 and draw the images of △*DEF* under the following transformations.

(a) *R*   (b) *M*   (c) *R* ∘ *M*

(d) *M* ∘ *R*   (e) *R* ∘ *R*   (f) *M* ∘ *M*

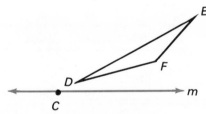

Figure 14-6

3. Given that

     L is reflection in *l*

     M is reflection in *m*

     R is rotation of 180° about 0,

copy Figure 14-7 and draw the images of △*OPQ* under the following transformations.

(a) *L* ∘ *M*   (b) *M* ∘ *L*   (c) *R*   (d) *M* ∘ *M*

(e) *R* ∘ *R*   (f) *R* ∘ *L*   (g) *R* ∘ *M*

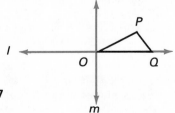

Figure 14-7

4. Given that

    F is reflection in the x-axis,
    G is reflection in the y-axis,
    T is the translation $(x, y) \rightarrow (x - 2, y + 3)$,
    R is rotation through $180°$ about the origin,

complete Table 14-2 in your notebook by finding the coordinates of the images of the given points under the given transformations.

	$A(1, 2)$	$B(3, 0)$	$C(-2, 5)$	$P(x, y)$
$T \circ T$				
R				
$F \circ G$				
$G \circ F$				
$T \circ R$				
$R \circ T$				
$T \circ F$				
$F \circ T$				

Table 14-2

5. What do you conclude by comparing parts (a), (b), and (c) of question 3 and rows R, $F \circ G$, $G \circ F$ of Table 14-2?

6. (a) If T is the translation defined by the vector $[2, 1]$ and S is the translation defined by the vector $[3, 5]$ find the images of the following points under $S \circ T$.
(i) $(1, 1)$ (ii) $(-2, 3)$ (iii) $(6, 4)$ (iv) (x, y)
(b) If T is the translation defined by the vector $\vec{a}$ and S is the translation defined by the vector $\vec{b}$, describe the transformation $S \circ T$.

7. If M and L are reflections in lines m and l, where m and l are parallel, what kind of transformation is $M \circ L$?

8. If R_θ means a rotation about C of $\theta°$, what is
(a) $R_{30} \circ R_{60}$ (b) $R_{45} \circ R_{70}$ (c) $R_\theta \circ R_\alpha$?

9. Suppose T is a translation, F is a reflection, and R is a rotation. Which of the following transformations are rigid motions? Explain.
(a) $T \circ F$ (b) $F \circ R$ (c) $R \circ T$

14.5 SYMMETRY

Tyger! Tyger! burning bright
In the forests of the night,
What immortal hand or eye
Dare frame thy fearful symmetry?

William Blake (1757-1827)

Figure 14-8

Artists use the word symmetry to indicate a kind of pleasing balance or harmony in painting, sculpture, architecture, or nature. The human body, a snowflake, a honeycomb, and many great works of art possess a sense of order, regularity, and balance that we call symmetry.

How can mathematics give a precise meaning to this word? There are two kinds of symmetry that we shall discuss—reflectional symmetry and rotational symmetry.

The design in Figure 14-8 has the property that it is unchanged when reflected in *m*, i.e., reflection in *m* maps the design onto itself. We say that *m* is a line of symmetry and that the design is symmetric about *m*.

> A figure is called *symmetric about a line m* if the figure is mapped onto itself by reflection in *m*. This kind of symmetry is called *reflectional symmetry* (or *line symmetry*) and *m* is called the *line of symmetry* (or *axis of symmetry*.)

Is it possible for a figure to have more than one line of symmetry?

EXAMPLE 1. How many lines of symmetry does an equilateral triangle have?

Solution

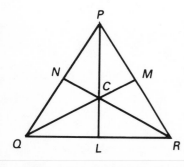

Given the equilateral triangle *PQR*, draw the medians *PL, QM, RN*. Then △*PLR* ≅ △*PLQ* and so *PL* is the perpendicular bisector of *QR*. This means that the image of △*PLQ* after reflection in *PL* is △*PLR*, and the image of △*PLR* is △*PLQ*. Thus △*PQR* is symmetric about the median *PL*. Similarly △*PQR* is symmetric about the other two medians *QM* and *RN*. Therefore an equilateral triangle has three lines of symmetry.

In example 1, △*PQR* also has the property that it is unchanged when rotated about *C* through 120° or 240° or 360°. We say that △*PQR* has rotational symmetry of order three.

A figure is called *symmetric about a point C* if the figure is mapped onto itself by a rotation with centre C. This kind of symmetry is called *rotational symmetry of order n* if there are n rotations which map the figure onto itself.

The human body has reflectional symmetry (perhaps imperfect), but not rotational symmetry. A snowflake possesses both types of symmetry. Most snowflakes have six lines of symmetry and also have rotational symmetry of order six. Perhaps the mathematical laws which govern nature are the source of symmetry in nature.

EXERCISE 14-5

A **1.** Which of the following figures possess reflectional symmetry or rotational symmetry? In each case state the number of lines of symmetry or the order of rotational symmetry.

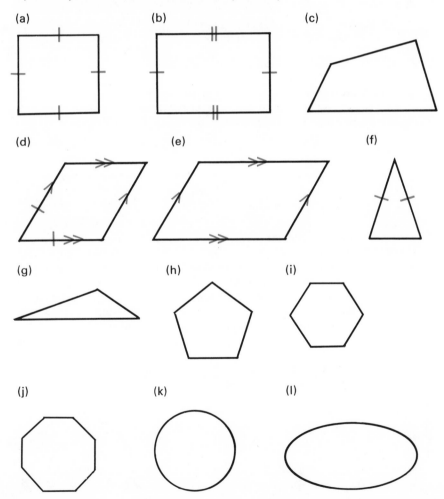

(a) (b) (c)

(d) (e) (f)

(g) (h) (i)

(j) (k) (l)

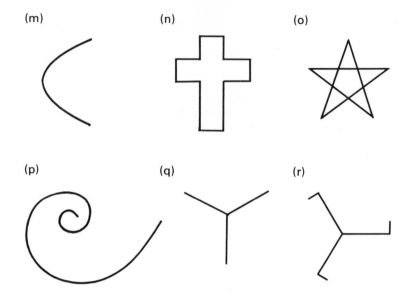

(m)   (n)   (o)

(p)   (q)   (r)

B   **2.** (a) List the capital letters of the alphabet which are symmetric about a vertical line.
(b) Which are symmetric about a horizontal line?
(c) Which are symmetric about both vertical and horizontal lines?
(d) Which possess rotational symmetry?

14.6 DILATATIONS

If you wash a new pair of jeans in very hot water, they will probably shrink. We say that the jeans have undergone a dilatation because they are the same shape but smaller. If you look at some object through a microscope it appears many times enlarged. We say the object has undergone a dilatation because it appears to have the same shape but is larger. We have an example of a dilatation anytime that something is enlarged, magnified, contracted, or shrunk.

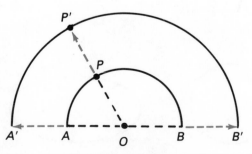

Figure 14-9

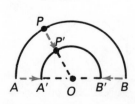

Figure 14-10

Figure 14-9 shows a semicircle *APB* with centre *O* and a magnified semicircle *A'P'B'*. The distance *OA'* is twice the distance *OA* and *OB'* = 2(*OB*). In fact all of the points on the larger semicircle, such as *P'*, were obtained by drawing a line through *O* and *P* and then locating the point *P'* on it so that *OP'* = 2(*OP*). The transformation *P* → *P'* is called a dilatation by a factor of 2.

In Figure 14-10, however, the image semicircle *A'P'B'* is smaller than the original semicircle *APB*. In fact, here *OA'* = $\frac{1}{2}$*OA*, *OB'* = $\frac{1}{2}$*OB*, and *OP'* = $\frac{1}{2}$*OP*. The transformation *P* → *P'* is called a dilatation by a factor of $\frac{1}{2}$.

A dilatation is a transformation which maps any point *P* into a point *P'* such that *OP'* = *kOP* and *O*, *P*, and *P'* are collinear. The fixed point *O* is called the *centre of the dilatation*, and the number *k* is called the *factor*, (or *dilatation factor*, or *magnification factor*).

EXAMPLE 1. *In Figure 14-11 find the image of △ABC under the dilatation with centre O and magnification factor 4.*

Solution
Draw the line *OA* and mark the point *A'* on *OA* such that *OA'* = 4(*OA*). Similarly, we draw *OB* and *OC* and mark the points *B'* on *OB* and *C'* on *OC* such that *OB'* = 4(*OB*) and *OC'* = 4(*OC*). Then △*A'B'C'* is the image of △*ABC* under the dilatation.

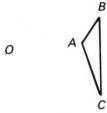

Figure 14-11

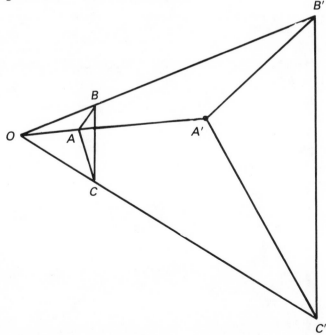

EXAMPLE 2. *Graph the image triangle* $A'B'C'$ *of the triangle* $A(0, -1)$, $B(-1, 2)$, $C(1, 1)$ *under the dilatation with centre* $O(0,0)$ *and factor* 3. *Show that*

$$(a) \quad \frac{A'B'}{AB} = \frac{B'C'}{BC} = \frac{C'A'}{CA} = 3,$$

$$(b) \quad A'B' \parallel AB, \quad B'C' \parallel BC, \quad C'A' \parallel CA.$$

$$(c) \quad \triangle A'B'C' \sim \triangle ABC.$$

Solution

As in example 1, we draw A', B', C' so that $OA' = 3(OA)$, $OB' = 3(OB)$, $OC' = 3(OC)$, and we find that the image vertices are $A'(0, -3)$, $B'(-3, 6)$, and $C'(3, 3)$.

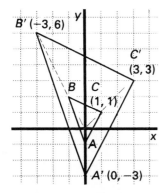

(a) $A'B' = \sqrt{(0+3)^2 + (-3-6)^2}$
$= \sqrt{9+81}$
$= \sqrt{90}$
$= 3\sqrt{10}$

$AB = \sqrt{(0+1)^2 + (-1-2)^2}$
$= \sqrt{1+9}$
$= \sqrt{10}$

So $\dfrac{A'B'}{AB} = \dfrac{3\sqrt{10}}{\sqrt{10}}$.
$= 3$

$B'C' = \sqrt{(-3-3)^2 + (6-3)^2}$
$= \sqrt{36+9}$
$= \sqrt{45}$
$= 3\sqrt{5}$

$BC = \sqrt{(-1-1)^2 + (2-1)^2}$
$= \sqrt{4+1}$
$= \sqrt{5}$

So $\dfrac{B'C'}{BC} = \dfrac{3\sqrt{5}}{5}$
$= 3.$

$C'A' = \sqrt{(3-0)^2 + (3+3)^2}$
$= \sqrt{9+36}$
$= \sqrt{45}$
$= 3\sqrt{5}$

$CA = \sqrt{(1-0)^2 + (1+1)^2}$
$= \sqrt{1+4}$
$= \sqrt{5}$

So $\dfrac{C'A'}{CA} = \dfrac{3\sqrt{5}}{\sqrt{5}}$
$= 3.$

(b) Slope $A'B' = \dfrac{-3-6}{0+3}$
$= \dfrac{-9}{3}$
$= -3$

Slope $AB = \dfrac{-1-2}{0+1}$
$= -3$

Therefore $A'B' \parallel AB.$

Slope $B'C' = \dfrac{6-3}{-3-3}$ Slope $BC = \dfrac{2-1}{-1-1}$

$\qquad = \dfrac{3}{-6}$ $\qquad = -\frac{1}{2}$

$\qquad = -\frac{1}{2}$

Therefore $B'C' \parallel BC$.

Slope $C'A' = \dfrac{3+3}{3-0}$ Slope $CA = \dfrac{1+1}{1-0}$

$\qquad = \frac{6}{3}$ $\qquad = 2$

$\qquad = 2$

Therefore $C'A' \parallel CA$.

(c) Since $B'C' \parallel BC$, we have $\angle OB'C' = \angle OBC$.   corresponding angles

Since $A'B' \parallel AB$, we have $\angle OB'A' = \angle OBA$.

$$\angle OB'C' + \angle OB'A' = \angle OBC + \angle OBA$$

Thus $\angle A'B'C' = \angle ABC$

Similarly $\angle B'C'A' = \angle BCA$ and

$\angle C'A'B' = \angle CAB$.

Therefore $\triangle A'B'C' \sim \triangle ABC$.

Example 2 suggests, and Exercise 14-6 confirms that

> Under a dilatation with factor k, all distances are magnified by a factor k, and the image of any triangle is a similar triangle.

EXAMPLE 3.   *What are the coordinates of the image P' of the point P(x, y) under the dilatation with centre O(0, 0) and factor k?*

Solution
We shall give the solution for the case where $x > 0$ and $y > 0$, but similar reasoning gives the same answer for any position of $P(x, y)$.
We know that $OP' = kOP$.
Let the coordinates of P' be x' and y'.
Draw the perpendiculars PQ, $P'Q'$ to the x-axis.
Then $\triangle OPQ \sim \triangle OP'Q'$ and so

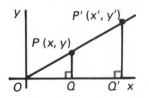

$$\frac{OQ'}{OQ} = \frac{P'Q'}{PQ} = \frac{OP'}{OP} = k.$$

If

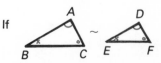

But $OQ' = x'$ and $OQ = x$, and so the equation $OQ' = kOQ$ becomes $x' = kx$. Also $P'Q' = y'$ and $PQ = y$, and so $P'Q' = kPQ$ becomes $y' = ky$. Therefore the coordinates of P are kx and ky.

then $\dfrac{AB}{DE} = \dfrac{BC}{EF} = \dfrac{CA}{FD}$

The result of example 3 is summarized as follows.

> Under a dilatation with centre $O(0, 0)$ and magnification factor k, we have
>
> $$(x, y) \rightarrow (kx, ky).$$

EXAMPLE 4. *Use the result of example 3 to find the image of the triangle $P(2, 2)$, $Q(4, 0)$, $R(2, -1)$ under the dilatation with centre $O(0, 0)$ and magnification factor*
(a) $k = \frac{1}{2}$ (b) $k = -2$.

Solution
(a) We have $(x, y) \rightarrow (\frac{1}{2}x, \frac{1}{2}y)$, and so $P(2, 2) \rightarrow P'(1, 1)$, $Q(4, 0) \rightarrow Q'(2, 0)$, and $R(2, -1) \rightarrow R'(1, -\frac{1}{2})$.
(b) We have $(x, y) \rightarrow (-2x, -2y)$, and so $P(2, 2) \rightarrow P'(-4, -4)$, $Q(4, 0) \rightarrow Q'(-8, 0)$, and $R(2, -1) \rightarrow R'(-4, 2)$.

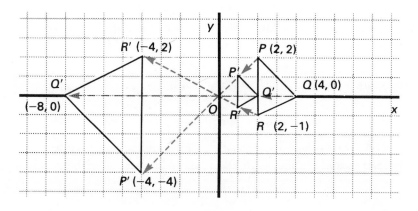

Observe that, in example 4 and in the following exercise, if $k > 0$, then P and P' are on the same side of O, but if $k < 0$, then P and P' are on opposite sides of O.

EXERCISE 14-6

A **1.** State the images of the following points under the dilatation with centre $O(0, 0)$ and magnification factor 3.
(a) $(1, 1)$ (b) $(3, -1)$ (c) $(0, 2)$
(d) $(-5, -2)$ (e) $(-1, \frac{1}{3})$ (f) (a, b)

3. State the images of the following points under the dilatation $(x, y) \rightarrow (\frac{1}{2}x, \frac{1}{2}y)$.
(a) $(6, 2)$ (b) $(-2, 0)$ (c) $(-8, -4)$
(d) $(1, 9)$ (e) $(2, -3)$ (f) (a, b)

3. State the images of the following points under the dilatation with centre $O(0, 0)$ and factor $k = -5$.

(a) $(1, 1)$ (b) $(0, 6)$ (c) $(-2, 9)$

(d) $(6, \frac{4}{5})$ (e) $(-7, -1)$ (f) (a, b)

How many words can you find that contain the letter sequence ARO?

4. Under a dilatation how many points are left unchanged? Are there any lines which are left unchanged?

B   **5.** Copy each of the following figures and construct their images under the dilatation with given centre O and given dilatation factor k.

(a) $k = 3$ (b) $k = 2$ (c) $k = -1$

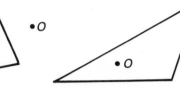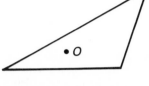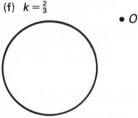

(d) $k = \frac{1}{2}$ (e) $k = 2$ (f) $k = \frac{2}{3}$

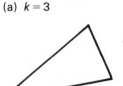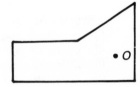

(g) $k = 3$ (h) $k = -2$ (i) $k = 1$

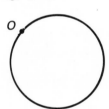

6. Given the triangle $A(-1, -1)$, $B(0, 1)$, $C(3, 2)$ and the dilatation with centre $O(0, 0)$ and factor 2.

(a) Find the vertices A', B', C' of the image of $\triangle ABC$ under the dilatation.

(b) Graph $\triangle ABC$ and $\triangle A'B'C'$.

(c) Find and compare the lengths of the sides of the two triangles.

(d) Show that corresponding sides of the two triangles are parallel.

(e) Prove that the angles of $\triangle ABC$ are equal to the angles of $\triangle A'B'C'$ so that $\triangle ABC \sim \triangle A'B'C'$.

7. Given the triangle $A(1, 1)$, $B(6, 1)$, $C(6, 5)$ and the dilatation with centre $O(0, 0)$ and factor 3.

(a) Find the vertices A', B', C' of the image triangle under the dilatation.

(b) Find and compare the lengths of the sides of the two triangles.

(c) Find the areas of $\triangle A'B'C'$ and $\triangle ABC$.

(d) Find the ratio of the areas of triangles $A'B'C'$ and ABC.

8. A dilatation maps $A \to A'$, $B \to B'$, $C \to C'$. If $AB = 6$, $BC = 9$, $CA = 4$, and $A'B' = 2$, find

(a) the dilatation factor k, (b) $B'C'$, (c) $C'A'$.

9. Given that

    D is dilatation with centre $O(0, 0)$ and factor 2,

    T is the translation $(x, y) \to (x+1, y+3)$,

    F is reflection in the x-axis,

    R is rotation through $180°$,

find, and graph, the image of the triangle $A(1, 1)$, $B(2, 3)$, $C(3, 2)$ under the following transformations.

(a) $D \circ T$ (b) $T \circ D$ (c) $D \circ F$ (d) $R \circ D$

C **10.** Suppose that under the dilatation $(x, y) \to (kx, ky)$ the image of $P(a, b)$ is P' and the image of $Q(c, d)$ is Q'. Show that

(a) $P'Q' = kPQ$ (b) $P'Q' \parallel PQ$

11. The image of triangle $A(-2, -1)$, $B(-2, 2)$, $C(4, -1)$ under the dilatation with factor k and centre $O(0, 0)$ is $A'B'C'$. Show that the ratio of the area of $\triangle A'B'C'$ to the area of $\triangle ABC$ is k^2.

REVIEW EXERCISE

A **1.** What kinds of transformations are the following?

(a) $(x, y) \to (x-2, y+3)$ (b) $(x, y) \to (x, -y)$

(c) $(x, y) \to (8x, 8y)$ (d) $(x, y) \to (x, y-1)$

(e) $(x, y) \to (-x, -y)$ (f) $(x, y) \to (-x, y)$

2. State the images of the following points under the transformations

  (i) reflection in the x-axis,

  (ii) dilatation with centre $O(0, 0)$ and factor 3,

  (iii) translation defined by the vector $[2, -4]$,

  (iv) reflection in the y-axis,

  (v) rotation through $180°$ about the origin.

(a) $(0, 0)$ (b) $(3, 4)$ (c) $(-2, 1)$ (d) $(-6, -6)$

(e) $(0, 5)$ (f) $(1, -1)$ (g) $(6, \frac{1}{2})$ (h) (a, b)

3. What transformations will map triangle 1 onto the other triangles in Figure 13-12?

Figure 14-12

How many words of four letters or more can you form using the letters in the word CARTESIAN?

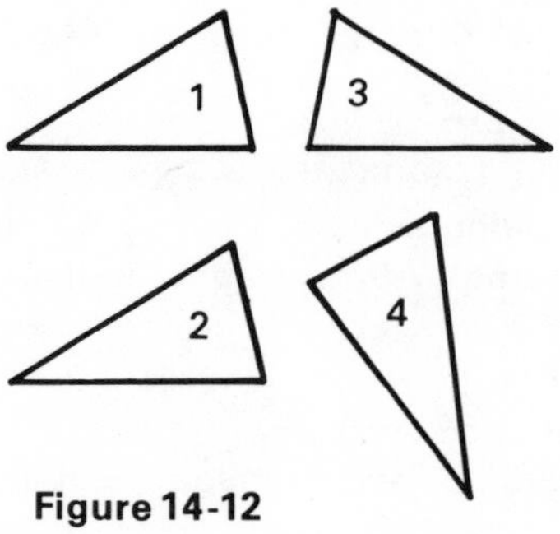

4. For each of the following figures, state the number of lines of symmetry and the order of rotational symmetry.

(a)   (b)   (c)

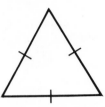 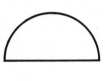

5. Which of the following transformations are rigid motions?

(a) translation   (b) rotation   (c) reflection   (d) dilatation

B   **6.** Copy the following figures and draw their images under
  (i)   rotation about O through 60°,
  (ii) dilatation with centre O and factor 2,
  (iii) reflection in m.

(a)   (b)   (c)

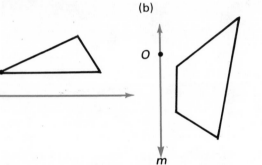 

7. Given the triangle $A(1,0)$, $B(2,5)$, $C(4,1)$ and the transformations
  (i)   reflection in the x-axis,
  (ii) the translation $(x, y) \rightarrow (x+1, y+4)$,
  (iii) dilatation with centre $O(0,0)$ and factor 3.

(a) Graph $\triangle ABC$ and its images under each of the transformations.
(b) Calculate the lengths of the sides of all four triangles.

8. Copy the following figures. If L is reflection in l and M is reflection in m, draw the images of these figures under the transformations L, M, $L \circ M$, and $M \circ L$.

(a)   (b)   (c)

 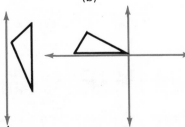

How many words can you find that contain the letter sequence ORP?

9. If F is reflection in the x-axis,

T is the translation $(x, y) \rightarrow (x+2, y-1)$,

D is the dilatation $(x, y) \rightarrow (\frac{1}{2}x, \frac{1}{2}y)$,

R is rotation through $180°$ about the origin,

complete Table 13-3 in your notebook by finding the coordinates of the images of the given points under the given transformations.

	$A(-2, -2)$	$B(4, 6)$	$C(2, 8)$	$P(x, y)$
F				
R				
T				
D				
$T \circ D$				
$D \circ T$				
$F \circ R$				
$D \circ F$				
$F \circ D$				
$D \circ D$				
$D \circ R$				
$F \circ T$				

Table 14-3

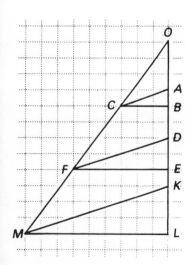

10. (a) Show that $\triangle ABC$, $\triangle DEF$, and $\triangle KLM$ are all similar.

(b) Show that $\triangle OBC$, $\triangle OEF$, and $\triangle OLM$ are all similar.

(c) Find the dilatation factor k for the following dilatations with centre O:

$\triangle ABC \rightarrow \triangle DEF$

$\triangle DEF \rightarrow \triangle KLM$

$\triangle KLM \rightarrow \triangle ABC$

$\triangle OEF \rightarrow \triangle OBC$

11. Copy the following figures and draw their reflections in the given mirror line.

(a)   (b)   (c)

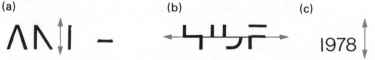

12. Find the centre of the rotation which maps triangle 1 onto triangle 4 in Figure 14-12.

REVIEW AND PREVIEW TO CHAPTER 15

PERCENT

EXERCISE 1

Express each of the following as (a) common fractions
(b) decimals.

1. 25%   **2.** 75%   **3.** $33\frac{1}{3}$%
4. 10%   **5.** 65%   **6.** 120%
7. 85%   **8.** 225%   **9.** 5%
10. 1.5%   **11.** 10.5%   **12.** $66\frac{2}{3}$%
12. $12\frac{1}{2}$%   **14.** 37.5%   **15.** 62.5%

EXERCISE 2

Express each of the following as a percent.

1. $\frac{2}{5}$ **2.** $\frac{3}{4}$ **3.** $\frac{7}{10}$ **4.** $\frac{3}{20}$
5. $\frac{3}{50}$ **6.** 0.25   **7.** 1.75   **8.** 0.575
9. 0.345   **10.** 2.025   **11.** 0.625   **12.** $\frac{1}{8}$
13. $\frac{3}{8}$ **14.** $1\frac{1}{4}$ **15.** $3\frac{7}{8}$

EXERCISE 3

Evaluate

1. 5% of 20   **2.** 18% of 24   **3.** 9% of 82
4. 125% of 600   **5.** 12% of 12   **6.** 5% of 3.75
7. $12\frac{1}{2}$% of 64   **8.** 62.5% of 88.8   **9.** 28% of 50
10. 45% of 1400   **11.** $1\frac{1}{2}$% of 240   **12.** $\frac{1}{3}$% of 330
13. $6\frac{1}{2}$% of 1800   **14.** $16\frac{2}{3}$% of 6600   **15.** $32\frac{1}{2}$% of 1000
16. 0.5% of 2500

17. How many students were absent from a school of 1450 with an absentee rate of 8%?

18. How much would you pay for a car listing at $8225 with a 17% fleet discount?

19. How much is a used car worth today if it cost $5680 when new and if it depreciated at a rate of 30%/a for the past three years?

20. How much would you charge for a $250 pump to make a 35% profit?

EXERCISE 4

Find the rate percent.

1. What percent of 24 is 9?

2. 6 is what percent of 35?

3. 24 is what percent of 18?

4. What percent is 12 of 36?

5. What percent is 13 of 65?

6. What percent of 18 is 30?

7. A merchant buys sweaters for $15.50 and sells them for $24.50. What was the percent markup?

8. A person earning $850/mon received a raise of $60/mon. What was the percent raise?

9. A class takes 4 min to get to work in a 70 min period. What percent of time is lost?

10. In 1940 a house sold for $3500, and in 1977 it was sold again for $28 000. Express the increase in value as a percent.

Statistics

CHAPTER 15

Number rules the universe.

Pythagoras

Statistics is the science of collecting, organizing, and interpreting collections of facts or numbers called data. Graphs are often used to display statistical information just as in previous chapters where graphs were helpful in analyzing relations and functions.

15.1 SAMPLING AND SURVEYING

When a TV producer wishes to determine public reaction to a new program, he finds it impractical to survey every viewer. He then selects a small group, called a *sample*, and asks these people for their reaction. He uses their comments to generalize for all television viewers. Hence we say that a *sample* is a small group of individuals (or objects) selected to stand for a larger group called the *population* The person who samples a population must ensure that the sample is
1. large enough to be typical of the population,
2. selected at random.

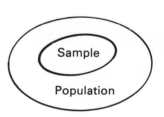

EXAMPLE 1. *The community college conducted a survey of the high school backgrounds of its first year students. The number of students surveyed was* 100 *and the data was collected.*

30 *took art*   19 *took music and French*
46 *took music*   11 *took art and French*
57 *took French*   8 *took art, music, and French*
15 *took art and music*

(*a*) *How many students did not take art, music, or French?*
(*b*) *How many students took French only?*
(*c*) *How many students took music and art with no French?*

Solution
The data can be sorted using a Venn Diagram.

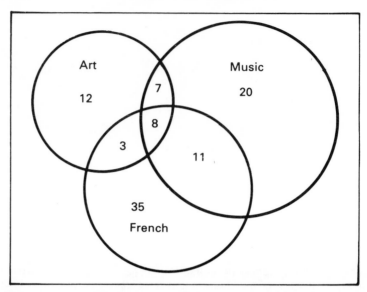

9	6	15	14
4	4	2	2
12	12	10	7
3	2		4

Determine the pattern. Find the missing number.

(a) Number of students who did not take art, music, or French is

$$100-(12+7+8+3+11+20+35)=100-96$$
$$=4$$

(b) Number of students who took French only is

$$57-(8+3+11)=57-22$$
$$=35$$

(c) Number of students who took music and art with no French is

$$15-8=7$$

EXERCISE 15-1

A **1.** State the reason why a sample is used rather than the entire population in each of the following:

(a) The Buck Shot Ammunition Company tests one bullet in every two hundred by actual firing.

(b) The East Bay Exploration Company tests ore samples to determine the value of the ore body.

(c) The Pacer Poll Company is commissioned to determine the popularity of the president of the United States.

(d) The Maison Bleu Winery employs a wine taster to determine the quality of the wine.

(e) The Fish and Game Association tags wild geese to determine their migratory habits.

2. The Sure Jump Parachute Company tests every chute before shipping. LIst three other examples where it is necessary to test the entire population rather than use a sample.

3. Give an example of a problem that could arise when:
(a) The sample is too small.
(b) The sample is too large.
(c) The members of the sample are not selected at random.

4. Examination of 350 samples of ore revealed the contents to be as follows
144 contain gold
134 contain silver
143 contain zinc
40 contain gold and silver
37 contain gold and zinc
46 contain silver and zinc
15 contain gold, silver and zinc
(a) How many samples contained no gold, silver, or zinc?
(b) How many samples contained only gold?
(c) How many samples contained gold and silver with no zinc?

5. The following data was collected to determine the magazine reading habits of 125 students.
41 read *Seventeen*
68 read *Rolling Stone*
48 read *Sport*
14 read *Seventeen* and *Rolling Stone*
3 read *Seventeen* and *Sport*
17 read *Rolling Stone* and *Sport*
1 read *Seventeen, Rolling Stone*, and *Sport*.
(a) How many students read only *Seventeen*?
(b) How many students read only *Rolling Stone*?
(c) How many students read *Seventeen* and *Sport*, but not *Rolling Stone*?
(d) How many students read none of these?

Use $+$, $-$, $\times$, $\div$, ( ) to make a true statement.

3 4 1 5 = 2 4 2 2

15.2 FREQUENCY DISTRIBUTION

When presented with a large mass of data it is convenient to express the information in a frequency distribution table. In order to make the task easier the data is often grouped into classes and all numbers in a given class are treated as though they were equal to the mid-value of the class. The class interval is chosen to give convenient class limits. Following is a table of masses in kilograms for 50 year two students.

48	61	55	56	52	58	55	52	57	51
59	55	54	55	54	58	54	56	52	54
56	56	51	48	51	60	53	59	57	53
55	56	54	57	53	49	54	50	50	58
57	51	56	51	55	53	53	55	56	53

This group of data is difficult to interpret as it is. We make a table with convenient class limits and the number of cases in each class. Such a table is called a frequency distribution table.

MASSES OF YEAR 2 STUDENTS		
CLASS LIMITS	**TALLY**	**FREQUENCY**
48–49	///	3
50–51	//// //	7
52–53	//// ////	9
54–55	//// //// ///	13
56–57	//// //// /	11
58–59	////	5
60–61	//	2

The graph form used for a frequency distribution is a modified form of bar graph called a *histogram*.

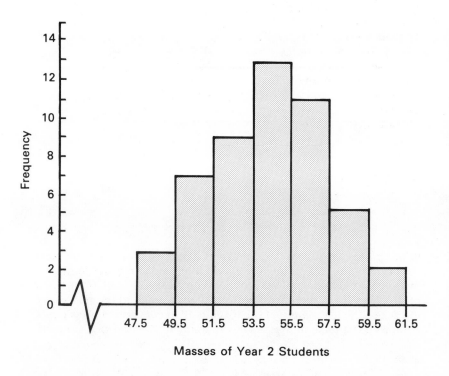

Masses of Year 2 Students

The widths of the bars correspond to the class intervals, and the boundaries are shown halfway between succeeding limits. The graph has a title and the axes are clearly labelled.

If we join the mid-value of each succeeding class we have another form of the graph called a *frequency polygon*.

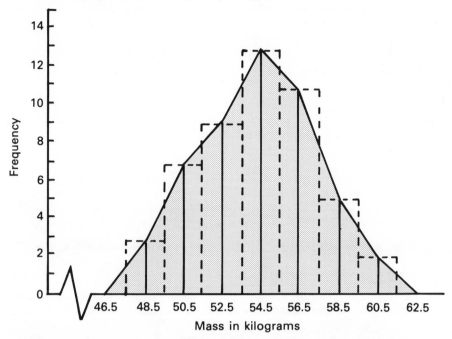

If the group of students was expanded to include all year two students we could estimate that it would more closely reflect the properties of the whole group if it were drawn as a smooth curve.

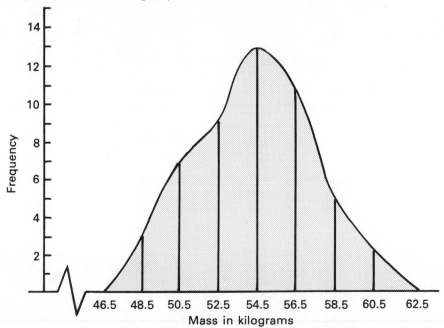

If $3! = 3 \times 2 \times 1$, evaluate $1! + 4! + 5!$

There are many frequency distributions whose graphs are bell shaped curves. We call such a graph a *normal curve* and the frequency distribution a *normal distribution*.

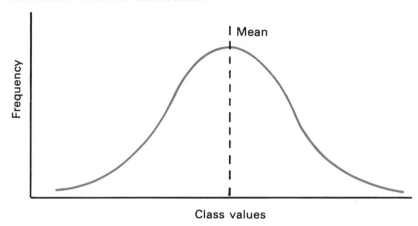

The normal distribution will be discussed further in section 15-4.

EXERCISE 15-2

B **1.** Construct a frequency distribution table for the following set of golf scores, using the classes 70–71, 72–73, 74–75, . . . , 88–89.

75	78	70	82	88	79	78	77
89	78	77	78	82	71	82	81
81	76	84	79	76	81	79	83
79	85	74	80	81	73	74	82
73	83	79	79	74	85	77	85
84	77	83	78	81	80	79	78
79	83	81	88	72	78	81	80
72	78	79	74	84	75	77	82

2. Draw a histogram to illustrate the following data.
Weekly earnings of students ages 13–17 from part-time work.

Earnings	Frequency
0–$10	7
$10–$20	9
$20–$30	10
$30–$40	9
$40–$50	8
$50–$60	6
$60–$70	4
$70–$80	2
$80–$90	1
$90–$100	1
over $100	2

3. The following table contains the number of basketball free throws sunk by 70 students, each taking 100 throws.

60	58	56	61	63	79	58	57	68	41
75	71	69	65	85	58	54	51	61	64
84	79	83	72	61	43	58	42	63	69
92	71	62	50	38	73	65	76	61	73
78	79	42	71	47	45	63	74	39	81
61	75	87	94	46	52	48	59	69	48
21	39	65	75	84	91	32	54	61	73

(a) Make a frequency distribution table using a class interval of 5.
(b) Draw a histogram.

4. A company is considering advertising in local movie houses. In order to analyze the movie going habits of a population, the following data was collected.

Number of movies attended in the past two years.	Frequency
0–4	51
5–9	87
10–14	131
15–19	96
20–24	68
25–29	37
30–34	19
34–39	8
40 and over	3

(a) Prepare a histogram to display the data.
(b) Draw the frequency polygon.
(c) What conclusions concerning the data can you draw from the histogram?

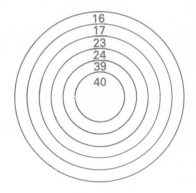

How many arrows will it take to score exactly 100 on this target?

15.3 MEASURE OF CENTRAL TENDENCY

In the previous section we grouped data into classes, then drew graphs of the *frequency distributions* to provide a "picture" to assist in the analysis. Statisticians are able to describe further a mass of data by indicating a centre of the distribution called a *measure of central tendency*. The three measures of central tendency are the *mode*, *median*, and *mean*. In this section you will learn how to find these and also when their use is meaningful.

(i) MODE:

The mode is the value that occurs most frequently in the data. In the following list of numbers:

$$1, 1, 2, 2, 2, \boxed{3, 3, 3, 3, 3,} 4, 4, 4, 5, 5, 5, 6, 6, 7$$

the mode is 3. The use of the mode is limited to cases such as the manager of a shoe store determining how many pairs of shoes of each size to stock. The sales of the most popular sizes would determine how many of each size should be ordered.

(ii) MEDIAN

The median is the mid-value of a group in which all values have been ranked. Knowing the median enables one to tell whether any value is in the top half or bottom half of the group. To find the median of any group of n values, we first arrange the values according to rank then

(i) select the mid-value if *n is odd*

(ii) find the average of the two mid-values if *n is even.*

If there are n values in the group, the median is located in the $\dfrac{n+1}{2}$ position when the data is arranged according to rank. The median is shown in the following groups of ranked data.

(i) n is odd

$$9\ 9\ 10\ 11\ 12\ \textcircled{13}\ 14\ 16\ 17\ 19\ 20$$

$$\frac{11+1}{2} = 6(\text{th position}) \text{ and the median is 13.}$$

(ii) n is even

$$4\ 9\ 9\ 10\ 11\ 11\ 12\ \bigcirc 14\ 15\ 16\ 19\ 20\ 21\ 22$$

$$\frac{14+1}{2} = 7\tfrac{1}{2}\ (\text{position}) \text{ and the median is the average of the 7th and}$$

8th values. $\dfrac{12+14}{2} = 13$ is the median.

(iii) MEAN:

The arithmetic mean is found by dividing the sum of all values in a group by the number of values in the group. For example if Tim Horvath, a basketball player, scored 22, 35, 47, 28, 25, and 35 points in 6 games then his mean score is

$$\frac{22+35+47+28+25+35}{6} = \frac{192}{6} = 32$$

We could now say that Tim "averaged" 32 points per game.

For a set of values $x_1, x_2, x_3, \ldots, x_n$, the mean is

$$\bar{x} = \frac{x_1 + x_2 + x_3 + \ldots + x_3}{n}$$

EXAMPLE 1. *A firm pays the following annual salaries:*
  1 *President at* $75 000
  1 *Vice-President at* $62 000
  1 *Secretary Treasurer at* $56 000
  3 *Accountants at* $40 000
  7 *Salesmen at* $30 000
  8 *Stenographers at* $16 000
Find (a) *the median salary*
     (b) *the mean salary*

Solution
(a) There are 21 people on the payroll, hence the *median* salary is in
the $\dfrac{21 + 1}{2} = 11$th position

The median salary is $30 000

(b) $\bar{x} = \dfrac{x_1 + x_2 + x_3 + \ldots + x_n}{n}$

$\bar{x} = \dfrac{75\,000 + 62\,000 + 56\,000 + \ldots + 16\,000}{21}$

$= \dfrac{651\,000}{21}$

$= 31\,000$

For large masses of data, we can use the following method:

x_i	f	$f \cdot x_i$
75 000	1	75 000
62 000	1	62 000
56 000	1	56 000
40 000	3	120 000
30 000	7	210 000
16 000	8	128 000
Total	21	651 000

$$\bar{x} = \frac{651\,000}{21}$$

$$= 31\,000$$

The mean salary is $31 000.

75 000
62 000
56 000
40 000
40 000
40 000
30 000
30 000
30 000
30 000
30 000
30 000
30 000
16 000
16 000
16 000
16 000
16 000
16 000
16 000
16 000

In the above example, we found the median to be $30 000, the mean to be $31 000, and we see that the mode is $16 000. Which is the better statistic to indicate the level of salary paid by the company?

EXAMPLE 2. *During a chocolate bar sale competition two classes were very close and each group had its own reason for feeling it was the winner. The number of chocolate bars sold by each student is given in the table.*

Class A		Class B	
35	22	33	24
34	20	31	24
30	20	29	23
30	20	29	23
28	20	27	20
26	19	25	19
26	18	25	19
25	16	25	16
22	16	25	16
		24	7

Find the (i) mode, (ii) median, and (iii) mean for each class.

Solution
Class A
  (i) The mode is 20
  (ii) The median is the average of the 9th and 10th values.

$$\frac{22+22}{2} = 22$$

      The median is 22.
  (iii) The mean is

$$\bar{x} = \frac{16+16+18+\ldots+34+35}{18}$$

$$= \frac{427}{18}$$

$$\doteq 23.7$$

Class B
  (i) The mode is 25.
  (ii) The median is the average of the 10th and 11th values

$$\frac{24+24}{2} = 24$$

      The median is 24.

(iii) The mean is

$$\bar{x} = \frac{7 + 16 + 16 + \ldots + 31 + 33}{20}$$

$$= \frac{464}{20}$$

$$= 23.2$$

The results of example 2 are summarized in the following table.

Class	Total	mode	median	mean
A	427	20	22	23.7
B	464	25	24	23.2

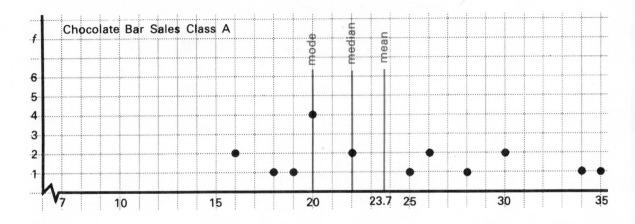

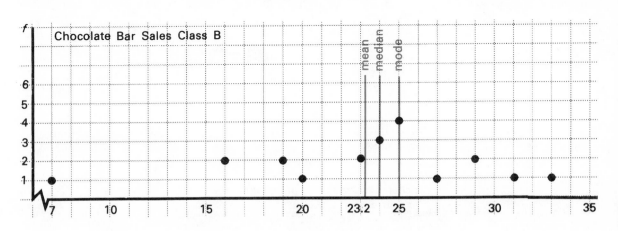

Which figure would you use to determine the winner?

EXERCISE 15-3

EIGHT
F I V E subtraction
FOUR

A **1.** State the measure of central tendency that best describes the following:
(a) level of salary paid by a company. *median*
(b) shoe sizes to be kept in stock. *mode*
(c) the mass of an offensive line on a football team. *mean*
(d) the number of cubic metres per hectare of corn. *mean*
(e) a set of class marks. *median*
(f) the helmet size of a hockey team. *mode*
(g) the rainfall in a certain area. *mean*
(h) the kilometre time for a race horse. *median*

B **2.** Order each of the following sets of data, then find the mode(s), median, and mean correct to one decimal place.
(a) 71 26 35 69 53 26 70 33 61
(b) 3 13 20 20 11 18 12 7 5
(c) 5 5 5 4 4 3 7 2
(d) 8 12 7 15 19 7 9 8 8 11
(e) 3 3 3 5 6 2 4 2 4 5 4 7 8

3. The following table gives the bulb life in hours of overhead projector bulbs. Find the mode, median, and mean.

mode = +1 after middle

8 0 0 11 36 65 84 120 144

Time (h)	8	9	10	11	12	13	14	15	16
Frequency	1	0	0	1	3	5	6	8	9

Mean = sum 1413 = 17.4
81

Mean = Average

204 126 76 160 126 110 69 24 50

Time (h)	17	18	19	20	21	22	23	24	25
Frequency	12	7	4	8	6	5	3	1	2

Median 18 numbers
18+1 = 19 = 9½
2
 # btwn 9+10
16+17 = 16½

4. Find the (i) mode, (ii) median and, (iii) mean of the following salaries:
1 president at $80 000
2 vice-presidents at $65 000
1 secretary treasurer at $50 000
1 controller at $45 000
3 managers at $40 000
14 salesmen at $31 000
10 stenographers at $17 000
2 receptionists at $13 000

5. The following is a set of marks on a college entrance examination.
(a) Make a frequency table.
(b) State the mode.
(c) Find the median.
(d) Calculate the mean.

43	61	51	51	71	65	62	86	77	51	64	56	30	56	85
68	60	55	41	72	57	63	68	65	41	62	80	46	54	60
45	61	49	48	53	66	69	84	51	69	74	60	61	58	53
75	88	40	81	83	71	51	65	71	62	48	80	80	55	53
71	51	66	52	60	56	65	48	67	66	82	54	87	77	75
77	70	68	41	56	59	72	58	61	79	46	57	61	85	68
65	60	66	64	40	57	70	76	84	53	62	88	78	67	93
61	61	74	70	52	57	70	62	80	72	50	65	51	92	69

6. The weekly closing prices for one year of the stock for A.T. & T. were as follows,

$55.50	$56.75	$57.25	$56.75	$56.25
$55.75	$55.75	$54.75	$54.75	$54.50
$53.00	$54.00	$55.00	$55.50	$55.75
$54.25	$53.00	$54.50	$55.25	$56.25
$57.75	$58.00	$57.50	$56.75	$55.00
$54.00	$54.00	$53.75	$53.00	$54.25
$55.50	$55.75	$57.00	$57.75	$58.00
$57.50	$58.25	$58.00	$58.50	$58.25
$58.75	$59.25	$59.00	$59.25	$58.75
$59.50	$60.00	$59.75	$60.25	$59.50
$60.00	$59.25			

Continue each pattern

1, 4, 7, 10, 13, . . .
1, 1, 2, 3, 5, 8, . . .
1, 3, 9, 27, 81, . . .
1, 4, 9, 16, 25, . . .

Find the (a) mode, (b) median, (c) mean for the stock.

15.4 MEASURES OF DISPERSION

In the previous section we studied the measures of central tendency of data. The mean or median might not tell someone everything they want to know about a set of data. It is possible for two sets of data to have the same mean or median and yet differ greatly in their *dispersion*, or spread.

One measure of dispersion is the *range*. The range of a set of data is found by subtracting the smallest number from the largest. The range is very sensitive to extreme values as shown in the table of fielding errors. By including the second baseman with 33 errors the range is increased from 18 to 30.

MAJOR LEAGUE BASEBALL FIELDING ERRORS IN ONE SEASON			
Second Basemen		**Third Basemen**	
33	12	22	14
21	11	18	11
18	11	16	11
18	11	16	11
16	10	15	10
15	9	15	10
14	8	14	9
13	7	13	8
13	7	13	8
13	5	13	6
12	4	14	6
12	4	14	5
12	3	14	4

$$R_{SB} = 33 - 3 \qquad R_{TB} = 22 - 4$$
$$= 30 \qquad\qquad = 18$$

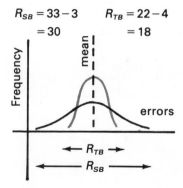

The range is determined by two numbers and unfortunately it does not tell us how the other numbers vary. Are the numbers evenly spread out or do they concentrate about the mean? To determine this we use another measure of dispersion called the *standard deviation*.

EXAMPLE 1. *Find the standard deviation of the fielding errors by second baseman found in Table 15-1.*

Solution
To determine the standard deviation of a set of numbers we find, in order
1. the mean of the numbers
2. the difference between each number and the mean
3. the square of each difference
4. the mean of the squares
5. the square root of the mean of the squares
The number that results is the standard deviation.

Table 15-1

Errors x_i	Differences $(x_i - \bar{x})$	Squares $(x_i - \bar{x})^2$
33	21	441
21	9	81
18	6	36
18	6	36
16	6	36
15	3	9
14	2	4
13	1	1
13	1	1
13	1	1
12	0	0
12	0	0
12	0	0
12	0	0
11	−1	1
11	−1	1
11	−1	1
10	−2	4
9	−3	9
8	−4	16
7	−5	25
7	−5	25
5	−7	49
4	−8	64
4	−8	64
3	−9	81

$$\text{Sum} = 312$$

$$\bar{x} = \frac{312}{26}$$

$$= 12$$

$$\text{Sum} = 966$$

$$\text{Mean} = \frac{966}{26}$$

$$\doteq 37.2$$

$$\text{S.D.} \doteq \sqrt{37.2} \doteq 6.1$$

The five steps may be abbreviated in the formula

$$S.D. = \sqrt{\frac{(x_1 - \bar{x})^2 + (x_2 - \bar{x})^2 + \ldots (x_n - \bar{x})^2}{n}}$$

The standard deviation becomes meaningful when the frequency distribution has a normal curve as its graph. When this is true then 68% of the population will lie within one standard deviation of the mean and 95% of the population will always be within two standard deviations of the mean. Almost all (99.7%) of the population will lie within three standard deviations of the mean.

How many words can you find that contain the letter sequence LBE?

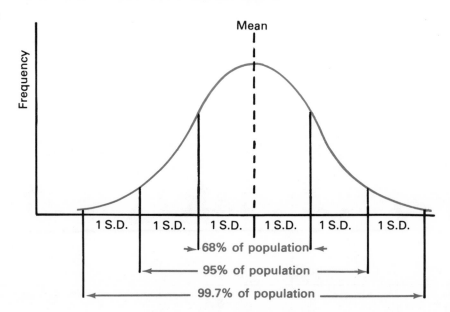

In order to facilitate calculations the distribution is simplified as follows.

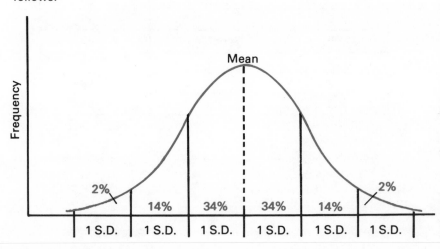

EXAMPLE 2. *A football coach graphed the masses of his players and found that the data was distributed normally. The mean was* 100 kg *and the standard deviation* 10 kg.

(*a*) *What percent of the players have masses between* 90 kg *and* 110 kg?

(*b*) *What percent of the players have masses between* 80 kg *and* 120 kg?

(*c*) *What percent of the players have masses between* 100 kg *and* 120 kg?

Solution
Draw a normal curve.

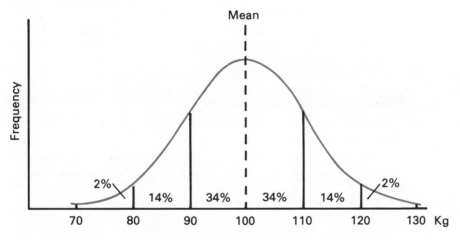

The standard deviation is 10, so 34% of the players have masses between 100 kg and 110 kg. Similarly we can place the remaining masses and percents on the horizontal axis.

(a) 68% of the players have masses between 90 kg and 110 kg.

(b) 96% of the players have masses between 80 kg and 120 kg.

(c) 48% of the players have masses between 100 kg and 120 kg.

EXERCISE 15-4

A **1.** State the range of each of the following.
   (a) 3, 5, 9, 14, 15, 22, 27
   (b) 8, 6, 24, 37, 81, 43
   (c) 58, 147, 318, 72, 14, 281
   (d) 185, 35, 167, 48, 93
   (e) 66, 78, 44, 75, 94

B **2.** A local hospital finds that the average stay for maternity cases is 5 d with a standard deviation of 1 d. Assuming a normal distribution,
   (a) what percent of mothers stay in the hospital between 4 and 5 d?
   (b) what percent of the mothers stay in the hospital between 3 and 6 d?
   (c) what percent of the mothers stay less than 6 d?

3. The quality controller at a pharmaceutical company finds that the mean number of vitamin pills in a bottle is 100 with a standard deviation of 1. Assuming a normal distribution,

(a) what percent of the bottles contain more than 101 pills?

(b) What percent of the bottles contain between 98 and 102 pills?

(c) what percent of the bottles contain less than 99 pills?

4. A factory ordered 1000 light bulbs from the Brite-Lite Company. The company claimed that the mean life of the bulbs was 800 h with a standard deviation of 100 h. Assuming a normal distribution,

(a) what percent of the bulbs will last between 700 h and 900 h?

(b) what percent of the bulbs will last longer than 600 h?

(c) how many bulbs could be expected to last over 900 h?

(d) how many bulbs will last longer than 1000 h?

5. The personnel manager of a factory employing 2000 people found that the average term of employment was 22 a with a standard deviation of 7 a. Assuming normal distribution,

(a) what percentage of the employees will work more than 15 a?

(b) how many employees will work between 15 and 29 a?

(c) how many people will work less than 8 a?

(d) how many employees will work longer than 29 a?

6. The quality controller at a candy factory finds that the mean mass of the Krunchy Nut chocolate bars is 60 g with a standard deviation of 2 g. The company produces 3000 bars a day. Assuming a normal distribution,

(a) what percent of the bars will have masses between 58 g and 64 g?

(b) on one day, how many bars will have a mass over 62 g?

(c) on one day, how many bars will have masses between 54 g and 60 g?

(d) what steps should be taken if the standard deviation increases to 10 g?

7. The Acme Paper Company makes rolls of paper towels. The mean length of each roll is 50 m with a standard deviation of 2 m. A grocery store ordered 500 rolls. Assuming a normal distribution,

(a) what percent of the rolls will have lengths between 44 m and 48 m?

(b) how many rolls will be longer than 52 m?

(c) how many rolls will be shorter than 52 m?

8. The Department of Health conducted a dental survey of 6000 sixteen year old high school students to determine the extent of dental decay. It was found that the mean number of teeth per student affected by decay was 8 with a standard deviation of 2. Assuming a normal distribution,

(a) what percent of the students has less than 6 teeth affected by decay?

(b) how many students had more than 10 teeth affected by decay?

(c) how many students had between 6 and 12 teeth affected by decay?

(d) what factors could contribute to bias in this survey?

9. A basketball coach measured the heights of his players and found them to be 172 cm, 176 cm, 176 cm, 178 cm, 180 cm, 180 cm, 181 cm, 181 cm, 182 cm, and 184 cm. Find the range, mean, and standard deviation of this set of data.

10. The quality controller removes 20 bags of potato chips at random from the production line and finds the masses to be 46 g, 46 g, 47 g, 47 g, 48 g, 48 g, 48 g, 50 g, 50 g, 50 g, 50 g, 50 g, 51 g, 51 g, 52 g, 52 g, 52 g, 53 g, 54 g, and 55 g. Find the range, mean, and standard deviation of this sample.

15.5 PROBABILITY

Probability theory has long been associated with games of chance. The first book on the subject was written by the Italian mathematician Girolamo Cardano (1501-1576) who supported himself as a professional gambler for several years. Later the French mathematicians Blaise Pascal (1623-1662) and Pierre Fermat (1601-1665) founded the modern development of probability theory with their correspondence on games played with dice.

When a single die is rolled, there are six equally likely outcomes which we can picture in a tree diagram.

The set of possible outcomes $\{1,2,3,4,5,6\}$ is called the sample space. There is only one way in six for a die to turn up the number 5, and so we say that the probability of rolling a 5 is $\frac{1}{6}$. In symbols we write

$$P(5) = \frac{1}{6}.$$

In general if a sample space consists of N equally likely outcomes and if S of those outcomes are considered successful (or favourable) for an event E, then we define probability as follows.

probability of an event E	$=$	$\dfrac{\text{number of successful outcomes}}{\text{total number of possible outcomes}}$
$P(E)$	$=$	$\dfrac{S}{N}$

How many words can you find that contain the letter sequence PTI?

EXAMPLE 1. A game is played by rolling a die. You win if the die shows 1 or 2. What is the probability of winning? Of losing?

Solution

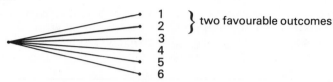

There are six equally likely outcomes. Two of them result in a win for you and the remaining four result in a loss.

$$P \text{ (winning)} = \frac{2}{6} \qquad\qquad P \text{ (losing)} = \frac{4}{6}$$

$$= \frac{1}{3} \qquad\qquad\qquad\qquad = \frac{2}{3}$$

Notice that the sum of the probabilities in Example 1 is 1. This always happens when we calculate the probabilities of the occurrence and non-occurrence of an event.

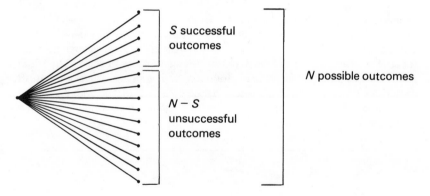

The probability of a successful outcome is $p = \dfrac{S}{N}$ and the probability of an unsuccessful outcome is $q = \dfrac{N-S}{N}$. Adding, we get

$$p + q = \frac{S}{N} + \frac{N-S}{N} = \frac{S + (N-S)}{N} = \frac{N}{N} = 1.$$

Thus $p + q = 1$.

If p is the probability that an event will occur, then $0 \leq p \leq 1$. If q is the probability that the event will not occur, then $p + q = 1$. If $p = 1$, the event is a certainty. If $p = 0$, it is impossible. The closer p is to 1, the more likely the event. The closer p is to 0, the less likely the event.

EXAMPLE 2. A game consists of tossing a penny and rolling a die. You win if the penny shows tails and the die shows 5. What is your probability of winning?

Solution

The tree diagram involves two events. Assume that the penny is tossed first and then the die is rolled. We can list all possible outcomes of the game by tracing from the starting point along the various branches of the tree.

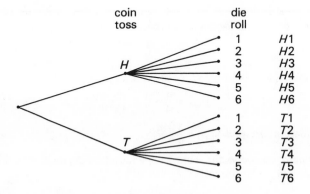

coin toss	die roll	
	1	H1
	2	H2
H	3	H3
	4	H4
	5	H5
	6	H6
	1	T1
	2	T2
T	3	T3
	4	T4
	5	T5
	6	T6

The sample space $\{H1,H2,H3,H4,H5,H6,T1,T2,T3,T4,T5,T6\}$ consists of twelve equally likely outcomes. For example $H4$ means the penny shows heads and the die shows 4. Only one of the outcomes is $T5$. Thus $N = 12$ and $S = 1$.

$$P\,(\text{winning}) = \frac{1}{12}.$$

Notice that this probability is the product of the individual probabilities of the two events.

$$P(\text{tails}) = \frac{1}{2} \qquad\qquad P(5) = \frac{1}{6}$$

The probability of both events happening is

$$P(\text{winning}) = \frac{1}{2} \times \frac{1}{6} = \frac{1}{12}.$$

The reason for multiplying the probabilities is seen in the tree diagram. There are six small branches on each of the two main branches and so there are twelve possible outcomes.

Two events are called independent if neither has an influence on the other. For instance in Example 2 the result of rolling the die is independent of the result of the coin toss.

> Suppose that two events are independent of each other. If p_1 is the probability that the first event will occur and p_2 is the probability that the second event will occur, then the probability that both events will occur is the product $p = p_1 p_2$.

EXAMPLE 3. (a) A card is dealt from a standard 52-card deck. The it is replaced, the deck is shuffled, and another card is dealt. What is the probability that both cards are spades? (b) If the first card is not replaced, what is the probability that both cards are spades?

Solution

(a) Since there are 13 spades in the deck,

$$P \text{ (spades)} = p_1 = \frac{13}{52} = \frac{1}{4}.$$

Since the card is replaced and the deck is shuffled, the second deal is independent of the first. Again the probability of dealing a spade is

$$p_2 = \frac{1}{4}.$$

Thus the probability that both cards are spades is

$$p_1 p_2 = \frac{1}{4} \times \frac{1}{4} = \frac{1}{16}.$$

(b) As in part (a), P(spades) $p_1 = \frac{1}{4}$.

If the first card is a spade, there are 12 spades left in the deck. The probability that the second card is a spade is

$$p_2 = \frac{12}{51} = \frac{4}{17}.$$

The probability that both cards are spades is

$$p_1 p_2 = \frac{1}{4} \times \frac{4}{17} = \frac{1}{17}.$$

Notice that if the first event has occurred before the second event and we know its outcome, then we can use the outcome of the first event as one of the conditions in calculating the probability of the second event.

EXERCISE 15-5

A **1.** A single die is rolled.

(a) How many possible outcomes are there?

(b) If a success is rolling an odd number, how many outcomes are successes?

(c) What is the probability of rolling an odd number?

(d) What is the probability of rolling an even number?

(e) What is the probability of rolling a number more than 4?

2. A box contains 3 red marbles, 4 black marbles, and 5 white marbles. You are to pick one marble at random.

(a) How many possible outcomes are there?

(b) If you hope to pick a red marble, how many possible outcomes are successes?

(c) What is the probability of picking a red marble?

(d) What is the probability of picking a black marble?

(e) What is the probability of picking a marble which is not red?

B 3. A coin is tossed twice. Find the probability of the following events and illustrate with a tree diagram.

(a) both heads   (b) both tails   (c) one heads, one tails

4. Draw tree diagrams to illustrate all possible outcomes for the following events.

(a) A die is rolled and then a coin is tossed.

(b) Three coins are tossed, one at a time.

(c) A man and his wife have two children. (Assume that it is equally likely for a child to be a boy or a girl.)

(d) Two teams, A and B, have a best 3 out of 5 playoff.

5. There are 12 boys and 18 girls in a mathematics class. The teacher chooses one student at random to answer a question.

(a) What is the probability that a girl is chosen?

(b) What is the probability that a boy is chosen?

6. A deck of playing cards is shuffled and a card is dealt. Find the probability that the card is

(a) a club,   (b) not a club,   (c) an ace,   (d) not an ace,

(e) black (a club or a spade),   (f) a red king,

(g) the 5 of hearts.

7. A deck of cards numbered from 1 to 100 is shuffled and a card is drawn at random. What is the probability that the number on the card

(a) is odd?   (b) ends in a 7?   (c) is divisible by 4?

8. Two dice are rolled.

(a) List the sample space of possible outcomes.

(b) Find the probabilities of rolling 1,2,3,4,5,6,7,8,9,10,11, and 12.

(c) Find the probability of getting 9 or more.

(d) Find the probability that the numbers on both dice are even.

9. Three dice are rolled. Find the probability that the total is

(a) 2   (b) 3   (c) 5

10. For families with three children, find the probabilities of the following, assuming that it is equally likely for a child to be a boy or a girl.

(a) All the children are girls.

(b) Two children are girls and one is a boy.

(c) At least one child is a boy.

11. Four coins are tossed. What is the probability of

(a) 2 heads and 2 tails?

(b) 3 heads and a tail?

(c) at least 2 heads?

C **12.** A card is dealt from a deck of playing cards and is replaced. The deck is reshuffled and another card is dealt. What are the probabilities of the following events?

(a) Both cards are red.

(b) The first card is red and the second is black.

(c) One card is red and the other is black.

(d) The first is clubs and the second is hearts.

(e) The king of hearts is dealt twice.

(f) The same card is dealt twice.

13. Do question 12 assuming that the first card is not replaced.

REVIEW EXERCISE

1. The Communications Broadcasting Poll Company surveyed 100 viewers to determine how many people watched the following programs on channel 4, on Tuesday night.

Time	Program
20:00	Stagecoach
21:00	Beth Green, M.D.
22:00	The Detectives

The results of the poll were as follows:

36 watched Stagecoach
30 watched Beth Green, M.D.
40 watched The Detectives
15 watched Stagecoach and Beth Green, M.D.
14 watched Stagecoach and The Detectives
12 watched Beth Green, M.D. and The Detectives
 8 watched all three.

(a) How many viewers did not watch any of these programs on channel 4?

(b) How many watched only

(i) Stagecoach?   (ii) Beth Green, M.D.?   (iii) The Detectives ?

2. The quality control division of a bar soap manufacturing company selects 40 bars of soap at random from every batch of 10 000. The masses in grams of 40 such soap bars are as follows

138	136	135	137	135	136	136	134	133	132
137	134	133	135	136	133	137	136	138	137
136	138	137	137	137	135	136	134	134	136
136	135	136	136	135	134	134	135	135	136

(a) Prepare a frequency distribution table.

(b) Determine the range.

(c) State the mode(s).

(d) Find the median.

(e) Calculate the mean.

(f) Find the standard deviation.

3. The federal government bought 10 000 Mark X tires from the BMA Tire Co. The company claims that the Mark X has a mean life of 150 000 km with a standard deviation of 15 000 km. Assuming normal distribution,

(a) what percent of the tires will last between 135 000 km and 180 000 km?

(b) what percent of the tires will wear out in less than 120 000 km?

(c) how many of the tires will last more than 165 000 km?

(d) how many tires will last less than 135 000 km?

4. The City of Blind Canyon did a traffic survey on the street where the high school was located in order to determine whether or not a traffic light should be installed. After clocking 1000 vehicles it was found that the mean speed was 45 km/h with a standard deviation of 4 km/h. Assuming normal distribution,

(a) what percent of the cars were travelling faster than 41 km/h?

(b) how many vehicles were travelling less than 49 km/h?

(c) how many vehicles were travelling between 45 km/h and 53 km/h?

5. A box contains 5 blue marbles, 6 yellow marbles, and 9 green marbles. Find the probability of picking at random a marble which is

(a) blue,   (b) not blue,   (c) yellow

(d) not yellow,   (e) green,   (f) not green.

6. If two dice are rolled, what is the probability of getting

(a) 4 or less?   (b) a 7 or an 11?   (c) an even number?

7. A card is drawn from a shuffled deck of playing cards. Find the probability that the card is

(a) a diamond,   (b) the jack of diamonds,

(c) not a diamond,   (d) not a jack,

(e) a face card,   (f) a king or queen.

8. Four dice are rolled. Find the probability that the total is

(a) 4   (b) 5 or less   (c) 6 or more   (d) 24

ANSWERS

REVIEW AND PREVIEW TO CHAPTER 1

Exercise 1

1. (a) $5x + 9y$ (b) $11x^2 + 13x$ (c) $27xy + 3w$
(d) $7x - y$ (e) $10x^2 - 17x$ (f) $11x^2 + 3x - 2$
(g) $9w - 12x - 4y$ (h) $5m^2 + 2m - 6$ (i) $2x^2 + 19x + 12$
(j) $8x^2 - 10xy - 4y^2$ (k) $4m + 5n + 6x - 3y$

2. (a) $3x + 3y$ (b) $4w + 9x + 4y$ (c) $4x + 6y$
(d) $-x^2 - 6x + 2$ (e) $-2w - 6x$ (f) $-8x^2 + 8x - 12$
(g) $7x^2 - 9x - 4$ (h) $10w + 9x - 8y$ (i) $-x^2 + 8xy - y^2$
(j) $-4m + 3n - 2$

Exercise 2

1. (a) 16 (b) 72 (c) 38 (d) -2 (e) 29
(f) -3 (g) -2 (h) -26 (i) -20 (j) -8
(k) -60 (l) -5 (m) -18 (n) 17 (o) 0

2. (a) -25 (b) -19 (c) 18 (d) -24 (e) -2
(f) 14 (g) -6 (h) 15 (i) 84 (j) 8
(k) 8 (l) 16 (m) -14 (n) -3 (o) -2

Exercise 3

1. (a) $12wxy$ (b) $-10wx$ (c) $40xy$ (d) $8x^3$
(e) $6w^5$ (f) $-12x^9$ (g) $12x^8$ (h) $-6x^6y$
(i) $10wxy^2$ (j) $-15m^5n^3$ (k) $-4x^6y^5$ (l) $12x^2y^2$
(m) $-14w^5x^4$ (n) $-2x^2y^5$ (o) $80x^9y^{14}$ (p) $-240x^2y^2$
(q) $-66s^3t^2$ (r) $-2x^3y^5$

2. (a) $3x + 15$ (b) $2x - 14$ (c) $18m - 9$
(d) $-3x + 18$ (e) $-x - 5$ (f) $21x - 14y - 56$
(g) $-4x^2 + 10x + 2$ (h) $3x^2 - 8x$ (i) $2x^3 - 2x^2 + 18x$
(j) $-4x^3 + 12x^2y + 4xy^2$ (k) $6x^2y - 10xy^2$ (l) $15t^6 - 12t^4 + 6t^3$
(m) $-12w^3 + 9w^2 - 12w$ (n) $-3x^3y + 12x^2y^2 + 6xy^3$
(o) $21tx - 9ty + 33t$ (p) $-4s^3t - 5s^2t^2 + 3st^3$
(q) $-3wx^2y + wxy^2 + w^2xy$ (r) $10x^{11} - 25x^9 - 45x^7$

CHAPTER 1

Exercise 1-1

1. (a) $2x - 10$ (b) $8x - 12$ (c) $7 - 21x$
(d) $18y - 24$ (e) $-8x - 10$ (f) $-18y + 9$
(g) $-x + 8$ (h) $8x - 20y$ (i) $-3x^2 + 9x + 6$
(j) $8x^2 + 12xy$ (k) $-12m^2 + 18mn$ (l) $-9xy + 12y^2 - 6y$

2. (a) $x^2 + 3x + 2$ (b) $x^2 + 5x + 6$ (c) $x^2 + 6x + 8$
(d) $x^2 - 4x + 3$ (e) $x^2 + 2x - 15$ (f) $x^2 + x - 2$
(g) $y^2 - 9y + 20$ (h) $t^2 + 15t + 56$ (i) $m^2 + 5m - 36$
(j) $n^2 - 11n + 18$ (k) $x^2 + x - 56$ (l) $y^2 - 6y - 7$
(m) $x^2 + 13x + 42$ (n) $t^2 - 14t + 45$ (o) $m^2 - 17m + 66$

3. (a) $x^2 + 6x + 9$ (b) $x^2 - 4x + 4$ (c) $x^2 + 10x + 25$
(d) $x^2 - 16$ (e) $y^2 + 4y + 4$ (f) $m^2 - 14m + 49$
(g) $t^2 - 25$ (h) $x^2 - 36$ (i) $y^2 + 2y + 1$
(j) $x^2 - 18x + 81$ (k) $x^2 + 20x + 100$ (l) $x^2 - 49$
(m) $x^2 + 24x + 144$ (n) $x^2 - 12x + 36$ (o) $y^2 - 1$

4. (a) $5x + 22$ (b) $8m + 18$ (c) -14
(d) $2y - 6$ (e) $5x - 11$ (f) $4m - 20$
(g) $5x - 4y - 42$ (h) -6 (i) $3x^2 - 19x + 32$
(j) $2x^2 - 16x + 6$ (k) $x^2 - 8xy - y^2$ (l) $-4x^2 - 3x$
(m) $5t^3 - 4t^2 - 8t$ (n) $4x^2 - 4x - 10$ (o) $3m^3 - 6m^2 + 2m$
(p) $6w^3 - w^2 + 11w$

5. (a) $2x^2 + 13x + 15$ (b) $6x^2 + 29x + 28$
(c) $14y^2 + 31y - 10$ (d) $6m^2 - 17m + 5$
(e) $12m^2 - 24m + 9$ (f) $9x^2 + 30x + 25$
(g) $4x^2 - 25$ (h) $8t^2 + 26t + 21$
(i) $25t^2 - 60t + 36$ (j) $49t^2 + 56t + 16$
(k) $12x^2 - 17xy + 6y^2$ (l) $20m^2 + 3mn - 2n^2$
(m) $9x^2 + 30xy + 25y^2$ (n) $-3x^2 + 5xy + 28y^2$
(o) $49 - 64t^2$ (p) $28x^2 - 55xy - 18y^2$
(q) $72x^2 + 107xy + 30y^2$ (r) $56m^2 - 19mn - 15n^2$
(s) $12x^4 - 11x^3 + 2x^2$ (t) $-x^4 + 5x^3y - 4x^2y^2$
(u) $4t^4 - 28t^2 + 49$ (v) $5x^8 - 21x^4 + 18$
(w) $-8x^2 + 26xy - 21y^2$ (x) $24a^2b^2c^2 - 22abcx + 3x^2$

6. (a) $2x^2 + 20x + 33$ (b) $5x^2 + 27x + 46$ (c) $-m^2 - 15m + 22$
(d) $60t - 210$ (e) $5m^2 + 4m + 29$ (f) $-10x^2 + 83x + 2$
(g) $70m^2 + 66m - 33$ (h) $-5x^2 - 60x - 17$ (i) $-40t^2 + 49t + 16$
(j) $-3x^2 - 48x - 67$ (k) $-84w^2 - 12w + 99$

7. (a) $x^3 + 3x^2 + 3x + 2$ (b) $2x^3 - x^2 - 14x - 12$
(c) $6x^3 - x^2 - 16x - 5$ (d) $3m^3 - 13m^2 + 6n + 8$
(e) $x^4 + x^3 - 8x^2 - 9x + 5$ (f) $6m^4 - 5m^3 + m^2 - 4m + 2$
(g) $x^4 + 9x^3 + 13x^2 - 34x - 24$
(h) $2w^2 - 15x^2 - 12y^2 + 7wx + 29xy - 2wy$

8. $2x^2 - 5x - 12$ 9. $9x^2 - 12x + 4$

10. (a) $4x^3 - 12x^2 - 31x + 60$ (b) $x^4 - 6x^3 + 7x^2 + 6x + 1$

(c) $x^2 - \dfrac{1}{x^2}$ (d) $-x^2 + x + 5$

(e) $w^2 + x^2 + y^2 + z^2 + 2wx + 2wy + 2wz + 2xy + 2xz + 2yz$

Exercise 1-2

1. (a) $2(x + 3)$ (b) $5(y - 2)$ (c) $3(x + 2)$
(d) $7(w - 1)$ (f) $2(x^2 - 41)$ (g) $3(1 - 3y)$
(h) $2x(x + 3)$ (j) $y(6y - 7)$ (k) $5w(2w - 1)$
(l) $4x(2w - 3)$ (m) $5(3x + 2y)$ (o) $2t(w + 2x - 3y)$

2. **(a)** $5x(5x^2+2x+3)$ **(b)** $y^2(y^3-y^2+y-1)$ **(c)** $9(4x^5-y^3)$
(d) $4x(3y+w-2z)$ **(e)** $3m(3m^2-2mt+t^2)$ **(f)** $7xy(z-2+3t)$
(h) $11y(2x-y+3w)$ **(i)** $4mn(9n-6m+7)$ **(j)** $7rst(1-2rs)$
(k) $9rs^2(2rs-1-3r^2)$
(l) $10m^5n^3(2mn-3n^2+4m^2-1)$
(n) $4x^5y^4(10y^3-8x^2y^2-7x^3-9x^2y)$

3. **(a)** $(x+y)(3m+2)$ **(b)** $(y-1)(3x+2)$ **(c)** $(m+3)(9x-2)$
(d) $(m+n)(5y+t)$ **(e)** $(x-2)(5w-3t)$ **(f)** $(x+5)(2t+1)$
(g) $(t-4)(4mn-1)$ **(h)** $2(x+y)(m+2)$ **(i)** $3x(m-n)(y-2)$
(j) $(t+5)(2t+7)$ **(k)** $5(2x-3)(t-2m)$ **(l)** $(w+3)^2(4w+17)$

Exercise 1-3

1. **(a)** $x+4$ **(b)** $x+2$ **(c)** $x-3$ **(d)** $m+3$
(e) $y-2$ **(f)** $t+4$ **(g)** $s-4$ **(h)** $w+5$
(i) $n-5$ **(j)** $x-7$ **(k)** $y-2$ **(l)** $x-8$

2. **(a)** $(x+5)(x+2)$ **(b)** $(m+6)(m+2)$ **(c)** $(n+4)(n+2)$
(d) $(w-5)(w-2)$ **(e)** $(x-5)(x-4)$ **(g)** $(r-6)(r+5)$
(h) $(m+7)(m-6)$ **(i)** $(n+9)(n+2)$ **(j)** $(x+10)(x+2)$
(l) $(s+8)(s-2)$ **(m)** $(y-7)(y+5)$ **(n)** $(x+8)(x-5)$
(o) $(t+8)(t+9)$ **(q)** $(r-10)(r-8)$ **(r)** $(m-3)^2$
(s) $(y+5)^2$ **(t)** $(x+9)(x-7)$ **(v)** $(x-10)^2$
(w) $(m-10)(m+2)$ **(x)** $(n+12)(n-2)$

3. **(a)** $2(x+1)^2$ **(b)** $3(w+3)(w+1)$ **(c)** $(m-11)(m+7)$
(d) $5(x-5)(x-2)$ **(e)** $(n+11)(n+5)$ **(f)** $(w-10)(w-3)$
(g) $3(x^2+x+1)$ **(h)** $2(x-9)(x-5)$ **(i)** $2(w+7)^2$
(j) $(5-m)(7-m)$ **(k)** $(8-x)(2+x)$ **(l)** $2(x^2-3x+5)$
(m) $4(x-6)^2$ **(n)** $(m+14)(m-3)$ **(o)** $(x-20)(x-15)$
(p) $(m-16)(m+7)$ **(q)** $(x+13)(x-9)$ **(r)** $(x-15)(x-13)$
(s) $(w-19)(w+4)$ **(t)** $(t+21)(t-6)$ **(u)** $(s-6)(s-2)$

Exercise 1-4

1. **(a)** $2,5$ **(b)** $2,3$ **(c)** $-3,-4$ **(f)** $3,6$
(g) $10,-3$ **(h)** $-4,-4$ **(i)** $4,-5$ **(j)** $7,-2$
(k) $1,1$ **(l)** $7,-5$ **(n)** $4,-6$ **(o)** $5,5$
(p) $3,-6$

2. **(a)** $(2x+1)(3x+5)$ **(b)** $(2w+3)(w+1)$ **(c)** $(3x-2)(2x-1)$
(d) $(m+6)(4m+3)$ **(e)** $(w-2)(3w-4)$ **(f)** $(5t-2)(3t+1)$
(g) $(m+2)(2m-5)$ **(h)** $(4x+1)(x+6)$ **(i)** $(3n-2)(2n-3)$

3. **(a)** $(t+7)(4t+3)$ **(b)** $(3m+4)(2m-1)$ **(c)** $(2x+5)(x+6)$
(d) $(3x+1)^2$ **(e)** $(4m-3)(m+6)$ **(f)** $(2x-5)(3x-2)$
(g) $(5x+2)(2x+5)$ **(h)** $(2t-7)(3t+2)$ **(i)** $(3w-4)^2$

Exercise 1-5

1. **(a)** $(x-4)(x+4)$ **(b)** $(m+3)^2$ **(c)** $(r-5)^2$
(d) $(m-7)(m+7)$ **(e)** $(t-4)^2$ **(f)** $(x-6)(x+6)$
(g) $(x+7)^2$ **(h)** $(m-2)^2$ **(i)** $(w+10)^2$

(j) $(y-1)^2$ **(k)** $(x-8)(x+8)$ **(l)** $(n+9)^2$
(m) $(s+8)^2$ **(n)** $(r-3)^2$ **(o)** $(x-12)(x+12)$

2. **(a)** $(2x-5)(2x+5)$ **(b)** $(2x+1)^2$ **(c)** $(3x-1)^2$
(e) $(4m-1)^2$ **(f)** $(10t-7)(10t+7)$ **(g)** $(2w-3)^2$
(h) $(5s+4)^2$ **(i)** $(3-7y)(3+7y)$ **(j)** $(2-5x)^2$
(k) $(7y+3)^2$ **(l)** $(1-7m)^2$ **(n)** $(2r+7)^2$

3. **(a)** $9(x-2)(x+2)$ **(b)** $(x-4)(x+2)$ **(c)** $(3x+2)(2x-5)$
(d) $3t(mn-2m^2-3n)$ **(e)** $(4x+1)^2$ **(f)** $2(x-4)(x+3)$
(g) $(x-2)(5m-4)$ **(h)** $x(5x^2+x+7)$ **(i)** $3(2x^2+3x+4)$
(j) $(3m-2)(2m+7)$ **(k)** $(3x-5)^2$ **(l)** $5(m-n)(x-2y)$

4. **(a)** $4(m+5)(m-3)$ **(b)** $2(2-3x)(2+3x)$ **(c)** $m(n+6)(n+3)$
(d) $(5y-4)(3y-2)$ **(e)** $(6x+5)^2$ **(f)** $(x+y)(2x+2y-m)$
(g) $7m^2n^5(7-4mn-2m^4n^2)$ **(h)** $(4x+7)(2x+5)$
(i) $3x(m+3)(9-x)$ **(j)** $3(4m-3)(4m+3)$
(k) $(6m+1)(4m-3)$ **(l)** $(7t+3)(3t+7)$

Exercise 1-6

1. **(a)** 2 **(b)** $\dfrac{3}{4}$ **(c)** $\dfrac{5}{18}$ **(d)** $\dfrac{7}{5t}$ **(e)** $\dfrac{2x}{y}$

(f) 28 **(g)** $\dfrac{x^2}{y^2}$ **(h)** $\dfrac{5x}{y}$ **(i)** $\dfrac{5}{7}$ **(j)** $\dfrac{1}{7}$

(k) y^2 **(l)** $\dfrac{y}{x}$ **(m)** $\dfrac{x+3}{x-5}$ **(n)** $\dfrac{x+y}{x-y}$

2. **(a)** $3x^2$ **(b)** $\dfrac{x^2y^4}{6}$ **(c)** $\dfrac{3m}{4}$ **(d)** $\dfrac{4ry}{3}$

(e) $\dfrac{6xy^2}{mn}$ **(f)** $\dfrac{6}{y}$

3. **(a)** $2x$ **(b)** $6x$ **(c)** $2t(x-3)$ **(d)** $\dfrac{2x(x+2)}{5}$

(e) $\dfrac{n^2}{2m}$ **(f)** $\dfrac{1}{2x^2}$

4. **(a)** 1 **(b)** $\dfrac{t}{t+1}$ **(c)** $\dfrac{w+5}{w-6}$ **(d)** $\dfrac{4}{x-7}$

(e) $\dfrac{10}{x-6}$ **(f)** $\dfrac{m+1}{m-1}$ **(g)** $\dfrac{x(x+8)}{(x+9)(x-4)}$ **(h)** $\dfrac{w+5}{w+3}$

5. **(a)** 1 **(b)** $\dfrac{3w+2}{4w+7}$ **(c)** $\dfrac{2x}{x-5}$ **(d)** $\dfrac{5t+3}{t-7}$

(e) $\dfrac{m}{2m+1}$

6. **(a)** $\dfrac{x-3}{2x}$ **(b)** $\dfrac{1}{x(x+7)}$ **(c)** $x(x+3)$ **(d)** 1

Exercise 1-7

1. **(a)** 40 **(b)** 200 **(c)** 180 **(d)** 1050 **(e)** 180 **(f)** 140

2. **(a)** $60x^4$ **(b)** $12x^2y^2$ **(c)** $6m^2n^2$ **(d)** $150x^3y^2$
(e) $18abc$ **(f)** $120a^2b^2$

3. **(a)** $(x-1)(x-4)$ **(b)** $(x+1)(x+2)(x-3)$
(c) $(x+3)(x+4)(x+5)$ **(d)** $x(x+1)(x-1)$
(e) $6(x-3)$ **(f)** $(x+1)(x+5)(x-3)$
(g) $(m+1)(m-2)(m-3)(m-5)$ **(h)** $3(x+4)(x+7)(x-8)$
(i) $x(x+5)(x-4)(x-5)$

Exercise 1-8

1. **(a)** $1\frac{2}{7}$ **(b)** $\frac{6}{11}$ **(c)** $\frac{11}{x}$ **(d)** $\frac{8}{m}$

(e) $\frac{x+y}{2}$ **(f)** $\frac{4x-1}{5}$ **(g)** $\frac{5}{x+1}$ **(h)** $\frac{m-n}{x-3}$

(i) $\frac{1}{(x+2)(x+1)}$ **(j)** $\frac{2m^2}{(x-3)(x+4)}$

2. **(a)** $\frac{17}{20}$ **(b)** $2\frac{7}{24}$ **(c)** $\frac{5x}{12}$ **(d)** $\frac{16x+11y}{6}$

(e) $\frac{m-17}{12}$ **(f)** $\frac{12-x-13y}{12}$ **(g)** $\frac{37x-1}{14}$ **(h)** $\frac{8t-13}{24}$

3. **(a)** $\frac{11}{6x}$ **(b)** $-\frac{1}{20x}$ **(c)** $\frac{26x-9}{12x^2}$ **(d)** $\frac{2t^2-3st+4s^2}{s^2t^2}$

(e) $\frac{6x-y+3}{xy}$ **(f)** $\frac{x^2+4x-1}{x}$ **(g)** $\frac{y^2+3y-2}{y}$ **(h)** $\frac{x+1+xy}{x}$

4. **(a)** $\frac{5x+7}{(x+1)(x+2)}$ **(b)** $\frac{5m-5}{(m-4)(m+1)}$ **(c)** $\frac{x+22}{(x-3)(x+2)}$

(d) $\frac{x-5}{2(x+1)}$ **(e)** $\frac{23x+18}{5(x+1)}$ **(f)** $\frac{2x^2-2x-2}{x(x-2)}$

(g) $\frac{4x^2+x-23}{(x+3)(x-2)}$ **(h)** $\frac{4x^2-6}{(x+1)(x-1)}$

5. **(a)** $\frac{5x+3}{(x+2)(x-1)(x+3)}$ **(b)** $\frac{8x-22}{(x-2)(x-1)(x-4)}$

(c) $\frac{2x+26}{(x+5)(x-1)(x+6)}$ **(d)** $\frac{6t+50}{(t-4)(t-1)(t+7)}$

(e) $\frac{-m^2-14m}{(m+5)(m+1)(m-4)}$ **(f)** $\frac{3x^2+6x}{x(x+5)(x+3)}$

6. **(a)** $\frac{16x-9}{(2x-1)(x+6)(3x-2)}$ **(b)** $\frac{2m+14}{(3m-1)(3m+1)(2m+3)}$

(c) $\frac{-3x^2-20x-17}{(x+3)(x+1)(x-5)}$ **(d)** $\frac{-6x+16}{(x+4)(x-4)}$

Exercise 1-9

1. **(a)** 2×3 **(b)** 2×2 **(c)** 3×2 **(d)** 1×4
(e) 3×1 **(f)** 1×1 **(g)** 3×3 **(h)** 2×1
(i) 1×3

3. **(a)** 3×2 **(b)** 2×2 **(c)** 2×3 **(d)** 4×1
(e) 1×3 **(f)** 1×1 **(g)** 3×3 **(h)** 1×2
(i) 3×1

4. **(a)** $-3, 4, 1$ **(b)** $-2, 0, 4$ **(c)** $1, 0, 6$ **(d)** -2
(e) 6 **(g)** 3×3

5. **(a)** $x = 7, y = 0$ **(b)** $x = -3$ **(c)** $x = -1, y = -4$
(d) $x = 7, y = 4, z = 3$ **(e)** $x = 4, y = 6$ **(f)** $x = -4, y = 3, z = -3$

6. **(a)** $\begin{pmatrix} 7 & 11 \\ 8 & 9 \end{pmatrix}$ **(b)** $\begin{pmatrix} -3 & 1 \\ -3 & 3 \\ 5 & 6 \end{pmatrix}$ **(d)** $\begin{pmatrix} 6 & 12 \\ 1 & -1 \end{pmatrix}$

(e) $\begin{pmatrix} 7 \\ -1 \\ 5 \end{pmatrix}$ **(g)** $(-4 \quad 3)$ **(h)** $\begin{pmatrix} -6 & 2 \\ -6 & 7 \end{pmatrix}$

7. **(a)** $\begin{pmatrix} -1 & 5 \\ 3 & 8 \end{pmatrix}$ **(b)** $\begin{pmatrix} 0 & 4 \\ 0 & 0 \end{pmatrix}$ **(c)** $\begin{pmatrix} 2 & 0 \\ 6 & 8 \end{pmatrix}$ **(d)** $\begin{pmatrix} -2 & 0 \\ -6 & -8 \end{pmatrix}$

(e) $\begin{pmatrix} -2 & 7 \\ 0 & 4 \end{pmatrix}$ **(f)** $\begin{pmatrix} -2 & 7 \\ 0 & 4 \end{pmatrix}$ **(g)** $\begin{pmatrix} 2 & -4 \\ 6 & 8 \end{pmatrix}$ **(h)** $\begin{pmatrix} -3 & 2 \\ 0 & 0 \end{pmatrix}$

(i) $\begin{pmatrix} -3 & 0 \\ -2 & 0 \end{pmatrix}$

8. **(a)** $\begin{pmatrix} 3 & 3 \\ -1 & -1 \end{pmatrix}$ **(b)** $\begin{pmatrix} 1 & -11 \\ 9 & 1 \end{pmatrix}$ **(c)** $\begin{pmatrix} 10 & 9 \\ 2 & -4 \end{pmatrix}$ **(d)** $\begin{pmatrix} 1 & -4 \\ 5 & 0 \end{pmatrix}$

Exercise 1-10

1. **(a)** $\begin{pmatrix} 12 & 0 \\ 3 & 15 \end{pmatrix}$ **(b)** $\begin{pmatrix} 0 \\ 2 \\ -12 \end{pmatrix}$ **(c)** $(-20 \quad 8 \quad 12)$

(d) $\begin{pmatrix} 4 & 3 \\ 2 & -5 \end{pmatrix}$ **(e)** $\begin{pmatrix} 15a & 10b \\ -25a & 15b \end{pmatrix}$ **(f)** $\begin{pmatrix} -10 & 14 \\ 6 & 2 \end{pmatrix}$

2. **(a)** $\begin{pmatrix} 23 & 6 \\ 8 & -1 \end{pmatrix}$ **(b)** $\begin{pmatrix} 9 & -3 \\ -4 & 3 \end{pmatrix}$ **(c)** $\begin{pmatrix} 1 & -7 \\ 15 & 15 \\ 11 & 8 \end{pmatrix}$

(d) $\begin{pmatrix} 21 & -5 \\ 14 & -5 \end{pmatrix}$ **(e)** $\begin{pmatrix} 21 & -8 & -6 \\ -1 & 2 & -7 \end{pmatrix}$ **(f)** $\begin{pmatrix} -5 & -8 \\ 5 & 6 \end{pmatrix}$

3. **(a)** $\begin{pmatrix} 6 & -9 \\ 12 & 0 \end{pmatrix}$ **(b)** $\begin{pmatrix} -2 & 4 \\ -6 & 10 \end{pmatrix}$ **(c)** $\begin{pmatrix} 3 & -5 \\ 7 & -5 \end{pmatrix}$

(d) $\begin{pmatrix} 4 & -5 \\ 6 & 10 \end{pmatrix}$ **(e)** $\begin{pmatrix} 7 & -12 \\ 17 & -15 \end{pmatrix}$ **(f)** $\begin{pmatrix} -10 & 16 \\ -22 & 10 \end{pmatrix}$

(g) $\begin{pmatrix} 6 & -10 \\ 14 & -10 \end{pmatrix}$ **(h)** $\begin{pmatrix} -9 & 15 \\ -21 & 15 \end{pmatrix}$

4. **(a)** $\begin{pmatrix} 2 & -4 \\ 3 & -5 \end{pmatrix}$ **(b)** $\begin{pmatrix} 3 \\ -2 \\ -4 \end{pmatrix}$ **(c)** $\begin{pmatrix} 2 & 2 \\ 1 & 4 \end{pmatrix}$

(d) $\begin{pmatrix} -5 & 6 \\ 2 & -1 \end{pmatrix}$ **(e)** $\begin{pmatrix} 8 & 1 \\ 11 & -12 \end{pmatrix}$ **(f)** $\begin{pmatrix} -1 & 12 \\ 1 & 2 \end{pmatrix}$

Exercise 1-11

1. (a) $\begin{pmatrix} 9 & 3 & 1 \\ 16 & 2 & 4 \end{pmatrix}$ **(b)** $\begin{pmatrix} 18 & 23 \\ 6 & -1 \end{pmatrix}$ **(d)** (-12)

(e) $\begin{pmatrix} 19 & 8 & 19 \\ -23 & -5 & -23 \\ 37 & 19 & 37 \end{pmatrix}$ **(f)** $\begin{pmatrix} 9 \\ -8 \\ 11 \end{pmatrix}$ **(g)** $\begin{pmatrix} 20 & -10 \\ 8 & -4 \\ -4 & 2 \\ 12 & -6 \end{pmatrix}$

(j) $\begin{pmatrix} 3 & -2 & 4 \\ 5 & 1 & 6 \\ 5 & 2 & -3 \end{pmatrix}$ **(k)** $\begin{pmatrix} -3 & 5 \\ 6 & 4 \end{pmatrix}$ **(l)** $\begin{pmatrix} -5 & -2 \\ 3 & -7 \end{pmatrix}$

(m) $\begin{pmatrix} -29 \\ -18 \\ -14 \\ -3 \end{pmatrix}$ **(n)** $\begin{pmatrix} -10 & 9 \\ 16 & 14 \\ 4 & 9 \end{pmatrix}$

2. (a) $\begin{pmatrix} 2 & -5 \\ 4 & -9 \end{pmatrix}, \begin{pmatrix} -3 & -2 \\ -5 & -4 \end{pmatrix}$ **(b)** $\begin{pmatrix} 1 & 2 \\ 5 & 10 \end{pmatrix}, \begin{pmatrix} 4 & -7 \\ -4 & 7 \end{pmatrix}$

(c) $\begin{pmatrix} 3 & -3 \\ 5 & -7 \end{pmatrix}, \begin{pmatrix} 3 & -3 \\ 5 & -7 \end{pmatrix}$ **(d)** $\begin{pmatrix} 1 & -7 \\ 3 & -11 \end{pmatrix}, \begin{pmatrix} 1 & -7 \\ 3 & -11 \end{pmatrix}$

(e) $\begin{pmatrix} 7 & 14 \\ 13 & 26 \end{pmatrix}, \begin{pmatrix} 7 & 14 \\ 13 & 26 \end{pmatrix}$ **(f)** $\begin{pmatrix} 14 & -2 \\ 27 & -5 \end{pmatrix}, \begin{pmatrix} 9 & 1 \\ 18 & 0 \end{pmatrix}$

(g) $\begin{pmatrix} 6 & 14 \\ 7 & 27 \end{pmatrix}, \begin{pmatrix} 1 & 17 \\ -2 & 32 \end{pmatrix}$ **(h)** $\begin{pmatrix} 4 & 0 \\ 5 & 1 \end{pmatrix}, \begin{pmatrix} 9 & -3 \\ 14 & -4 \end{pmatrix}$

Exercise 1-12

1. (c) #1, $1000; #2, $670; #3, $1480; #4, $1720
   (d) $4870

2. (c) Churchill, $970; Vanier, $1280; Central, $1610; High Park, $1580; Parkside, $1600
   (d) $3000 **(e)** $4040 **(f)** $7040

3. (c) January, $4810; February, $4880; March, $4060
   (d) $13 750

4. (c) 1, $4600; 2, $6850; 3, $5100; 4, $6700; 5, $7000
   (d) $16 500 **(e)** $30 250

5. (c) I, $670; II, $969; III, $944; IV, $682; V, $730
   (d) $3995

Review Exercise

1. (a) $x - 29$ **(b)** $x^2 - 13x + 40$ **(c)** $3m^2 - 2m - 36$
(d) $w^2 + 15w - 82$ **(e)** $4x^2 + 2x - 17$ **(f)** $11x^2 + 83x + 24$
(g) $2x^3 - 9x^2 - 26x - 12$ **(h)** $2x^3 - 5x^2 - 3x + 10$ **(i)** $8t^2 + 32t + 28$

(j) $-38x^2 + 79x - 47$

2. (a) $3mn(1-3m-4n)$ **(b)** $(x-6)(x+5)$　　**(c)** $(x-9)(x+9)$
(d) $(x+4)^2$　　　　　　　**(e)** $(2x+7)(x+4)$　　**(f)** $(3m-4)(2m-5)$
(g) $(6t-7)(6t+7)$　　　**(h)** $(m-7)(5x-3)$　　**(i)** $2(x-6)(x+10)$
(j) $(x-7)^2$　　　　　　　**(k)** $(5m+1)(2m-5)$　**(l)** $(10m-11)(10m+11)$
(m) $3x(3xy-1+4y^2)$　**(n)** $(5x-2)^2$　　　　**(o)** $(2m+7)^2$
(p) $(4x+1)(3x+7)$　　　**(q)** $x(m-n)(5x-2)$　**(r)** $3(x-4)(x+4)$

3. (a) $10mnx^2y$　　　**(b)** $\dfrac{9t^3xy^2w}{4}$　　　**(c)** x

(d) $\dfrac{m+1}{3}$　　　　**(e)** 1　　　　　　　**(f)** $\dfrac{t-3}{t+3}$

4. (a) $\dfrac{3}{7}$　　　　　**(b)** $\dfrac{17x}{15}$　　　　**(c)** $\dfrac{17x+2}{12}$

(d) $\dfrac{-10m-21}{18}$　**(e)** $\dfrac{-2x^2+15x+5}{6x^3}$　**(f)** $\dfrac{7x+1}{(x+1)(x-1)}$

(g) $\dfrac{5x+10}{(x+4)(x-1)(x-3)}$　　　**(h)** $\dfrac{x+11}{(x+3)(x+5)(x-5)}$

(i) $\dfrac{-m-6}{m(m-4)(m-6)}$　　　　**(j)** $\dfrac{x-13}{(x+3)(x+5)(x-1)}$

5. (a) $\begin{pmatrix} -2 & 6 \\ -6 & 13 \end{pmatrix}$　　**(b)** $\begin{pmatrix} 1 & -2 \\ 9 & -9 \\ 2 & 4 \end{pmatrix}$　　**(c)** $\begin{pmatrix} 8 & 1 \\ -6 & -8 \end{pmatrix}$

(d) $\begin{pmatrix} 5 & 9 & -2 \\ -5 & -1 & 4 \end{pmatrix}$　**(e)** $\begin{pmatrix} 10 & 9 \\ 14 & -22 \end{pmatrix}$　**(f)** $\begin{pmatrix} -2 & 26 \\ 32 & 14 \\ 0 & -4 \end{pmatrix}$

6. (a) $\begin{pmatrix} 2 & 4 \\ 4 & 1 \end{pmatrix}$　　**(c)** $\begin{pmatrix} -3 & 7 \\ 4 & 6 \end{pmatrix}$　　**(d)** $\begin{pmatrix} 32 & 14 \\ 9 & -11 \end{pmatrix}$

(e) (9)　　　　　　**(f)** $\begin{pmatrix} 3 & 4 & 1 \\ -2 & 4 & 2 \\ 3 & -1 & 5 \end{pmatrix}$

7. (c) Westview, \$3540; East, \$2760; St. Mary's, \$3550; Glendale, \$2440
(d) \$12 290

REVIEW AND PREVIEW TO CHAPTER 2

Exercise 1

1. (a) 0.5　　　**(b)** 0.25　　**(c)** 0.75　　**(d)** 0.2　　　**(e)** 0.6
　　(f) 0.375　　**(g)** 0.625　**(h)** 2.125　**(i)** 3.8　　　**(j)** 4.875
2. (a) $\frac{7}{20}$　　　**(b)** $\frac{3}{4}$　　　**(c)** $\frac{21}{50}$　　**(d)** $\frac{611}{1000}$　**(e)** $\frac{21}{40}$
　　(f) $\frac{37}{1000}$　　**(g)** $\frac{541}{1000}$　**(h)** $3\frac{13}{25}$　**(i)** $4\frac{16}{25}$　**(j)** $5\frac{5}{8}$
3. (a) 51.5751　**(b)** 17.125　**(c)** 0.7791　**(d)** 2.008
4. (a) 3.13　　**(b)** 5.14　　**(c)** 63.25　**(d)** 5.16　　**(e)** 10.03
5 (a) 3.1　　　**(b)** 5.1　　　**(c)** 63　　　**(d)** 5.2　　　**(e)** 10

Exercise 2

1. 187.5 km　　**2.** $500.80　　**3.** 33　　　　**4.** 29.76 g
5. 1239 MJ　　**6.** 32.69　　　**7.** $32.40
8. 7 365 000 km　**9.** 303.3 g
10. 3060 m

CHAPTER 2

Exercise 2-1

1. (a) Q　　(b($\bar{Q}$　　　(c) Q　　　(d) $\bar{Q}$　　　(e) $\bar{Q}$　　　(f) Q
2. (a) 205, 3　　　(b) 204, 3　　　(c) 542, 3　　　(d) 3427, 4
　　(e) 2, 1　　　　(f) 25, 2　　　(g) 36, 2　　　(h) 122, 3
　　(i) 012, 3　　　(j) 12, 2　　　(k) 1, 1　　　(l) 2473, 4
3. (a) 4　　(b) 5　　　(c) 6　　　(d) 12　　　(e) 16　　　(f) 30
　　(g) 42　　(h) 70
4. (a) 0.75　　　(b) 0.625　　　(c) 0.5625　　(d) 1.75　　　(e) 1.375
　　(f) 0.15625　(g) 0.82　　　(h) $0.2\dot{7}$　　(i) $1.3\dot{6}$　　(j) $0.7\dot{3}$
　　(k) 0.53　　(l) $0.5\dot{3}$　　(m) $0.\dot{1}$　　(n) $0.\dot{4}$　　(o) $1.0\dot{9}$
5. (a) $\frac{5}{8}$　　　(b) $\frac{183}{250}$　　(c) $\frac{321}{100}$　　(d) $\frac{93}{20}$　　(e) $\frac{8}{11}$
　　(f) $\frac{7}{9}$　　　(g) $\frac{215}{999}$　　(h) $\frac{3014}{9999}$　　(i) $\frac{17}{45}$　　(j) $\frac{27}{110}$
　　(k) $\frac{599}{1980}$　　(l) $\frac{649}{900}$　　(m) $\frac{322}{99}$　　(n) $\frac{4071}{999}$　　(o) $\frac{234\,35}{3330}$
　　(p) $\frac{703\,68}{9999}$
6. (a) $\frac{1}{7}$　　(b) $\frac{3}{7}$　　(c) $\frac{2}{7}$　　(d) $\frac{6}{7}$　　(e) $\frac{4}{7}$　　(f) $\frac{5}{7}$
7. (a) $\frac{1}{3}$　　(b) $\frac{1}{12}$　　(c) $\frac{1}{9}$　　(d) $\frac{1}{11}$　　(e) $\frac{1}{9}$　　(f) $\frac{2}{15}$
8. (a) $\frac{1}{2}$　　(b) $\frac{3}{10}$　　(c) $\frac{3}{5}$　　(d) 1
9 (a) no　　(b) yes
10. (a) $\frac{1}{9}$　　(b) $\frac{2}{9}$　　(c) $\frac{25}{99}$　　(d) $\frac{2}{11}$

Exercise 2-2

1. (a) Q　　(b) N　　(c) $\bar{Q}$　　(d) Q　　(e) Q　　(f) $\bar{Q}$
　　(g) Q　　(h) Q　　(i) $\bar{Q}$　　(j) N　　(k) Q　　(l) Q
　　(m) Q　　(n) Q　　(o) $\bar{Q}$
2. (a) $\{x \in R \mid x > {}^4\!-2\}$　　(b) $\{x \in R \mid x \leqq 3\}$　　(c) $\{x \in R \mid -1 \leqq x < 3\}$
　　(d) $\{x \in R \mid x < -2 \text{ or } x \geqq 2$　　(e) $\{x \in R \mid x < 0 \text{ or } x > 4\}$
　　(f) $\{x \in R \mid -3 < x \leqq 1\}$

3. (a) 　　(b) 　　(c)

　　(d) 　　(e) 　　(f)

4. (a) 　　(b)

　　(c) 　　(d)

5. (a) $\begin{array}{c}\text{—number line from }-2\text{ to }3\text{—}\end{array}$ **(b)** $\begin{array}{c}\text{—number line from }-4\text{ to }3\text{—}\end{array}$

(c) $\begin{array}{c}\text{—number line from }-3\text{ to }3\text{—}\end{array}$ **(d)** $\begin{array}{c}\text{—number line from }-2\text{ to }4\text{—}\end{array}$

7. (a) $\begin{array}{c}\text{—number line from }-4\text{ to }4\text{—}\end{array}$ **(b)** $\begin{array}{c}\text{—number line from }-3\text{ to }3\text{—}\end{array}$

(c) $\begin{array}{c}\text{—number line from }-4\text{ to }3\text{—}\end{array}$ **(d)** $\begin{array}{c}\text{—number line from }-4\text{ to }3\text{—}\end{array}$

Exercise 2-3

1. (a) $\{0.45, 0.5, 0.65\}$ **(b)** $\{-2, -1, 0, 3, 4\}$
   (c) $\{-\frac{1}{2}, \frac{1}{2}, \frac{2}{3}, 1\}$ **(d)** $\{-5, -4, -2, 0, 1\}$
2. (a) $\{0.75, 0.33, 0.28, 0.2\}$ **(b)** $\{5, 1, 0, -2, -3\}$
   (c) $\{3, \frac{2}{3}, 0, -\frac{1}{3}, -2\}$ **(d** $\{2, 1, 0, -2, -3\}$
3. (a) $x > 4$ **(b)** $x < 5$ **(c)** $x < 0$ **(d)** $x < -3$ **(e)** $x > 4$
   (f) $x < 3$ **(g)** $x < -2$ **(h)** $x > -2$ **(i)** $x < -3$ **(j)** $x < 6$
   (k) $x < -6$ **(l)** $x > -4$
4. (a) 3.5 **(b)** -1 **(c)** -4 **(d)** 42.5 **(e)** 2.55 **(f)** -2.65
   (g) -3.45 **(h)** 2.8 **(i)** $\frac{5}{12}$ **(j)** $-\frac{7}{24}$ **(k)** $\frac{23}{32}$ **(l)** $-\frac{1}{4}$
5. (a) $7.22, 7.221\,234\,56\ldots$ **(b)** $-0.271\,46, -0.271\,461\,611\,611\,1\ldots$
   (c) $4.274, 4.274\,142\,43\ldots$

Exercise 2-4

1. 3	**2.** 5	**3.** 2	**4.** -4	**5.** 2	**6.** 5
7. 1	**8.** -6	**9.** 3	**10.** 1	**11.** 2	**12.** 3
13. -10	**14.** 4	**15.** 7	**16.** 14	**17.** 22	**18.** 20
19. -2	**20.** 2	**21.** 2	**22.** 4	**23.** -16	**24.** -3
25. 5	**26.** -3	**27.** 2	**28.** 3	**29.** 9	**30.** 1

Exercise 2-5

1. 15	**2.** $10\frac{2}{3}$	**3.** 2	**4.** $\frac{1}{8}$	**5.** $\frac{5}{6}$
6. $\frac{1}{2}$	**7.** 6.4	**8.** 5	**9.** 4.24	**10.** 5
11. 5.4	**12.** 2	**13.** 19	**14.** 0	**15.** $\frac{9}{4}$
16. $-\frac{9}{4}$	**17.** $\frac{17}{2}$	**18.** $7\frac{1}{2}$	**19.** -2	**20.** -5
21. 9	**22.** $-\frac{2}{5}$	**23.** 1	**24.** 5	**25.** 0.6
26. -1.13	**27.** 4.968	**28.** 7.636	**29.** 1.398	**30.** 3.286

Exercise 2-6

1. (a) $x + 3$ **(b)** $2x$ **(c)** $x - 5$ **(d)** $3x$
   (e) $2x + 3$ **(f)** $x + 1, x + 2, x + 3$ **(g)** $2x, 2x + 2, 2x + 4$ **(h)** $x + 5$
2. $21, 22, 23$
3. $14, 16, 18$
4. $23, 25, 27$
5. 53

6. 15

7. 8, 16

8. 15, 10

9. 7 nickles, 5 dimes, 3 quarters

10. 75 ml and 125 ml

11. 90 km/h

12. 80 km

13. 350 km

14. 60 km/h

15. 5 h

Exercise 2-7

1. $x > 2$

2. $a < 11$

3. $x < 4$

4. $x \geqq 5$

5. $x \leqq 4$

6. $x \leqq 4$

7. $x < -2$

8. $x \geqq -2$

9. $x < -3$

10. $x \geqq 7$

11. $m \leqq -3$

12. $x > -7$

13. $a \leqq -11$

14. $x \leqq 2$

15. $x \geqq 5$

16. $x \leqq -3$

17. $m < -6$

18. $x \leqq 16$

19. $c \leqq 6$

20. $x > 1$

21. $a \geqq 12$

22. $b \geqq 6$

23. $x \leqq 11$

24. $a < -4$

25. $x > \frac{5}{4}$

26. $x \geqq -3$

27. $x \leqq \frac{15}{7}$

28. $x < 2$

29. $x \geqq 1$

30. $x < 0$

Exercise 2-8

1. $x < 6$

2. $x \leqq 9$

3. $x \leqq -6$

4. $x > 8$

5. $x > 7$

6. $m \geqq 40$

7. $b \geqq -4$

8. $x \leqq 1.1$

9. $x > \frac{5}{2}$

10. $a \leqq \frac{1}{4}$

11. $m \leqq \frac{15}{4}$

12. $b < -8$

13. $m \geqq -30$

14. $x \geqq 24$

15. $a \leqq 2.5$

16. $x > -2$

17. $x \leqq 2.5$

18. $x > 2$

19. $x \leqq 4.5$

20. $x \geqq -2.5$

21. $a > -10$

22. $b \geqq -7$

23. $x < -\frac{3}{2}$

24. $x \leqq 3$

25. $x > 2$

26. $x > 1$

27. $x \leqq 2.5$

28. $x \geqq -3$

29. $x \leqq 4$

30. $x > 2.56$

Exercise 2-9

1. $\{2, -2\}$ 2. $\{5, -5\}$ 3. $\{3, -3\}$ 4. $\{3, -3\}$ 5. $\{3, -3\}$
6. $\{2, -2\}$ 7. $\{x \in R \mid -1 < x < 1\}$ 8. $\{x \in R \mid x \le -6 \text{ or } x \ge 6\}$
9. $\{x \in R \mid -3 \le x \le 3\}$
10. (a) $-2 < x < 2$ (b) $-4 < x < 4$ (c) $-3 < x < 3$
    (d) $x \le -2 \text{ or } x \ge 2$ (e) $x < -2 \text{ or } x > 2$ (f) $x \le -6 \text{ or } x \ge 6$
11. (a) $4, -3$ (b) $2, -5$ (c) $\frac{4}{3}, -2$
    (d) $-1, 2$ (e) -1.4 (f) $-2, \frac{10}{3}$

12. (a)   (b)

    (c)   (d)

    (e)   (f)

13. (a)   (b)

    (c)   (d)

    (e)   (f)

14. (a) $2, -2$ (b) $8, -8$ (c) $2, -2$ (d) $-\frac{3}{16}, -\frac{33}{16}$
    (e) $3, -\frac{1}{3}$ (f) -7
15. absolute value is never negative (a), (c), (d)
16. (a) sometimes true   (b) sometimes true   (c) sometimes true
    (d) true   (e) true   (f) sometimes true
    (g) sometimes true   (h) sometimes true

Review Exercise

1. (a) 0.875 (b) $0.\dot{3}8461\dot{5}$ (c) $0.\dot{2}$ (d) $0.7\dot{2}$ (e) $0.\dot{2}3076\dot{9}$
2. (a) $\frac{9}{11}$ (b) $\frac{2}{15}$ (c) $\frac{14}{13}$ (d) $\frac{235}{999}$ (e) $\frac{67}{495}$

3. (a)   (b)   (c)

4. (a)   (b)   (c)

5. (a) $\{-0.25, 0, 0.3, 0.54, 1.3\}$ **(b)** $\{1.3, 0.54, 0.3, 0, -0.25\}$

6. (a) 3.5, 3.512 345 6... **(b)** 2.56, 2.561 661 666 1...

(c) 3.123, 3.123 456...

7. (a) -7 **(b)** 1 **(c)** 5 **(d)** 5 **(e)** 2

(f) $-\frac{3}{8}$ **(g)** 1.25 **(h)** -6

8. (a) $x < 2$ **(b)** $x \geqq -1$ **(c)** $x \leqq -4$

(d) $x \geqq 1$ **(e)** $x \leqq 1$ **(f)** $x < -\frac{2}{7}$

(g) $x > 2.5$ **(h)** $x \geqq 1$

9. (a) $7, -7$ **(b)** $2, -4$ **(c)** $4, -4$

(d) $2, -3$ **(e)** 3 **(f)** $-1, 2$

10. (a) **(b)**

(c) **(d)**

(c) **(f)**

REVIEW AND PREVIEW TO CHAPTER 3

Exercise 1

1. $5x^2 + 8x$ 2. $12ab + 2b$ 3. $a^2b - ab$

4. $6ab^2 - 2ab$ 5. $xy + 7x^2 + y^2$ 6. $2a^2 - 3a$

7. $8a - 1$ 8. $2x - 2$ 9. $2a^2 - 8a$

10. $11a^2 - 10a$

Exercise 2

1. $6a^2 - 11a - 10$ 2. $x^2 - 9$ 3. $a^2 + 10a + 25$

4. $x^2 - 49$ 5. $6x^2 + 5x - 25$ 6. $2x^2 - x - 6$

7. $a^2 - 6a + 9$ 8. $x^2 - x - 42$ 9. $x^2 + x - 42$

10. $a^2 - 100$ 11. $a^2 - 12a + 36$ 12. $3a^2 + a - 10$

13. $4x^2 + 12x + 9$ 14. $9a^2 - 4$ 15. $-15a^2 - 29a + 14$

Exercise 3

1. 9 2. 12 3 13 4. 14 5. 24

6. 25 7. 19 8. 17 9. 31 10. 27

11. 32 12. 45 13. 0.1 14. 11 15. 0.07

16. 4.5

Exercise 4

1. $3x^3 + x^2 - 8x + 4$ 2. $2x^3 - 11x^2 + 22x - 21$

3. $2x^4 - 19x^3 + 46x^2 - 41x + 12$ 4. $-x^3 - x^2 + 10x - 8$

5. $6x^4 + 4x^3 - 7x^2 + 2x - 5$ 6. $2x^3 - 5x^2 - 4x + 10$

7. $2x^2 - 5x + 3$ 8. $a^2 - 2a + 5$

9. $a^2 - 3a + 9$ 10. $x^2 + 2x + 4$

Exercise 5

1. 5 2. 5 3. 8 4. 17 5. 7 6. 25

CHAPTER 3

Exercise 3-1

1. **(a)** 4　　　　**(b)** 7　　　　**(c)** 9　　　　**(d)** 10　　　　**(e)** 11
   (f) $\frac{2}{3}$　　　**(g)** $\frac{6}{5}$　　　**(h)** $\frac{8}{9}$　　　**(i)** $\frac{6}{7}$　　　**(j)** $\frac{1}{4}$
   (k) 14　　　**(l)** 17　　　**(m)** 0.2　　**(n)** 21　　　**(o)** 0.03

2. **(a)** $\sqrt{6}$　　　**(b)** $\sqrt{66}$　　　**(c)** $\sqrt{15}$　　　**(d)** $\sqrt{35}$　　　**(e)** $\sqrt{77}$
   (f) $\sqrt{30}$　　**(g)** $\sqrt{42}$　　**(h)** $\sqrt{22}$　　**(i)** $\sqrt{143}$　　**(j)** $\sqrt{85}$
   (k) $\sqrt{39}$　　**(l)** 6

3. **(a)** $6\sqrt{10}$　　**(b)** $5\sqrt{21}$　　**(c)** $4\sqrt{15}$　　**(d)** $42\sqrt{10}$　　**(e)** $6\sqrt{30}$
   (f) $8\sqrt{35}$　　**(g)** $12\sqrt{10}$　　**(h)** $6\sqrt{6}$　　**(i)** $15\sqrt{6}$　　**(j)** $8\sqrt{21}$
   (k) $30\sqrt{10}$　　**(l)** 24

4. **(a)** $2\sqrt{3}$　　**(b)** $3\sqrt{2}$　　**(c)** $2\sqrt{5}$　　**(d)** $4\sqrt{2}$　　**(e)** $3\sqrt{5}$
   (f) $5\sqrt{3}$　　**(g)** $5\sqrt{2}$　　**(h)** 32　　　**(i)** $6\sqrt{2}$　　**(j)** $2\sqrt{17}$
   (k) $10\sqrt{2}$　　**(l)** $2\sqrt{6}$　　**(m)** $7\sqrt{2}$　　**(n)** $2\sqrt{7}$　　**(o)** $10\sqrt{3}$
   (p) $2\sqrt{2}$

5. **(a)** $\sqrt{12}$　　**(b)** $\sqrt{50}$　　**(c)** $\sqrt{45}$　　**(d)** $\sqrt{75}$　　**(e)** $\sqrt{99}$
   (f) $\sqrt{250}$　　**(g)** $\sqrt{300}$　　**(h)** $\sqrt{28}$　　**(i)** $\sqrt{200}$　　**(j)** $\sqrt{126}$
   (k) $\sqrt{252}$　　**(l)** $\sqrt{242}$　　**(m)** $\sqrt{1875}$　　**(n)** $\sqrt{800}$　　**(o)** $\sqrt{160}$
   (p) $\sqrt{175}$

6. **(a)** $2\sqrt{3}$　　**(b)** $2\sqrt{15}$　　**(c)** $7\sqrt{2}$　　**(d)** $3\sqrt{2}$　　**(e)** $5\sqrt{3}$
   (f) $5\sqrt{10}$　　**(g)** $2\sqrt{15}$　　**(h)** $15\sqrt{6}$　　**(i)** $10\sqrt{30}$　　**(j)** $70\sqrt{2}$
   (k) $30\sqrt{5}$　　**(l)** 36　　　**(m)** 6　　　**(n)** $5\sqrt{6}$　　**(o)** 30
   (p) 36　　　**(q)** $90\sqrt{3}$　　**(r)** 144

7. **(a)** $5x^2$　　**(b)** $7|x|$　　**(c)** x^4　　**(d)** $5x^2$　　**(e)** $15x|x|$
   (f) $|x|\sqrt{30x}$　　**(g)** $5x^2\sqrt{3x}$　　**(h)** $3x^2\sqrt{2}$　　**(i)** $3|x|\sqrt{5x}$
   (j) $3x^2\sqrt{2}$　　**(k)** $2\sqrt{5x}$　　**(l)** $3x^3\sqrt{3}$　　**(m)** $3x|x|\sqrt{3x}$
   (n) $|x|\sqrt{6}$　　**(o)** $2|x|\sqrt{2x}$　　**(p)** $3|x^3|\sqrt{3}$　　**(q)** $5x^2\sqrt{5}$
   (r) $8x^2\sqrt{x}$　　**(s)** $3|x|\sqrt{11x}$　　**(t)** $2|x^3|\sqrt{30x}$

Exercise 3-2

1. **(a)** $8\sqrt{2}$　　**(b)** $3\sqrt{3}$　　**(c)** $13\sqrt{11}$　　**(d)** $7\sqrt{5}$
   (e) $9\sqrt{13}$　　**(f)** $5\sqrt{5}$　　**(g)** $6\sqrt{2}$　　**(h)** $7\sqrt{3}$
   (i) $6\sqrt{2}$　　**(j)** $18\sqrt{3}$　　**(k)** $2\sqrt{7}$　　**(l)** $\sqrt{2}$
   (m) $11\sqrt{2}$　　**(n)** $8\sqrt{3}$

2. **(a)** $2\sqrt{2}+9\sqrt{11}$　　　**(b)** $14\sqrt{13}-3\sqrt{7}$　　　**(c)** $10\sqrt{3}+2\sqrt{2}$
   (d) $4\sqrt{7}-\sqrt{11}$　　　**(e)** $3\sqrt{5}+\sqrt{7}$　　　**(f)** $6\sqrt{3}$
   (g) $8\sqrt{10}-7$　　　**(h)** $16-11\sqrt{11}$

3. **(a)** $4\sqrt{3}+3$　　　**(b)** $10\sqrt{3}+5$　　　**(c)** $11+\sqrt{5}$
   (d) $7\sqrt{5}+5\sqrt{3}$　　**(e)** $\sqrt{7}$　　　**(f)** $2\sqrt{2}-11$

4. **(a)** $5\sqrt{3}$　　**(b)** $\sqrt{2}$　　**(c)** $9\sqrt{2}$　　**(d)** $2\sqrt{2}$
   (e) $5\sqrt{2}$　　**(f)** $\sqrt{3}$　　**(g)** $11\sqrt{2}$　　**(h)** $2\sqrt{3}$
   (i) $2\sqrt{6}-4\sqrt{2}$　　**(j)** $4\sqrt{2}$　　**(k)** $23\sqrt{3}$　　**(l)** $2\sqrt{2}$
   (m) $10\sqrt{2}$　　**(n)** $8\sqrt{2}$　　**(o)** $-3\sqrt{2}$　　**(p)** $18\sqrt{2}+\sqrt{3}$

5. **(a)** $3\sqrt{x}$　　**(b)** $4\sqrt{a}$　　**(c)** $21\sqrt{x}$　　**(d)** $2\sqrt{a}$
   (e) $2\sqrt{2x}$　　**(f)** 0　　　**(g)** $8|x|\sqrt{x}$　　**(h)** $4|x|\sqrt{2x}$

Exercise 3-3

1. (a) $\sqrt{15}+\sqrt{6}$ (b) $2\sqrt{7}+\sqrt{21}$ (c) $12\sqrt{2}-8\sqrt{5}$
   (d) $2\sqrt{2}-4$ (e) $\sqrt{6}+3\sqrt{2}$ (f) $6+3\sqrt{6}$
   (g) $6\sqrt{2}-2\sqrt{3}$ (h) $2\sqrt{3}+3\sqrt{6}$
2. (a) $3-\sqrt{2}$ (b) $\sqrt{5}+\sqrt{3}$ (c) $2\sqrt{3}-2\sqrt{5}$
   (d) $3\sqrt{7}+\sqrt{6}$ (e) $2\sqrt{5}-3$ (f) $3\sqrt{5}+1$
   (g) $2\sqrt{5}-\sqrt{3}$ (h) $3\sqrt{2}+\sqrt{5}$ (i) $2\sqrt{7}-\sqrt{5}$
3. (a) $11+6\sqrt{3}$ (b) $11+3\sqrt{15}$ (c) $4+\sqrt{6}$
   (d) $24-5\sqrt{5}$ (e) $37-6\sqrt{14}$ (f) $-9-8\sqrt{10}$
   (g) $16-8\sqrt{21}$ (h) $18-\sqrt{5}$
4. (a) $5+2\sqrt{6}$ (b) $7-2\sqrt{10}$ (c) $9-6\sqrt{2}$
   (d) $13-2\sqrt{42}$ (e) $22+12\sqrt{2}$ (f) $278-160\sqrt{3}$
   (g) $50-8\sqrt{6}$ (h) $372+24\sqrt{30}$ (i) $51+36\sqrt{2}$
   (j) $116-48\sqrt{5}$
5. (a) 1   (b) -1 (c) 18   (d) 8   (e) -5
   (f) 78   (g) 50   (h) 94
6. (a) $29+8\sqrt{3}$ (b) $-45+6\sqrt{2}$ (c) -4
7. (a) $6x+10\sqrt{x}$ (b) $x-25$ (c) $3x\sqrt{x}+3x$
   (d) $x-6\sqrt{x}+9$ (e) $x\sqrt{6}+x\sqrt{3}$ (f) $9x-1$
   (g) $16x-16\sqrt{x}+4$ (h) x^2-x

Exercise 3-4

1. (a) $\sqrt{2}$ (b) $\sqrt{6}$ (c) $9\sqrt{3}$ (d) 2   (e) $\sqrt{3}$
   (f) 6   (g) 5   (h) 15
2. (a) 2.65   (b) 1.41   (c) 2.45   (d) 47.4   (e) 44.7
   (f) 3.46   (g) 3.61   (h) 6.71   (i) 4.47   (j) 4.45
   (k) 1.27   (l) 0.764

3. (a) $\dfrac{\sqrt{15}}{3}$ (b) $\sqrt{2}$ (c) $\dfrac{\sqrt{30}}{4}$ (d) $\dfrac{2\sqrt{14}}{5}$

   (e) $\dfrac{\sqrt{21}}{2}$ (f) $\dfrac{\sqrt{15}}{5}$ (g) $\dfrac{3\sqrt{14}}{8}$ (h) $\sqrt{2}$

   (i) $\dfrac{\sqrt{10}+\sqrt{15}}{5}$ (j) $\dfrac{\sqrt{21}-4\sqrt{3}}{6}$ (k) $\dfrac{2\sqrt{15}-3}{6}$

   (l) $\dfrac{\sqrt{10}+\sqrt{14}-2}{4}$

4. (a) 1.15   (b) 1.89   (c) 1.10
   (d) 1.31   (e) 0.387   (f) 1.19
   (g) 1.39   (h) 1.09   (i) 6.15
   (j) 1.49   (k) 0.818   (l) 6.55

5. (a) $\dfrac{\sqrt{5}+\sqrt{3}}{2}$ (b) $\sqrt{3}-\sqrt{2}$ (c) $\dfrac{\sqrt{15}-\sqrt{6}}{3}$

   (d) $3\sqrt{2}+\sqrt{3}$ (e) $\sqrt{6}+\sqrt{2}$ (f) $\dfrac{14\sqrt{5}-7\sqrt{2}}{18}$

(g) $\dfrac{20+5\sqrt{3}}{13}$ **(h)** $\dfrac{11+6\sqrt{2}}{7}$ **(i)** $\dfrac{43+25\sqrt{3}}{13}$

(j) $-12-9\sqrt{2}$ **(k)** $6+\sqrt{35}$ **(l)** $\dfrac{57-12\sqrt{15}}{33}$

6. (a) $\dfrac{\sqrt{a}+\sqrt{b}}{a-b}$ **(b)** $\dfrac{2\sqrt{x}-4}{x-4}$ **(c)** $\dfrac{a+b-2\sqrt{ab}}{a-b}$

(d) $\dfrac{6x+9\sqrt{x}}{4x-9}$ **(e)** $\dfrac{\sqrt{x^2+x}-2\sqrt{x}}{x-3}$ **(f)** $\dfrac{2a+b+2\sqrt{a^2+ab}}{-b}$

7. (a) $\dfrac{2\sqrt{3}+3\sqrt{2}+3\sqrt{30}}{4}$ **(b)** $\dfrac{48\sqrt{2}+20\sqrt{6}-8\sqrt{3}-56}{23}$

8. (a) $\dfrac{\sqrt{2}}{3}$ **(b)** $\dfrac{\sqrt{6}}{3}$ **(c)** $\dfrac{\sqrt{2}}{3}$

(d) $3\sqrt{2}+3$ **(e)** $\sqrt{5}+\sqrt{2}$ **(f)** $\dfrac{2\sqrt{6}+\sqrt{2}+4\sqrt{3}+2}{11}$

Exercise 3-5

1. (a) 6.71 **(b)** 11.3 **(c)** 5.39 **(d)** 11.8
(e) 18.6 **(f)** 7.83 **(g)** 0.186 **(h)** 0.0524
2. (a) 5.83 **(b)** 9.80 **(c)** 11.5
3. 4.58 m **4.** 7.75 cm **5.** 5.29 cm
6. 46.6 cm **7. (a)** 8.88 s **(b)** 1.99 s
8. (a) 36.0 m^2 **(b)** 1180 m^2 **(c)** 358 m^2
9. 9.90 cm **10.** 8.60 cm **11.** 4.24 cm
12. 28.4 m **13.** 12.2 km **14.** 15.5 km
15. 9 m **16.** 6.93 cm **17.** 9.54 cm

Review Exercise

1. (a) $\sqrt{18}$ **(b)** $\sqrt{175}$ **(c)** $\sqrt{44}$ **(d)** $\sqrt{98}$ **(e)** $\sqrt{125}$
2. (a) $4\sqrt{2}$ **(b)** $5\sqrt{3}$ **(c)** $12\sqrt{2}$ **(d)** $11\sqrt{2}$ **(e)** $7\sqrt{3}$
3. (a) $30\sqrt{2}$ **(b)** $36\sqrt{2}$ **(c)** $40\sqrt{3}$ **(d)** $42\sqrt{2}$

(e) $48\sqrt{2}$ **(f)** $18\sqrt{10}$ **(g)** $\dfrac{\sqrt{2}}{12}$ **(h)** $6\sqrt{7}$ **(i)** $\sqrt{6}$

4. (a) $\sqrt{6}-5\sqrt{3}$ **(b)** $6\sqrt{6}-10\sqrt{2}$ **(c)** $2\sqrt{15}-\sqrt{10}$
(d) $4+2\sqrt{2}$ **(e)** $15\sqrt{2}-5\sqrt{6}$ **(f)** $6+6\sqrt{2}$
5. (a) 1 **(b)** $19+3\sqrt{35}$ **(c)** $31+12\sqrt{3}$
(d) $59-30\sqrt{2}$ **(e)** 23 **(f)** 2
6. (a) $\sqrt{6}$ **(b)** $\sqrt{5}$ **(c)** 1 **(d)** $\sqrt{7}$ **(e)** 10
7. (a) $2\sqrt{2}$ **(b)** $4\sqrt{3}$ **(c)** $8\sqrt{2}$ **(d)** $2\sqrt{10}$
(e) $15\sqrt{6}$ **(f)** $\sqrt{5}$ **(g)** $10\sqrt{7}$
8. (a) $4\sqrt{3}+8\sqrt{2}$ **(b)** $12\sqrt{3}+6\sqrt{2}$ **(c)** $14\sqrt{2}-4\sqrt{3}$
(d) $30\sqrt{5}$ **(e)** $18\sqrt{2}+8$

9. (a) $\dfrac{3\sqrt{2}}{2}$ **(b)** $\sqrt{10}$ **(c)** $\sqrt{21}$ **(d)** $\dfrac{2\sqrt{6}}{3}$

(e) $\dfrac{3\sqrt{2}}{2}$ **(f)** $\sqrt{2}$ **(g)** $\dfrac{2\sqrt{15}}{5}$ **(h)** $\sqrt{6}$

(i) $\sqrt{5}-\sqrt{2}$ **(j)** $8\sqrt{3}+4\sqrt{10}$ **(k)** $\dfrac{9\sqrt{6}+3\sqrt{2}}{26}$

(l) $\dfrac{5\sqrt{15}-\sqrt{6}}{3}$ **(m)** $\dfrac{3\sqrt{42}-10\sqrt{3}}{12}$ **(n)** $\dfrac{3\sqrt{15}+6\sqrt{6}}{6}$

(o) $\dfrac{21+4\sqrt{5}}{19}$ **(p)** $7-2\sqrt{6}$ **(q)** $\dfrac{23-2\sqrt{14}}{11}$

10. (a) 1.3   **(b)** 3.1   **(c)** 1.7   **(d)** 3.7   **(e)** 1.6
    (f) 2.7   **(g)** 4.6   **(h)** 0.69   **(i)** 0.31   **(j)** 1.6
    (k) 2.1

11. 6.6 m

12. 37 km

13. 2.83 cm

14. (a) $6\sqrt{x}$ **(b)** $|a|\sqrt{b}$ **(c)** $a^2|b|\sqrt{b}$
    (d) $|a|\,b^2\sqrt{ab}$

15. (a) 0   **(b)** $y\sqrt{x}$ **(c)** $5a\sqrt{b}-5b\sqrt{a}$

REVIEW AND PREVIEW TO CHAPTER 4

Exercise 1
A(4, 2), B(5, 6), C(8, 3), D(−4, 3), E(−8, 6), F(−6, −2), G(−2, −6), H(2, −3), I(6, −2), J(7, 0), K(0, 3), L(−6, 0), M(0, −9), N(7, −8).

CHAPTER 4

Exercise 4-1
1. (b) {1, 2, 3, 4, . . . 50}   **(c)** {6, 12, 18, 24, . . . 300}
    (d) 25 teams need 150 players
    (f) (20, 120), (31, 186), (40, 240)

2. (a) Domain: {5, 7, 8}, Range: {6, 12, 41}
    (b) Domain: {−3, 0, 3, 5}, Range: {−7, 6, 11, 20}
    (c) Domain: {2, 5}, Range: {7}
    (d) Domain: {−6}, Range: {3, 8, 14}
    (e) Domain: {a, c, e, g}, Range: {b, d, f, h}
    (f) Domain: {3, 4, 7, 15}, Range: {11}

3. (a) (1, 400), (2, 800), (9, 3600), $(13\frac{1}{2}, 5400)$, (20, 8000)
    (b) He ran 2400 m in 6 min
    (c) (8, 3200), (7, 2800), (11, 4400)
    (d) He ran 2000 m in 5 min; he ran 1000 m in 25 min; no meaning.

4. (b) {(1, 1), (2, 2), (3, 4), (4, 8), (5, 16), (6, 32), (7, 64), (8, 128), (9, 256), (10, 512),
       (11, 1024), (12, 2048), (13, 4096), (14, 8192)}.
    (c) Domain: {1, 2, 3, . . . 14}
    (d) Range: {1, 2, 4, . . . 8192}

5. (b) {(3, 0), (4, 2), (5, 5), (6, 9), (7, 14), (8, 20)}

  (c) Domain: {3, 4, 5, 6, 7, 8}

  (d) Range: {0, 2, 5, 9, 14, 20}

  (f) $\dfrac{n(n-3)}{2}$

6. Domain: {B, I, N, G, O}, Range: {1, 2, 3, ... 75}

7. Domain: {0, 1, 2, 3, 4}, Range: {0, 1, 2, 3}

8. (b) {(0, 1), (1, 2), (2, 4), (3, 7), (4, 11), (5, 16)}

  (c) {0, 1, 2, 3, 4, 5} **(d)** {1, 2, 4, 7, 11, 16}

  (e) There are no partial cuts. **(f)** 22

Exercise 4-2

1. (a), (d) **2.** (a), (b)

8. (a) {(1, 2), (1, 3), (2, 2), (2, 3), (3, 2), (3, 3)}

  (b) {(2, 2), (2, 3), (3, 2), (3, 3)}

  (c) {(1, 1), (1, 2), (1, 3), (2, 1), (2, 2), (2, 3), (3, 1), (3, 2), (3, 3)}

9. (a) (i) 6 (ii) 4 (iii) 9

  (b) The product of the number of elements in each set.

10. (a) {(6, 4), (6, 5), (7, 4), (7, 5)} **(b)** {(4, 8), (4, 9), (5, 8), (5, 9)}

  (c) {(8, 6), (8, 7), (9, 6), (9, 7)} **(d)** {(4, 4), (4, 5), (5, 4), (5, 5)}

11. (a) (i) {(−3, 0), (−3, 1), (−2, 0), (−2, 1), (−1, 0), (−1, 1)}

    (ii) {(0, 3), (0, 4), (1, 3), (1, 4)}

    (iii) {(−3, 3), (−3, 4), (−2, 3), (−2, 4), (−1, 3), (−1, 4)}

    (iv) {(3, 3), (3, 4), (4, 3), (4, 4)}

  (b) $K \times K$ **(c)** $K \times K$ **(d)** $G \times K, H \times K, K \times K$

  (e) $G \times H, H \times K, G \times K, K \times K$

12. (a) no **(b)** 2 **(c)** $P \times M, M \times S, S \times M$

13. $A = B$

Exercise 4-3

1. {(2, 2), (3, 3), (4, 4), (5, 5)}

2. {(0, 4), (4, 0), (1, 3), (3, 1), (2, 2)}

3. {(1, 0), (2, 1), (3, 2), (4, 3), (5, 4)}

4. (a) {(0, 1), (0, 2), (1, 2)} **(b)** {(1, 0), (2, 0), (2, 1)}

  (c) Domain: {0, 1} **(d)** Domain: {1, 2}

5. (a) {(7, 6), (7, 7), (7, 8), (7, 9)}

  (b) {(6, 9), (7, 9), (8, 9), (9, 9)}

  (c) Domain: {7}, Range: {6, 7, 8, 9}

  (d) Domain: {6, 7, 8, 9}, Range: {9}

6. (a) {(1, 1), (1, 2), (1, 3), (1, 4), (2, 1), (2, 2), (2, 3), (2, 4)

    (3, 1), (3, 2), (3, 3), (3, 4), (4, 1), (4, 2), (4, 3), (4, 4)}

  (b) (i) {(1, 1), (2, 2), (3, 3), (4, 4)}

    (ii) {(1, 2), (1, 3), (1, 4), (2, 3), (2, 4), (3, 4)}

    (iii) {(2, 1), (3, 1), (3, 2), (4, 1), (4, 2), (4, 3)}

    (iv) {(1, 2), (2, 2), (3, 2), (4, 2)}

7. (a) {(−2, −2), (−1, −1), (0, 0), (1, 1), (2, 2)}

  (b) {(−1, −2), (0, −2), (0, −1), (1, −2), (1, −1), (1, 0), (2, −2), (2, −1), (2, 0), (2, 1)}

  (c) {(−2, 2), (−1, 1), (0, 0), (1, −1), (2, −2)}

  (d) {(−1, −2), (−1, −1), (−1, 0), (−1, 1), (−1, 2)}

8. (a) {(−4, −4), (−3, −3), (−2, −2), (−1, −1), (0, 0), (1, 1)}

(b) $\{(-4,-3), (-4,-2), (-4,-1), (-4,0), (-4,1), (-3,-2), (-3,-1), (-3,0), (-3,1),$
$(-2,-1), (-2,0), (-2,1), (-1,0), (-1,1), (0,1)\}$
(c) $\{(-4,0), (-3,-1), (-2,-2), (-1,-3), (0,-4)\}$
(d) $\{(0,-4), (0,-3), (0,-2), (0,-1), (0,0), (0,1), (1,-4), (1,-3), (1,-2), (1,-1),$
$(1,0), (1,-1)\}$
(e) $\{(-4,-4), (-3,-4), (-2,-4), (-1,-4), (0,-4), (1,-4), (-4,-3), (-3,-3),$
$(-2,-3), (-1,-3), (0,-3), (1,-3)\}$

Exercise 4-6

1. **(a), (b), (d), (e), (h)**   **2.** **(a), (b), (d), (e)**
3. (a) 12   **(b)** 7   **(c)** 4   **(d)** 1   **(e)** 14   **(f)** -7
(g) -9 **(h)** 2   **(i)** -15
4. (a) 2   **(b)** 10   **(c)** 6   **(d)** 9   **(e)** 4   **(f)** 1
(g) -9 **(e)** -14 **(i)** -2
5. (a) yes **(b)** no   **6.** No
7. (b) Domain: $\{1, 2, 3, 4, 5\}$, Range: $\{-1, 1, 3, 5, 7\}$
(c) Yes
8. (b) Domain: $\{-2, -1, 0, 1, 2\}$, Range: $\{2, 3, 6\}$
(c) Yes
9. (b) Domain: $\{0, 1, 2, 3, 4\}$, Range: $\{4, 7, 10, 13, 16\}$
(c) Yes
10. (b) Yes
11. (a) $\{(0, -4), (1, 1), (2, 6), (3, 11), (4, 16)\}$
(b) Domain: $\{0, 1, 2, 3, 4\}$, Range: $\{-4, 1, 6, 11, 16\}$
(c) Yes
12. (a) $\{(0, 3), (2, 4), (4, 5), (6, 6)\}$
(b) Yes
13. (a) $\{(-2, 4), (-1, -2), (0, -4), (1, -2), (2, 4)\}$
(b) Yes
14. $\{(0, 0), (0, 1), (0, 2), (0, 3), (1, 0), (1, 1), (1, 2), (1, 3), (2, 0), (2, 1), (2, 2), (2, 3), (3, 0),$
$(3, 1), (3, 2), (3, 3), (4, 0), (4, 1), (4, 2), (4, 3)\}$.
Not a function.
15. $\{(4, -2), (1, -1), (0, 0), (1, 1), (4, 2)\}$. Not a function.
16. (a) $f : x \to 3x - 7$ **(b)** $f : x \to 4x + 6$
(c) $f : x \to -5x + 13$ **(d)** $f : x \to \dfrac{4 - 2x}{3}$

Exercise 4-7

1. (a) 7   **(b)** 11   **(c)** -5 **(d)** 3   **(e)** 43   **(f)** -25
(g) -397 **(h)** 203   **(i)** 27   **(j)** -17 **(k)** $4a + 3$ **(l)** $4b + 3$
2. (a) 1   **(b)** 16   **(c)** -14 **(d)** -5 **(e)** 25   **(f)** -35
(g) -26 **(h)** 55   **(i)** -17 **(j)** $3m - 5$ **(k)** $3t - 5$ **(l)** $3a^2 - 5$
3. (a) 4   **(b)** -8 **(c)** 5   **(d)** 0   **(e)** 13   **(f)** 4
(g) -7 **(h)** -11 **(i)** 13   **(j)** $\frac{1}{4}$ **(k)** 6   **(l)** 0
4. (a) 8, (2, 8)   **(b)** 13, $(-3, 13)$ **(c)** 40, (6, 40)
(d) 8, $(-2, 8)$
5. (a) -3, (2, -3)   **(b)** -6, $(-4, -6)$ **(c)** -1, (6, -1)
(d) $\frac{1}{2}$, $(9, \frac{1}{2})$
6. (a) 5   **(b)** 5   **(c)** 25   **(d)** 7
7. (a) 9   **(b)** 25   **(c)** 0   **(d)** 9

8. (a) 6   **(b)** 18   **(c)** -24 **(d)** -23
9. (a) 18   **(b)** 14   **(c)** 1   **(d)** 20
10. (a) 39   **(b)** 7   **(c)** 78   **(d)** 35
11. (a) -13 **(b)** 1   **(c)** 5   **(d)** -9 **(e)** 2   **(f)** -19
12. (a) 16   **(b)** 6   **(c)** 4   **(d)** 18
13. (a) 2   **(b)** 7   **(c)** -5
14. $-1, 2$
15. (a) $3x + 5$ **(b)** $3x - 1$ **(c)** $6x - 7$

Exercise 4-8

1. (a), (d), (i), (j),
2. (a) $-3 \leqq x \leqq 4$, $0 \leqq y \leqq 3$, yes   **(b)** $-4 \leqq x \leqq 4$, $-2 \leqq y \leqq 2$, yes
   (c) $-3 \leqq x \leqq 4$, $-4 \leqq y \leqq 1$, yes   **(d)** $-2 \leqq x \leqq 1$, $-4 \leqq y \leqq 4$, yes
   (e) $-6 \leqq x \leqq 2$, $y = 2$, yes   **(f)** $x = -2$, $-2 \leqq y \leqq 4$, no
   (g) $x \in R$, $y \in R$, yes   **(h)** $-3 \leqq x \leqq 3$, $-3 \leqq y \leqq 3$, no
   (i) $-3 \leqq x \leqq 3$, $0 \leqq y \leqq 4$, yes   **(j)** $-3 \leqq x \leqq 3$, $-1 \leqq y \leqq 3$, no ✓
   (k) $x \in R$, $y \geqq 0$, yes   **(l)** $x \leqq 0$, $y \in R$, no
3. (a) $-20 \leqq x \leqq 20$, $-10 \leqq y \leqq 20$, yes   **(b)** $-8 \leqq x \leqq 8$, $-8 \leqq y \leqq 8$, no
   (c) $x \in R$, $y \geqq 0$, yes   **(d)** $-30 \leqq x \leqq 50$, $-20 \leqq y \leqq 40$, no
   (e) $x \in R$, $y \leqq 3$, yes   **(f)** $x \in R$, $y \in R$, yes
   (g) $-20 \leqq x \leqq 0$, $-20 \leqq y \leqq 20$, no
   (h) $x \geqq 0$, $y \in R$, no   **(i)** $-9 \leqq x \leqq 6$, $-12 \leqq y \leqq 15$, no
5. (a), (b), (d)
6. (a), (c), (e), (g)
8. (b), (c), (d)

Review Exercise

1. (a) Domain: {5, 6, 7, 9}, Range: {11, 14, 28, 43}
   (b) Domain: {−3, −1, 0, 3}, Range: {4, 5, 7, 12}
   (c) Domain: {−3}, Range: {6, 7, 8, 9, 10}
   (d) Domain: {−5, −4, −3}, Range: {−2}
   (e) Domain: {5, 6, 7}, Range: {−4, −3, −2, −1, 0}
   (f) Domain: {a, c, e, g}, Range: {b, d, f, h}
2. (b), (c), (e), (f)
3. (a) {(0, −1), (0, 0), (1, −1), (1, 0), (2, −1), (2, 0)}
   (b) {(−1, 0), (−1, 1), (−1, 2), (0, 0), (0, 1), (0, 2)}
   (c) {(6, −1), (6, 0), (7, −1), (7, 0)}
   (d) (i) 12   (ii) 8   (iii) 6   (iv) 16
4. (a) {(1, 1), (2, 2), (3, 3), (4, 4)}
   (b) {(1, 2), (1, 3), (1, 4), (2, 3), (2, 4), (3, 4)}
   (c) {(2, 1), (3, 1), (4, 1), (3, 2), (4, 2), (4, 3)}
   (d) {(4, 1), (4, 2), (4, 3), (4, 4)}
   (e) {(1, 2), (2, 2), (3, 2), (4, 2)}
5. (a), (b), (f)
6. (a) 7   **(b)** 13   **(c)** 5   **(d)** -1 **(e)** 5   **(f)** -5
   (g) -6 **(h)** -10
7. (a) 5   **(b)** 11   **(c)** 4   **(d)** 59   **(e)** 9   **(f)** 0
   (g) -19 **(h)** -16 **(i)** 2   **(j)** -2 **(k)** $2a + 1$ **(l)** $3b - 1$
8. (a) $x \in R$, $y \in R$, yes   **(b)** $-2 \leqq x \leqq 2$, $-1 \leqq y \leqq 3$, yes
   (c) $-4 \leqq x \leqq 3$, $-1 \leqq y \leqq 3$, no   **(d)** $-2 \leqq x \leqq 2$, $-3 \leqq y \leqq 3$, no

(e) $-2 \leq x \leq 2, -3 \leq y \leq 2$, yes **(f)** $-3 \leq x \leq 3, -3 \leq y \leq 3$, no

(g) $-10 \leq x \leq 10, 0 \leq y \leq 20$, yes **(h)** $-6 \leq x \leq 6, -6 \leq y \leq 6$, no

(i) $x \in R, y \leq 12$, yes

9. (a) $\{(-1, -1), (0, 0), (1, 1), (2, 2), (3, 3)\}$

(b) $\{(-1, 0), (-1, 1), (-1, 2), (-1, 3), (0, 1) (0, 2)$
$(0, 3), (1, 2), (1, 3), (2, 3)\}$

(c) $\{(1, -1), (2, 0), (3, 1)\}$

(d) $\{(0, -1), (0, 0), (0, 1), (0, 2), (0, 3)\}$

(e) $\{(-1, -1), (0, -1), (1, -1), (2, -1), (3, -1)\}$

13. (a) -14 **(b)** 16 **(c)** 2 **(d)** 12 **(e)** 5 **(f)** 28

15. (a), (b), (d), (e)

REVIEW AND PREVIEW TO CHAPTER 5

Exercise 1

1. (a) **(b)** **(c)**

(d) **(e)** **(f)**

(g) **(h)**

2. (a) **(b)** **(c)**

(d) **(e)** **(f)**

(g)

Exercise 2

1. (a) $l = \dfrac{A}{w}, w = \dfrac{A}{l}$ **(b)** $p = \dfrac{I}{rt}, t = \dfrac{I}{pr}$ **(c)** $r = \dfrac{C}{2\pi}$

(d) $l = \dfrac{V}{wh}, w = \dfrac{V}{lh}$ **(e)** $S = \dfrac{D}{T}, T = \dfrac{D}{S}$ **(f)** $h = \dfrac{2A}{b}, b = \dfrac{2A}{h}$

(g) $l = \dfrac{P - 2w}{2}, w = \dfrac{P - 2l}{2}$ **(h)** $h = \dfrac{2A}{(a+b)}, b = \dfrac{2A - ha}{h}$

(i) $x = \dfrac{-By - C}{A}, y = \dfrac{-Ax - C}{B}$ **(j)** $r = \sqrt{\dfrac{A}{\pi}}$

CHAPTER 5

Exercise 5-1

1. (a) second   (b) first   (c) fourth   (d) first   (e) third
   (f) fifth   (g) second   (h) second   (i) second   (j) third
   (k) sixth   (l) third   (m) first   (n) second   (o) fourth

2. (a) $y=-2x+7$ (b) $y=4x-3$ (c) $y=-5x$ (d) $y=3$
  (e) $y=2x-7$ (f) $y=6x$ (g) $y=-3x+6$ (h) $y=-3x+4$

3. (a) $y=x-6$ (b) $y=4x+7$ (c) $y=-3x-5$ (d) $y=-6x+5$
  (e) $y=4x$ (f) $y=2$ (g) $y=7x-3$ (h) $y=-x$

4. (a) $y=-\frac{3}{2}x+\frac{5}{2}$ (b) $y=-\frac{5}{4}x+\frac{3}{4}$ (c) $y=-\frac{2}{3}x-\frac{8}{3}$ (d) $y=-\frac{2}{7}x$

  (e) $y=-\frac{x}{3}+1$ (f) $y=2x-\frac{3}{2}$ (g) $y=-2x+\frac{3}{2}$ (h) $y=\frac{x}{3}+\frac{4}{3}$

5. (a) $y=\frac{2}{3}x-\frac{7}{3}$ (b) $y=\frac{x}{4}+\frac{5}{4}$ (c) $y=\frac{5}{2}x-5$ (d) $y=x-\frac{7}{2}$

  (e) $y=2x+\frac{4}{5}$ (f) $y=\frac{7}{2}x+3$ (g) $y=\frac{4}{5}x$ (h) $y=\frac{1}{5}$

6. (a) $y=-\frac{x}{6}+\frac{4}{3}$ (b) $y=-\frac{x}{6}+4$ (c) $y=\frac{4}{3}x-10$ (d) $y=\frac{2}{5}x-3$

  (e) $y=\frac{4}{5}x+12$ (f) $y=4x+\frac{20}{3}$

7. (a) $y=-2x+7$ (b) $y=-3x+4$ (c) $y=-4x-4$ (d) $y=2x-5$

  (e) $y=3x-\frac{5}{2}$ (f) $y=\frac{3}{2}x+3$ (g) $y=\frac{5}{2}x$ (h) $y=-\frac{x}{3}$

  (i) $y=3x-\frac{2}{3}$ (j) $y=-\frac{4}{3}x+\frac{7}{3}$

Exercise 5-2

1. (a) $x=3, y=2$ (b) $x=3, y=4$ (c) $x=3, y=9$
  (d) $x=8, y=2$ (e) $x=2, y=-5$ (f) $x=3, y=-7$
  (g) $x=-5, y=4$ (h) $x=-5, y=3$ (i) $x=2, y=7$
  (j) $x=-3, y=8$ (k) $x=2, y=-8$ (l) $x=4, y=12$

2. (a) $x=5, y=4$ (b) $x=4, y=-3$ (c) $x=2, y=4$
  (d) $x=3, y=5$ (e) $x=-7, y=7$ (f) $x=-2, y=-5$
  (g) $x=7, y=2$ (h) $x=-6, y=2$

3. (a) $x=2, y=-6$ (b) $x=2, y=4$ (c) $x=-3, y=-3$
  (d) $x=-4, y=2$ (e) $x=3, y=1$ (f) $x=2, y=3$
  (g) $x=12, y=-6$ (h) $x=-3, y=8$

4. (a) $x=\frac{3}{2}$ (b) $y=-3$ (c) $x=3, -3, y=-9$
  (d) $x=2, -2, y=-8$ (e) $x=5, -5, y=5, -5$ (f) $x=2, -2, y=3, -3$

Exercise 5-3

1. a, c, d, f 2. a, d, f 3. a, d, h
4. a, b, f, g 5. a, c, d, f, g

6. (a) yes   (b) no   (c) no   (d) no   (e) yes   (f) yes
  (g) yes   (h) yes   (i) yes   (j) no   (k) yes   (l) no
  (m) yes   (n) no

7. (a) yes   (b) yes   (c) no   (d) yes   (e) no   (f) no
  (g) no   (h) yes   (i) yes   (j) no   (k) yes   (l) no
  (m) no   (n) no

9. (a) 2   (b) 5   (c) -4 (d) 3   (e) -3 (f) 4
  (g) 2   (h) $-\frac{1}{2}$

Exercise 5-6

1. (a) First   (b) second   (c) first, second, fourth
   (d) fourth   (e) second, third, fourth   (f) third
   (g) first, second, third

Review Exercise

1. (a) first,   (b) third   (c) third   (d) second   (e) third
   (f) second   (g) fifth   (h) second   (i) sixth
2. (a) $x = 5, y = 4$ (b) $x = 10, y = 5$ (c) $x = 2, y = -6$
   (d) $x = 2, y = -7$ (e) $x = -3, y = 2$ (f) $x = 1, y = -4$
   (g) $x = 9, y = 2$ (h) $x = 3, y = 12$ (i) $x = -5, y = 6$
3. a, e, f
4. b, c, e, h
5. (a) $y = -3x + 14$ (b) $y = -2x + \frac{9}{2}$ (c) $y = \frac{5}{3}x - 2$
   (d) $y = \frac{7}{2}x + 2$ (e) $y = x - 7$ (f) $y = \frac{3}{2}x - 6$
6. (a) $y = -3x + 4$ (b) $y = 2x - 5$ (c) $y = 2x - \frac{7}{2}$

   (d) $y = \frac{1}{2}x - \frac{3}{4}$ (e) $y = \frac{4}{3}x$ (f) $y = \dfrac{x}{4} + \dfrac{3}{2}$

8. (a) yes   (b) yes   (c) no   (d) yes   (e) no
   (f) yes   (g) yes   (h) no

REVIEW AND PREVIEW TO CHAPTER 6

Exercise 1

1. (a) $a = 10$ (b) $b = 12$ (c) $c = 12$ (d) $b \doteq 6.93$
   (e) $a \doteq 9.22$ (f) $b = 32$ (g) $a \doteq 17$ (h) $c = 48$
2. (a) $x \doteq 16.9$ (b) $x \doteq 4.90$ (c) $x = 5$ (d) $x = 2$

Exercise 2

1. (a) $y = -2x + 7, m = -2, b = 7$ (b) $y = -\frac{3}{2}x + 2, m = -\frac{3}{2}, b = 2$
   (c) $y = x - 4, m = 1, b = -4$ (d) $y = -\frac{5}{3}x + \frac{5}{3}, m = -\frac{5}{3}, b = \frac{5}{3}$

   (e) $y = -\dfrac{x}{3} + \dfrac{7}{3}, m = -\frac{1}{3}, b = \frac{7}{3}$ (f) $y = \frac{4}{3}x + \frac{7}{3}, m = \frac{4}{3}, b = \frac{7}{3}$

   (g) $y = \frac{5}{3}x - \frac{2}{3}, m = \frac{5}{3}, b = -\frac{2}{3}$ (h) $y = 3x + \frac{11}{2}, m = 3, b = \frac{11}{2}$
   (i) $y = \frac{2}{5}x - 1, m = \frac{2}{5}, b = -1$ (j) $y = -\frac{7}{3}x + \frac{4}{3}, m = -\frac{7}{3}, b = \frac{4}{3}$

Exercise 3

1. (a) $x = 3, y = 6$ (b) $x = 3, y = 4$ (c) $x = 4, y = -6$
   (d) $x = 3, y = -5$ (e) $x = 2, y = 7$ (f) $x = -4, y = 5$
   (g) $x = 0, y = 0$ (h) $x = -2, y = 3$ (i) $x = 4, y = -2$
   (j) $x = 2, y = -10$ (k) $x = 3, y = 6$ (l) $x = -3, y = -3$

CHAPTER 6

Exercise 6-1

2. (a) $\frac{2}{3}$ (b) 1   (c) 1   (d) $\frac{6}{5}$ (e) 0   (f) $-\frac{3}{4}$
   (g) -4 (h) $-\frac{7}{2}$

3. (a) $-\frac{10}{9}$ **(b)** 0 **(c)** no slope **(d)** 1 **(e)** no slope **(f)** -1
(g) -4 **(h)** $\frac{6}{5}$ **(i)** $-\frac{35}{57}$ **(j)** no slope **(k)** -2.4
(l) 0.35 **(m)** 0.26 **(n)** 4.6

4. (a) 3 **(b)** -1 **(c)** $-\frac{2}{3}$ **(d)** $\frac{5}{3}$ **(e)** $\frac{1}{3}$ **(f)** 2
(g) 2 **(h)** -3

5. (a) $y=8$ **(b)** $y=-8$ **(c)** $y=-3$ **(d)** $x=2$

Exercise 6-2

1. (a) $5x+3y-7=0$ **(b)** $3x-2y+4=0$ **(c)** $4x+5y-3=0$
(d) $7x+3y+2=0$ **(e)** $3x+5y-2=0$ **(f)** $7x-2y+3=0$
(g) $4x-3y+5=0$ **(h)** $3x-4y=0$ **(i)** $2x+7=0$
(j) $-4y+3=0$ **(k)** $4x-3y+2=0$ **(l)** $2x-y-7=0$

2. (a) $4x-y-10=0$ **(b)** $2x-y-3=0$ **(c)** $3x+y+13=0$
(d) $x+y+5=0$ **(e)** $3x-y+14=0$ **(f)** $6x+y-22=0$
(g) $x-2y+10=0$ **(h)** $x+3y-12=0$ **(i)** $2x+4y+7=0$
(j) $20x-30y-11=0$ **(k)** $0.1x-y+0.58=0$ **(l)** $1.2x+y+0.24=0$
(m) $6.1x-y-24=0$ **(n)** $4.6x-y+15.06=0$

3. (a) $2x-y=0$ **(b)** $6x-y+3=0$ **(c)** $2x+y-2=0$
(d) $3x+y+13=0$ **(e)** $3x-y+1=0$ **(f)** $x-2y-6=0$
(g) $x+2y+4=0$ **(h)** $x-3y-14=0$ **(i)** $0.1x+y-0.36=0$
(j) $1.4x+y-0.08=0$

4. $2x-y-10=0$ **5.** $3x+y+2=0$

6. (a) $4x-y+26=0$ **(b)** $y=6$ **(c)** $x=-5$

7. $y=0$ **8.** $x=0$ **9.** $2x-y+12=0$

Exercise 6-3

1. (a) $m=4, b=6$ **(b)** $m=1, b=-4$ **(c)** $m=-2, b=-3$
(d) $m=-7, b=4$ **(e)** $m=\frac{1}{2}, b=-6$ **(f)** $m=-\frac{2}{3}, b=7$
(g) $m=3, b=-7$ **(h)** $m=-2, b=6$ **(i)** $m=0, b=5$
(j) no slope, no y-intercept   **(k)** $m=0, b=-2$
(l) no slope, no y-intercept   **(m)** $m=-3, b=2$
(n) $m=2, b=0$ **(o)** $m=-2, b=5$

2. (a) $y=2x+3$ **(b)** $y=4x-2$ **(c)** $y=-2x-4$
(d) $y=3$ **(e)** $y=-x$ **(f)** $y=-\frac{1}{2}x-2$
(g) $y=0.2x+1.7$ **(h)** $y=-1.5x-4.6$ **(i)** $y=-\frac{4}{5}x$
(j) $y=-\frac{1}{5}$ **(k)** $y=15.3x-45.6$ **(l)** $y=-9.8x+23.1$

3. (a) $y=-3x+7$ **(b)** $y=-\frac{1}{2}x+2$ **(c)** $y=-\frac{2}{3}x+3$
(d) $y=4x-5$ **(e)** $y=\frac{3}{2}x+2$ **(f)** $y=-\frac{1}{3}x+\frac{5}{6}$
(g) $y=\frac{4}{3}x+\frac{2}{3}$ **(h)** $y=\frac{4}{5}x+\frac{1}{5}$ **(i)** $y=-\frac{2}{3}x$
(j) $y=-7$

4. (a) $m=-\frac{2}{3}, b=\frac{8}{3}$ **(b)** $m=\frac{3}{2}, b=-\frac{5}{2}$ **(c)** $m=-\frac{5}{2}, b=-2$
(d) $m=-\frac{2}{5}, b=0$ **(e)** $m=\frac{7}{3}, b=\frac{2}{3}$ **(j)** $m=\frac{7}{2}, b=2$
(g) $m=0, b=\frac{7}{2}$ **(h)** no slope, no y intercept
(i) $m=-6, b=8$ **(j)** $m=4, b=-0.4$ **(k)** $m=-0.8, b=0.4$
(l) $m=-12, b=0$

6. $y=m(x-a)$

Exercise 6-4

1. (a) $2x-y-1=0$ **(b)** $3x-y+1=0$ **(c)** $5x+y+10=0$
(d) $2x+y+8=0$ **(e)** $4x+y+4=0$ **(f)** $x-2y=0$

(g) $x - 3y + 11 = 0$ **(h)** $y - 4 = 0$ **(i)** $x - 3 = 0$

(j) $9x + 2y - 19 = 0$ **(k)** $4x - y - 3 = 0$ **(l)** $3x - 2y + 1.8 = 0$

(m) $3x + 2y - 4.2 = 0$ **(n)** $5x + 2y + 18 = 0$

2. $4x - y + 18 = 0$ **3.** $3x + 4y - 8 = 0$ **4.** $4x - 5y - 20 = 0$

5. $5x - y - 5 = 0$ **6.** $2x + y - 8 = 0$ **7.** $3x - y - 2 = 0$

8. $bx + ay - ab = 0$

Exercise 6-5

2. (a) $2, -\frac{1}{2}$ **(b)** $3, -\frac{1}{3}$ **(c)** $-3, \frac{1}{3}$ **(d)** $-1, 1$ **(e)** $\frac{1}{2}, -2$

(f) $-\frac{2}{3}, \frac{3}{2}$ **(g)** $-\frac{3}{4}, \frac{4}{3}$ **(h)** $\frac{5}{4}, -\frac{4}{5}$ **(i)** $-7, \frac{1}{7}$ **(j)** $3, -\frac{1}{3}$

(k) $-3, \frac{1}{3}$ **(l)** $-\frac{5}{2}, \frac{2}{5}$ **(m)** $\frac{5}{4}, -\frac{4}{5}$ **(n)** $3, -\frac{1}{3}$ **(o)** $\frac{5}{7}, -\frac{7}{5}$

(p) $-\frac{3}{2}, \frac{2}{3}$

3. $2x - y + 8 = 0$ **4.** $2x + y + 7 = 0$ **5.** $x + 2y - 7 = 0$

6. $3x - 4y + 18 = 0$ **7. (b)** $3x + 4y - 20 = 0$ **(c)** $x + 2y = 0$

Exercise 6-6

1. (a) 5   **(b)** 6   **(c)** 11   **(d)** 11   **(e)** 7   **(f)** 17

(g) 15   **(h)** 10   **(i)** 8   **(j)** 1   **(k)** 4   **(l)** 3.2

2. (a) $\sqrt{58}$ **(b)** $\sqrt{89}$ **(c)** $\sqrt{34}$ **(d)** $\sqrt{234}$ **(e)** $\sqrt{265}$ **(f)** $\sqrt{85}$

(g) $5\sqrt{10}$ **(h)** $\sqrt{113}$ **(i)** $\sqrt{17}$ **(j)** $\sqrt{8}$ **(k)** $\sqrt{5}$ **(l)** $\sqrt{89}$

(m) 2.6   **(n)** $\sqrt{49.46}$

3. $AB = 2\sqrt{13}, BC = \sqrt{29}, AC = \sqrt{97}$ **4.** $AC = \sqrt{202}, BD = 3\sqrt{10}$

5. $AC = \sqrt{41}, BC = \sqrt{41}$ **6.** 5

8. (b) $5x - 3y + 14 = 0$ **(d)** $AS = \sqrt{34}, SB = \sqrt{34}$

(e) $6x + y - 20 = 0$ **(g)** $AT = \sqrt{37}, CT = \sqrt{37}$

(h) $m_{ST} = -\frac{1}{4}, m_{BC} = -\frac{1}{4}$ **(i)** $ST = \sqrt{17}, BC = 2\sqrt{17}$

(j) $ST = \frac{1}{2}BC$

9. (b) $3x - 5y + 2 = 0$ **(e)** $m_{AC} = \frac{3}{5}, m_{CB} = \frac{3}{5}$

(g) (i) Yes   (ii) No   (iii) Yes

Exercise 6-7

1. (b) $c = 9n + 350$ **(c)** \$2150   **(d)** \$1700

(e) cost per meal   **(f)** 350   **(g)** 220

(i) $0 < p \leq 300, 350 < c \leq 3050$

2. (b) $t = 12.5h + 10$ **(c)** temperature rise per hour   **(d)** 22.5°C

(e) 10°C, cold water temperature   **(f)** $3.2h$

(g) $0 \leq h \leq 4, 10 \leq t \leq 60$

3. (b) $c = 3x + 1000$ **(c)** $0 < n \leq 500, 1000 \leq c \leq 2500$

(d) \$2200   **(e)** 450   **(f)** cost of lunch per person

(g) \$1000, cost of band

4. (b) $l = -0.2d + 100$ **(c)** litres per kilometre   **(d)** 20ℓ

(e) 100ℓ **(f)** 500 km   **(g)** 70ℓ

(h) $0 \leq d \leq 500, 0 \leq \ell \leq 100$

5. (b) $d = 330t$ **(c)** distance per second time interval

(d) 2046 m.

Review Exercise

1. (a) $m = 7, b = 6$ **(b)** $m = -3, b = 14$

(c) $m = 4, b = -7$ **(d)** $m = \frac{1}{3}, b = -4$

(e) $m = -2, b = \frac{7}{2}$ **(f)** no slope, no y intercept
(g) $m = 0, b = -4$ **(h)** $m = \frac{3}{5}, b = -\frac{9}{5}$
(i) $m = \frac{4}{7}, b = \frac{11}{7}$

2. (a) 5   **(b)** 2   **(c)** 7   **(d)** 16   **(e)** 6   **(f)** 11
   (g) 7   **(h)** 15
3. (a) -1 **(b)** $-\frac{1}{3}$ **(c)** $-\frac{1}{2}$ **(d)** 6   **(e)** -6 **(f)** -5
4. (a) $7x - y - 22 = 0$ **(b)** $x + y + 8 = 0$ **(c)** $2x + y + 2 = 0$
   (d) $x - 2y - 17 = 0$ **(e)** $1.4x + y + 5.6 = 0$ **(f)** $0.2x + y + 0.52 = 0$
5. (a) $2x + y + 13 = 0$ **(b)** $x = -4$ **(c)** $y = -5$
6. (a) $5x - 2y - 7 = 0$ **(b)** $4x - 9y - 38 = 0$ **(c)** $12x + 5y - 1 = 0$
   (d) $x + 2y = 0$
7. $2x - y - 17 = 0$ **8.** $x - 2y - 5 = 0$
9. (a) $3\sqrt{10}$ **(b)** $3\sqrt{2}$ **(c)** $\sqrt{261}$ **(d)** $2\sqrt{5}$
10. $AC = \sqrt{269}, BD = \sqrt{194}$
11. (a) $(4, 6), (-6, 2), (2, -2)$ **(b)** $\sqrt{116}, 2\sqrt{17}, 4\sqrt{5}$ **(c)** No
12. (c) $x + 3y - 4 = 0, 3x - 5y + 2 = 0$
   (d) $(1, 1)$ **(e)** $PT = \sqrt{34}, QT = \sqrt{10}, RT = \sqrt{34}, ST = \sqrt{10}$
   (f) No
13. (b) $C = 5x + 1000$ **(c)** cost/book   **(d)** \$2500   **(e)** \$2000
   (f) 500   **(g)** $(0, 1000)$

REVIEW AND PREVIEW TO CHAPTER 7

Exercise 1
1. (a) 15   **(b)** 4   **(c)** 5   **(d)** 12   **(e)** 7   **(f)** 8
   (g) 15   **(h)** 7   **(i)** 5
2. (a) 5   **(b)** -8 **(c)** 0   **(d)** -1 **(e)** 2   **(f)** -4
   (g) -20 **(h)** -1 **(i)** -10

Exercise 2
1. (a) -5 **(b)** 4   **(c)** 4   **(d)** 4   **(e)** 1   **(f)** -3
2. (a) 9   **(b)** -12 **(c)** -3 **(d)** 3   **(e)** 5   **(f)** 2

Exercise 3
1. (a) $\frac{3}{2}$ **(b)** 19   **(c)** $\frac{9}{4}$ **(d)** -8 **(e)** 5   **(f)** 7
   (g) 26   **(h)** 7
2. (a) 3   **(b)** -1 **(c)** 1   **(d)** 1   **(e)** -1 **(f)** 3
   (g) -1 **(h)** 2

CHAPTER 7

Exercise 7-1
1. (a) $(2, 12), (0, 14), (20, -6)$
   (b) $(1, 11), (7, -1), (10, -7)$
   (c) $(9, 1), (2, -6), (-6, -14), (3, -5)$
   (d) $(4, 6), (-3, -1), (-2, 0)$
   (e) $(5, 3), (-2, -11), (0, -7), (-1, -9)$
   (f) $(2, 6), (8, 12), (5, 9), (-4, 0)$

(g) $(-1, -4)$, $(5, 14)$, $(0, -1)$

(h) $(8, 1)$, $(-12, -3)$, $(3, 0)$

2. (a) $(4, 5)$, $(8, 1)$, $(-3, 12)$, $(14, -5)$, $(12, -3)$

   (b) $(9, 3)$, $(8, 2)$, $(5, -1)$, $(3, -3)$, $(-8, -14)$

   (c) $(1, 13)$, $(5, 5)$, $(7, 1)$, $(6, 3)$, $(10, -5)$

   (d) $(3, 7)$, $(-2, -3)$, $(6, 13)$, $(6, 13)$, $(4, 9)$

   (e) $(2, 0)$, $(0, 3)$, $(4, -3)$, $(-4, 9)$, $(4, -3)$

3. (a) $(3, 1)$ **(b)** $(4, 3)$ **(c)** $(2, 3)$ **(d)** $(2, 4)$

4. (a) 6 **(b)** 4 **(c)** $7, 3$ **(d)** $7, 1$

   (e) $5, 5$ **(f)** $7, 5$ **(g)** $9, 4$ **(h)** $2, -5$

Exercise 7-2

3. (a) $(1, 3)$ **(b)** $(3, 5)$ **(c)** $(-2, 5)$ **(d)** $(-2, 6)$

   (e) $(1, 1)$ **(f)** $(1, 7)$

4. (a) $(-2, 2)$ **(b)** $(2, -3)$ **(c)** $(6, 0)$ **(d)** $(2, 0)$

5. (a) none   **(b)** infinite   **(c)** none   **(d)** infinite

6. (a) consistent   **(b)** dependent   **(c)** inconsistent

   (d) inconsistent   **(e)** consistent   **(f)** dependent

   (g) inconsistent   **(h)** consistent   **(i)** dependent

   (j) inconsistent

Exercise 7-3

1. (a) $y = -3x + 7$ **(b)** $x = -2y + 4$ **(c)** $y = \dfrac{-2x + 2}{3}$

   (d) $x = \dfrac{-2y + 4}{3}$ **(e)** $y = \dfrac{-5x + 20}{2}$ **(f)** $x = \dfrac{-2y + 20}{5}$

   (g) $x = \dfrac{2y + 12}{3}$ **(h)** $y = \dfrac{4x + 11}{3}$ **(i)** $y = 5x - 7$

   (j) $x = 2y - 4$ **(k)** $a = \dfrac{-3b - 4}{2}$ **(l)** $b = \dfrac{5a - 2}{3}$

   (m) $y = \dfrac{2x - 4}{3}$ **(n)** $x = \dfrac{2y - 3}{3}$ **(o)** $a = \dfrac{3b - 6}{5}$

   (p) $n = \dfrac{3m - 4}{7}$

2. (a) $(2, 8)$ **(b)** $(1, -1)$ **(c)** $(2, -1)$ **(d)** $(-3, -6)$

   (e) $(-11, -7)$ **(f)** $(-5, 2)$ **(g)** $(-26, -11)$ **(h)** $(1, 1)$

3. (a) $(2, 2)$ **(b)** $(2, -2)$ **(c)** $(2, 1)$ **(d)** $(1, 2)$

4. (a) $(0, 2)$ **(b)** $(1, 0)$ **(c)** $(2, -1)$ **(d)** $(2, -\tfrac{1}{4})$

   (e) $(2, -\tfrac{1}{4})$ **(f)** $(-2, 0)$ **(g)** $(-1, 4)$ **(h)** $(2, \tfrac{1}{3})$

   (i) $(3, -\tfrac{2}{3})$ **(j)** $(-1, \tfrac{2}{3})$

Exercise 7-4

1. (a) $(2, 2)$ **(b)** $(1, -1)$ **(c)** $(-1, 1)$ **(d)** $(2, -1)$

   (e) $(2, -\tfrac{1}{2})$ **(f)** $(1, 0)$ **(g)** $(1, \tfrac{1}{3})$ **(h)** $(3, \tfrac{1}{2})$

2. (a) $(2, \tfrac{3}{4})$ **(b)** $(1, 0)$ **(c)** $(13, -4)$ **(d)** $(-1\tfrac{1}{2}, 2)$

   (e) $(2, \tfrac{1}{2})$ **(f)** $(2, 3)$ **(g)** $(\tfrac{2}{5}, -\tfrac{3}{4})$ **(h)** $(6, 2)$

Exercise 7-5

1. (a) $(5, 1)$ (b) $(5, 2)$ (c) $(3, 5)$ (d) $(1, 7)$ (e) $(1, 3)$
   (f) $(0, 2)$ (g) $(2, 0)$ (h) $(1, -\frac{1}{2})$ (i) $(1, 2)$
2. (a) $(4, 2)$ (b) $(3, 3)$ (c) $(4, 2)$ (d) $(7, 2)$ (e) $(2, 3)$
   (f) $(2, 1)$
3. (a) $(3, 2)$ (b) $(-1, -2)$ (c) $(-2, 1)$ (d) $(-2, 5)$
   (e) $(-2, -3)$ (f) $(-1, 5)$ (g) $(-1, -2)$ (h) $(6, 2)$
4. (a) $(-\frac{1}{2}, -\frac{2}{3})$ (b) $(\frac{5}{2}, -\frac{7}{3})$ (c) $(-\frac{7}{4}, 0)$
   (d) $(-6, 4)$ (e) $(-5, -4)$ (f) $(-\frac{1}{2}, -\frac{1}{3})$
   (g) $(\frac{1}{2}, \frac{1}{4})$ (h) $(-\frac{2}{3}, -\frac{5}{2})$
5. (a) $a = 2, b = 3, c = 2$ (b) $x = 4, y = 2, t = 5$
   (c) $a = 3, b = -2, c = -3$ (d) $x = -2, y = -3, m = -4$
   (e) $a = -1, b = 0, c = 1$ (f) $x = 2, y = -2, d = -\frac{1}{2}$
   (g) $a = 2, b = 3, c = -1, d = -2$ (h) $x = -2, y = -3, m = 4$

Exercise 7-6

1. (a) $(3, 4)$ (b) $(6, -4)$ (c) $(3, -3)$ (d) $(-6, -8)$
   (e) $(-4, -2)$ (f) $(1, -1)$
2. (a) $(4, 3)$ (b) $(3, 4)$ (c) $(-1, -3)$ (d) $(0.1, -0.2)$
   (e) $(-0.5, 0.3)$ (f) $(-0.7, -0.3)$ (g) $(-0.4, -1.1)$
   (h) $(1.2, -0.8)$
3. (a) $(1, 6)$ (b) $(-1, -5)$ (c) $(4, 5)$ (d) $(-3, -7)$
   (e) $(5, -3)$ (f) $(-3, -4)$ (g) $(20, 10)$ (h) $(0, 0)$
4. (a) $(5, 4)$ (b) $(-4, 7)$ (c) $(8, -6)$ (d) $(8, 6)$
   (e) $(6, 9)$ (f) $(7, 6)$

Exercise 7-7

1. (a) $\dfrac{b}{a}$ (b) $\dfrac{n}{m}$ (c) $\dfrac{a+b}{n}$ (d) $\dfrac{a+b}{m+n}$ (e) ab (f) $-mn$

   (g) $\dfrac{4}{a+b}$ (h) $\dfrac{-2y}{m-n}$ (i) $\dfrac{6}{a+b}$ (j) $\dfrac{t}{c-d}$ (k) $\dfrac{c+d}{g-h}$ (l) $\dfrac{t-s}{b-a}$

   (m) $\dfrac{m}{2a+b}$ (n) $\dfrac{b-a}{4c-3t}$

2. (a) $(a, -b)$ (b) $(3a, -b)$ (c) $(-\frac{3}{2}n, m)$ (d) $(5b, -3a)$

   (e) $\left(\dfrac{23b}{13}, -\dfrac{a}{13}\right)$ (f) $\left(\dfrac{2a}{3} - \dfrac{(a+3b)}{3}\right)$

3. (a) $\left(\dfrac{m+n}{2a+b}, \dfrac{bm-2an}{2a+b}\right)$ (b) $\left(\dfrac{3b-2}{ab-1}, \dfrac{3-2a}{1-ab}\right)$

   (c) $\left(\dfrac{8-6a}{6-a^2}, \dfrac{4a-18}{a^2-6}\right)$ (d) $\left(\dfrac{6}{a+b}, \dfrac{2b-4a}{a+b}\right)$

   (e) $\left(\dfrac{eg-hn}{en-dn}, \dfrac{dg-hm}{dn-em}\right)$ (f) $\left(\dfrac{ce-bf}{ae-bd}, \dfrac{dc-af}{ae-bd}\right)$

Exercise 7-8

1. (a) $(3, 2)$ (b) $(4, 1)$ (c) $(3, -2)$ (d) $(5, 3)$ (e) $(\frac{1}{2}, -3)$
   (f) $(1, 6)$ (g) $(-3, -2)$ (h) $(3, -4)$ (i) $(-3, 4)$ (j) $(-4, 2)$
2. (a) $(1, 2, 3)$ (b) $(-1, 3, -2)$ (c) $(4, 2, -2)$ (d) $(3, 0, -1)$

Review Exercise

2. **(a)** $(3, 0), (0, 4)$ **(b)** $(3, 0), (0, 6)$ **(c)** $(2, 0), (0, -3)$
 (d) $(2, 0), (0, -5)$ **(e)** $(-3, 0), (0, 7)$ **(f)** $(4, 0), (0, -4)$

3. **(a)** $y = 4 - 2x$ **(b)** $x = 3y + 7$ **(c)** $y = \dfrac{5 - 3x}{2}$

 (d) $a = \dfrac{4 - 3b}{2}$ **(e)** $m = \dfrac{2n + 2}{3}$ **(f)** $e = \dfrac{4d - 7}{3}$

 (g) $x = \dfrac{3y}{4}$ **(h)** $y = \dfrac{4 - 2x}{3}$

4. **(a)** $(-1, 2)$ **(b)** $(5, 2)$ **(c)** $(3, 5)$ **(d)** $(-4, 2)$
5. **(a)** inconsistent **(b)** dependent **(c)** consistent **(d)** inconsistent
 (e) consistent **(f)** dependent
6. **(a)** $(-1, 2)$ **(b)** $(3, 4)$ **(c)** $(-1, 2)$ **(d)** $(-\frac{1}{2}, 3)$
 (e) $(-3, -4)$ **(f)** $(1, 3)$ **(g)** $(\frac{1}{2}, \frac{1}{3})$ **(h)** $(6, -3)$
 (i) $(-\frac{2}{3}, -\frac{1}{5})$ **(j)** $(-\frac{3}{7}, \frac{1}{2})$,
7. **(a)** $(3, 4)$ **(b)** $(4, 6)$ **(c)** $(-10, 6)$ **(d)** $(3, 3)$
 (e) $(-0.1, -0.5)$ **(f)** $(3, -4)$ **(g)** $(-0.3, 0.5)$ **(h)** $(3, -4)$
8. **(a)** $(4, -6)$ **(b)** $(-5, -1)$ **(c)** $(-1, -3)$ **(d)** $(\frac{1}{2}, -3)$
9. **(a)** $(3b, a)$ **(b)** $(-\frac{9}{2}b, -8a)$ **(c)** $(2b, 0)$

 (d) $\left(\dfrac{cn + bd}{an + bm}, \dfrac{cm - ad}{bm + am} \right)$

10. **(a)** $a = 2, b = 3, c = -2$ **(b)** $a = -3, b = -4, c = 0$
 (c) $a = 5, b = -6, c = 4$ **(d)** $a = 2, b = -2, c = 3, d = -1$

REVIEW AND PREVIEW TO CHAPTER 8

Exercise 1
 1. \$162.64 2. \$5938.50 3. \$135.00 4. \$377.50
 5. \$9360.00 6. \$3.25 7. \$467.50 8. \$3.21
 9. \$2700.00 10. \$38.52 11. \$165.85 12. \$132.00
 13. \$82.39 14. \$0.84 15. \$625.95 16. \$5007.60
 17. \$312.50 18. \$362.00 19. \$1908.00 20. \$35.31

CHAPTER 8

Exercise 8-1
 1. **(a)** $3x$ **(b)** $x + 4$ **(c)** $x - 3$ **(d)** $x + 5$ **(e)** $x - 2$
 (f) $x + 5$ **(g)** $2x + 3$ **(h)** $\frac{1}{2}x$ **(i)** $x - 8$ **(j)** $3x - 20$
 (k) $25x$ **(l)** $\frac{1}{2}(x - 6)$ **(m)** $\frac{1}{3}(x + 10)$ **(n)** $6x - 2$
 (o) $4x$ **(p)** $10y$ **(q)** $0.09x$ **(r)** $0.12x$
 (s) $0.1x$ **(t)** $0.12x$
 2. **(a)** 47 **(b)** 37 **(c)** 85 **(d)** 82 **(e)** 181
 (f) 22 **(g)** 14 **(h)** 21 **(i)** 30 **(j)** 11
 (k) 33 **(l)** 64 **(m)** 67 **(n)** 50 km/h **(o)** 450 km
 (p) 14 h **(q)** \$600 **(r)** \$20 **(s)** 71
 3. **(a)** $l + w$ **(b)** $2l + 3w$ **(c)** $3l - w$ **(d)** $x + 3y$
 (e) $5x + 10y$ **(f)** $5x + 25y$ **(g)** $2x + 5y$ **(h)** $5x - 4y$
 (i) $2l + 3 + 4w$

4. (a) $x + y = 50$ (b) $x - y = 40$ (c) $b + g = 35$
 (d) $c - t = 8$ (e) $h + p = 170$ (f) $2x + 3y = 48$
 (g) $4d - 2q = 33$ (h) $s + b = 35$ (i) $8t + (h - 2) = 251$
 (j) $l + 3w = 48$ (k) $7l - 5w = 38$ (l) $12l - 5w = 487$
 (m) $10d + 25q = 180$ (n) $10x + 5y = 765$ (o) $5n + 10d = 795$
 (p) $0.08x + 0.09y = 195$ (q) $0.12x + 0.09y = 240$

Exercise 8-2

1. 51, 33   2. 147, 108   3. 821, 763   4. 747, 464
5. 156, 93   6. 12, 6   7. 15, 11   8. 12, 10
9. 16, 14   10. 21, 20   11. 173, 81   12. 147, 41
13. 224, 101   14. 576, 358   15. 25, 21   16. 14
17. 18   18. 17   19. 21   20. 13
21. 26   22. 31 dimes, 69 quarters   23. 13
24. 121 students, 242 adults   25. 210   26. 60
27. 34   28. 143 m by 58 m   29. 160 m by 40 m
30. 33 m by 4 m   31. 22 m by 8 m
32. 15   33. 14   34. 13   35. 30
36. 27   37. 60 m by 10 m   38. 13   39. 3000

Exercise 8-3

1. (a) $200   (b) $27   (c) $360   (d) $0.07x   (e) $0.11y
 (f) $0.125w
2. (a) $20   (b) $15   (c) $60   (d) $3.10x   (e) $4.50y
 (f) $3.07m
3. (a) 30   (b) 200   (c) 100   (d) 0.3x   (e) 0.35y
 (f) 0.09m

4. (a) 240   (b) 12   (c) 50   (d) 40x   (e) $\dfrac{y}{50}$
 (f) 8m   (g) $\dfrac{n}{30}$
5. $600 at 8%, $400 at 9%
6. $6000 at 9%, $2000 at 10%
7. $3000 at 7.5%, $3000 at 8.5%
8. $5000
9. $1200 at 8%, $800 at 12%
10. $1800 at 8%, $1200 at 7%
11. $3840 at 8%, $2560 at 6%
12. 350
13. 400 kg of $3.60/kg, 800 kg of $2.40/kg
14. 60 kg of $1.10/kg, 40 kg of $1.20/kg
15. 120 kg of $2.20/kg, 80 kg of $2.40/kg
16. 240 kg of cashews, 160 kg of pecans
17. 90 kg of $1.50/kg, 110 kg of $1.90/kg
18. 60 kg of 30%, 140 kg of 40%
19. 200 kg of 40%, 300 kg of 20%
20. 40 kg of 40%, 60 kg of 30%
21. 200 kg of 9%, 300 kg of 12%

22. 100 kg of 35%, 400 kg of 45%

23. 20 kg of 20%, 80 kg of 40%

24. 400 km   **25.** 5 h   **26.** 1.5 h   **27.** 3 h   **28.** 3.5 h

29. 60 km   **30.** 250 km   **31.** 350   **32.** 30 km/h

33. 1.5 km/h   **34.** 74   **35.** 25 km/h   **36.** 240 km

37. 100 km   **38.** 84   **39.** 27

Exercise 8-4

1. (a) (i) maximum of 27 at A, minimum of -6 at C
   (ii) maximum of 12 at C, minimum of -14 at B
   (iii) maximum of 24 at A, minimum of -13 at C

(b) (i) maximum of 6 at C, minimum of -21 at B
   (ii) maximum of 30 at A, minimum of -14 at C
   (iii) maximum of 2 at C, minimum of -8 at B

(c) (i) maximum of 18 at D, minimum of -21 at B
   (ii) maximum of 32 at A, minimum of -18 at C
   (iii) maximum of 25 at A, minimum of -12 at C

(d) (i) maximum of 30 at E, minimum of -36 at B
   (ii) maximum of 27 at B, minimum of -19 at E
   (iii) maximum of 25 at D, minimum of -25 at A

(e) (i) maximum of 14 at A, minimum of -36 at D
   (ii) maximum of 49 at C, minimum of 0 at $(0, 0)$
   (iii) maximum of 7 at A, minimum of -9 at D

(f) (i) maximum of 44 at C, minimum of 0 at $(0, 0)$
   (ii) maximum of 25 at B, minimum of -10 at D
   (iii) maximum of 16 at C, minimum of -8 at A

2. (a) maximum of 20 at $(0, 5)$, minimum of 0 at $(0, 0)$

(b) maximum of 62 at $(4, 6)$, minimum of 0 at $(0, 0)$

(c) maximum of 70 at $(10, 0)$, minimum of 0 at $(0, 0)$

(d) maximum of 14 at $(1, 6)$, minimum of -42 at $(3, -10)$

(e) maximum of 43 at $(3, 7)$, minimum of 0 at $(0, 0)$

3. 80 Standard and 20 Championship

4. 15 bracelets and 12 necklaces

5. 10 portable and 12 table

6. 60 Super I and 30 Super II

7. 12 bears and 40 rabbits

8. 100 Standard and 100 Deluxe

Review Exercise

1. 242, 135   **2.** 530, 248   **3.** 427, 385   **4.** 31, 28

5. 56, 24   **6.** 29, 28   **7.** 56   **8.** 183

9. 161 m by 142 m   **10.** 17   **11.** 71

12. 65 m by 23 m   **13.** 15   **14.** 62

15. 142   **16.** $3000   **17.** 150

18. 60 kg of 40% and 40 kg of 20%

19. 150 km   **20.** 180 kg   **21.** $1500   **22.** 3 h

23. 20 kg of $3.60/kg, 80 kg of $4.60/kg   **24.** $1800

25. 300 kg   **26.** 80 kg of $2.30/kg, 70 kg of $3.20/kg

27. 400 km   **28.** 26

29. 40 bikinis and 60 trunks   **30.** 80 Super Dupers, 60 Supers

REVIEW AND PREVIEW TO CHAPTER 9

Exercise 1

1. $\angle BAC = 73°$
2. $\angle AED = 99°, \angle DEB = 81°$
3. $\angle ABC = \angle ACB = 70°$
4. $\angle PQR = \angle QRP = \angle RPQ = 60°$
5. $\angle ACD = 108°$
6. $\angle BEC = 70°$
7. $x = 30°$
8. $x = 9°$
9. $x = 39°$
10. $x = 16°$
11. $x = 10°$
12. $x = 41°$

CHAPTER 9

Proofs of deductions are left for the student.

Exercise 9-1

1. (a) authority   **(b)** inspection   **(c)** authority   **(d)** analogy
    (e) induction   **(f)** authority   **(g)** inspection   **(h)** induction
    (i) induction   **(j)** deduction

Exercise 9-2

1. (c)

Sides	3	4	5	6	7	8	100	n
Diagonals	0	1	2	3	4	5	97	$n-3$
Triangles	1	2	3	4	5	6	98	$n-2$
Sum	180°	360°	540°	720°	900°	1080°	17640°	$(n-2)180°$

    (d) $(n-2)180°$
2. (a) 60°   **(b)** 90°   **(c)** 108°   **(d)** 120°   **(e)** 171°
7. 64   **8. (a)** no   **(b)** yes   **(c)** no
9. 5   **10.** no

Exercise 9-3

1. $\angle DEF \rightarrow \angle RST, \angle DFE \rightarrow \angle RTS, \angle EDF \rightarrow \angle SRT$
    $EF \rightarrow ST, DE \rightarrow RS, DF \rightarrow RT$
2. $PQ = ST, SU = PR, QR = TU, \angle PQR = \angle STU, \angle RPQ = \angle UST, \angle QRP = \angle TUS$
3. (a) $AB = AC, BD = CD, AD = AD, \angle ABD = \angle ACD, \angle ADB = \angle ADC, \angle BAD = \angle CAD$
    (b) $AB = AC, AC = AB, BC = CB, \angle ABC = \angle ACB, \angle BCA = \angle CBA, \angle BAC = \angle CAB$
    (c) $TQ = PR, QS = RS, ST = SP, \angle TQS = \angle PRS, \angle QST = \angle RSP, \angle STQ = \angle SPR$
5. (b) yes

Exercise 9-4

1. $\triangle ABC \cong \triangle FED, \triangle GHI \cong \triangle VWX, \triangle JKL \cong \triangle UST$
    $\triangle MNO \cong \triangle QPR$
2. (a) $AO = BO, \angle AOD = \angle COB, DO = CO$
    (b) $AC = EC, \angle ACB = \angle ECD, BC = DC$
    (c) $AB = CD, \angle ABD = \angle CDB, DB = BD$
    (d) $BD = CD, \angle BDA = \angle CDA, AD = AD$
    (e) $AD = CD, \angle DAB = \angle DCB, DB = DB$
    (f) $BA = DA, \angle BAC = \angle DAC, AC = AC$

Exercise 9-5

1. $\triangle ABC \cong \triangle WVX$, $\angle BCA = \angle VXW$, $\angle BAC = \angle VWX$, $\angle ABC = \angle WVX$
   $\triangle DEF \cong \triangle RPQ$, $\angle DEF = \angle RPQ$, $\angle DFE = \angle RQP$, $\angle EDF = \angle PRQ$
   $\triangle GHI \cong \triangle UTS$, $\angle GHI = \angle UTS$, $\angle GIH = \angle UST$, $\angle IGH = \angle SUT$
   $\triangle JKL \cong \triangle MON$, $\angle JKL = \angle MON$, $\angle JLK = \angle MNO$, $\angle KJL = \angle OMN$

2. **(a)** $CO = AO$, $BO = DO$, $CB = AD$ **(b)** $AB = AC$, $BD = CD$, $AD = AD$
   (c) $AB = AD$, $BC = DC$, $CA = CA$ **(d)** $AD = CB$, $AB = CD$, $BD = DB$
   (e) $AB = CB$, $AD = CD$, $BD = BD$ **(f)** $AD = CB$, $AB = CD$, $BD = DB$

Exercise 9-6

1. $\triangle ABC \cong \triangle RPQ$, $\triangle DEF \cong \triangle OMN$, $\triangle HGI \cong \triangle XVW$, $\triangle JKL \cong \triangle SUT$

2. **(a)** $\angle BAC = \angle EDC$, $AC = DC$, $\angle ACB = \angle DCE$
   (b) $\angle ABD = \angle CDB$, $BD = DB$, $\angle ADB = \angle CBD$
   (c) $\angle ABD = \angle ACD$, $BD = CD$, $\angle ADB = \angle ADC$
   (d) $\angle AOD = \angle COB$, $OD = OB$, $\angle ADO = \angle CBO$
   (e) $\angle BAC = \angle DEC$, $AC = EC$, $\angle ACB = \angle ECD$
   (f) $\angle ABD = \angle CBD$, $BD = BD$, $\angle ADB = \angle CDB$

REVIEW AND PREVIEW TO CHAPTER 10

Exercise 1

1. $32°$ 2. $83°$ 3. $40°$ 4. $26°$ 5. $20°$
6. $25°$ 7. $65°$ 8. $50°$ 9. $30°$

Exercise 2

1. **(a)** $A = 63$ cm^2, $P = 32$ cm   **(b)** $A = 36$ cm^2, $P = 30$ cm
   (c) $A = 56$ cm^2, $P = 32$ cm   **(d)** $A = 8$ cm^2, $P = 16$ cm
2. **(a)** 28.3 cm^2 **(b)** 157 cm^2 **(c)** 19.6 cm^2 **(d)** 66.0 cm^2
3. **(a)** 157 cm   **(b)** 42.8 cm   **(c)** 45.7 cm   **(d)** 357 m
4. **(a)** 77 cm^2 **(b)** 144 cm^2 **(c)** 43.5 cm^2 **(d)** 62.5 cm^2

CHAPTER 10

Exercise 10-1

1. **(a)** Alternate: c and d, b and e; corresponding: a and e, b and f; interior: b and d, c and e.
   (b) interior: a and b, b and c, c and d, a and d.
   (c) alternate: a and d, e and f; corresponding: a and b, d and f, a and e; interior: c and d, c and e.
2. **(a)** $a = 110°$, $b = c = 70°$ **(b)** $a = 60°$, $b = 60°$, $c = 120°$
   (c) $a = c = 65°$, $b = 115°$ **(d)** $a = 30°$, $b = 80°$, $c = 70°$
   (e) $a = 45°$, $b = 25°$, $c = 110°$ **(f)** $a = b = 60°$, $c = 120°$
3. **(a)** $x = 50°$, $y = 55°$, $z = 75°$ **(b)** $a = 65°$, $b = 75°$, $c = 40°$
   (c) $x = 50°$, $y = 70°$, $z = 60°$ **(d)** $x = 70°$, $y = 50°$, $z = 70°$
   (e) $x = 35°$, $y = 80°$, $z = 65°$ **(f)** $x = 80°$, $y = 60°$, $z = 40°$

Exercise 10-4

1. **(a)** 5   **(b)** 13   **(c)** 17   **(d)** 25
   (e) 30   **(f)** 12   **(g)** $r = 11$ **(h)** $g = 18$, $w = 7$

2. (a) 10 cm   **(b)** 13 m   **(c)** 17 m   **(d)** 50 cm
   (e) 50 cm   **(f)** 26 cm
3. 5.39 cm   **4.** 283 mm   **5.** 323 m
6. 2.3 m   **7.** 3 m   **8.** $\sqrt{2}, \sqrt{3}, 2\sqrt{5}$
9. 21 cm   **10.** 220 cm
11. (a) 9.9   **(b)** 8.3   **(c)** 25
13. 195 cm

Exercise 10-5

1. (a) yes   **(b)** no   **(c)** yes   **(d)** no
2. (a) no   **(b)** yes   **(c)** yes
   (d) yes   **(e)** yes   **(f)** yes
3. (a) 6   **(b)** 30   **(c)** 60
   (d) 84   **(e)** 24   **(f)** 7.5

Review Exercise

1. (a) $a = 108°$, $b = 72°$, $c = 108°$
   (b) $a = 62°$, $b = 43°$, $c = 75°$
   (c) $a = 38°$, $b = 103°$, $c = 65°$
   (d) $a = 45°$, $b = 100°$, $c = 35°$
   (e) $a = 52°$, $b = 78°$, $c = 50°$
   (f) $a = 78°$, $b = 60°$, $c = 42°$
2. (a) 50   **(b)** 20   **(c)** 8
   (d) $\sqrt{7}$ **(e)** $\sqrt{14}$ **(f)** $\sqrt{30}$
3. (a) yes   **(b)** yes   **(c)** no
   (d) no   **(e)** no   **(f)** yes
4. (a) 6   **(b)** 30   **(c)** 120
   (d) 78   **(e)** 3   **(f)** 126

REVIEW AND PREVIEW TO CHAPTER 11

Exercise 1

1. (a) 60   **(b)** 490   **(c)** 600
2. (a) 27   **(b)** 133   **(c)** 72
3. (a) 502.4   **(b)** 445   **(c)** 620
4. (a) 14 130 cm^3 **(b)** 524 cm^3 **(c)** 1436 cm^3

CHAPTER 11

Exercise 11-2

1. (a) infinitely many
2. (a) one   **(c)** no
3. (a) one   **(b)** infinitely many   **(c)** one
4. (a) the line, and the two sets of points on either side.
   (b) the plane, and the two sets of points on either side.

Exercise 11-3

1. (a) *ABFE* and *DCGH*, *EADH* and *FBCG*, *ABCD* and *EFGH*
   (b) * *AD* and *BCGF*   * not the only solutions.
   (c) * *AB* and *BCGF*
   (d) * *EADH*, *ABCD*, and *EABF*
2. $\angle XOY$, $\angle AOX$, $\angle AOY$, $\angle AOZ$, $\angle BOX$, $\angle BOY$, $\angle BOZ$.
3. Line segment *PQ* (a) intersects *A* (b) lies in the plane *A*.
4. (a) * *G* and *H*, *G* and *I*, *D* and *A*, *B* and *C*
   (b) * *E*, *F*, *G*, and *D*   (c) * *C*, *G*, *H*, *I*, and *B*
   (d) *B*   (e) *B* and *C*   (f) no
5. (a) always true   (b) sometimes true   (c) always true
   (d) always true   (e) sometimes true   (f) always true
   (g) sometimes true
6. (a) 13   (b) 20

Exercise 11-4

1. (a) 126, 166
2. (a) 60, 96

Review Exercise

3. (a) $a = 25$, $b = 20$, $c = 5\sqrt{41}$
   (b) $a = 2\sqrt{29}$, $b = 4\sqrt{13}$, $c = 2\sqrt{13}$
   (c) $a = b = 13$
4. (a) $F + V - E = 2$
   (b) (i) no   (ii) no   (iii) yes
5. (a) 13, 260   (b) 72, 96   (c) 11, 368

REVIEW AND PREVIEW TO CHAPTER 12

1. (a) $x = 70°$, $y = 110°$ (b) $a = 45°$, $b = 45°$
   (c) $a = 70°$, $b = c = 55°$ (d) $x = 30°$, $2x = 60°$
2. (a) 1.75   (b) 1.35   (c) 6.91   (d) 2.4
   (e) 15.4   (f) 9.06   (g) 4.50   (h) 226
3. (a) 50   (b) 4.04   (c) 1.41   (d) 13

CHAPTER 12

Exercise 12-2

1. (a) $\sin A = \dfrac{8}{17}$, $\cos A = \dfrac{15}{17}$, $\tan A = \dfrac{8}{15}$ (d) $\sin A = \dfrac{\sqrt{3}}{2}$, $\cos A = \dfrac{1}{2}$, $\tan A = \sqrt{3}$

   (b) $\sin A = \dfrac{1}{\sqrt{2}}$, $\cos A = \dfrac{1}{\sqrt{2}}$, $\tan A = 1$ (e) $\sin A = \dfrac{1}{2}$, $\cos A = \dfrac{\sqrt{3}}{2}$, $\tan A = \dfrac{1}{\sqrt{3}}$

   (c) $\sin A = \dfrac{5}{13}$, $\cos A = \dfrac{12}{13}$, $\tan A = \dfrac{5}{12}$ (f) $\sin A = \dfrac{3}{5}$, $\cos A = \dfrac{4}{5}$, $\tan A = \dfrac{3}{4}$

2. **(a)** $\tan B = \dfrac{8}{7}$ **(b)** $\cos B = \dfrac{4}{\sqrt{20}}$ **(c)** $\tan B = 1$ **(d)** $\cos B = \dfrac{7}{10}$

3. **(a)** $\sin B = \dfrac{3}{5}$, $\cos B = \dfrac{4}{5}$, $\tan B = \dfrac{3}{4}$ $\sin C = \dfrac{4}{5}$, $\cos C = \dfrac{3}{5}$, $\tan C = \dfrac{4}{3}$

   (b) $\sin A = \dfrac{3}{5}$, $\cos A = \dfrac{4}{5}$, $\tan A = \dfrac{3}{4}$ $\sin C = \dfrac{4}{5}$, $\cos C = \dfrac{3}{5}$, $\tan C = \dfrac{4}{3}$

   (c) $\sin A = \dfrac{5}{13}$, $\cos A = \dfrac{12}{13}$, $\tan A = \dfrac{5}{12}$ $\sin B = \dfrac{12}{13}$, $\cos B = \dfrac{5}{13}$, $\tan B = \dfrac{12}{5}$

4. **(a)** 0.8   **(b)** 0.6   **(c)** 0.8

5. **(a)** $\dfrac{1}{\sqrt{2}}$ **(b)** $\dfrac{1}{\sqrt{2}}$ **(c)** $\dfrac{1}{\sqrt{2}}$ **(d)** 1

6. **(a)** $\sqrt{2}$ **(b)** $\sin 45° = \cos 45° = \dfrac{1}{\sqrt{2}}$, $\tan 45° = 1$

7. **(a)** $BD = 1$, $AD = \sqrt{3}$

   (b) $\sin 60° = \dfrac{\sqrt{3}}{2}$, $\cos 60° = \dfrac{1}{2}$, $\tan 60° = \sqrt{3}$

   $\sin 30° = \dfrac{1}{2}$, $\cos 30° = \dfrac{\sqrt{3}}{2}$, $\tan 30° = \dfrac{1}{\sqrt{3}}$

Exercise 12-3

1. **(a)** $\csc \theta = \dfrac{17}{8}$, $\sec \theta = \dfrac{17}{15}$, $\cot \theta = \dfrac{15}{8}$

   (b) $\csc \theta = \dfrac{5}{3}$, $\sec \theta = \dfrac{5}{4}$, $\cot \theta = \dfrac{4}{3}$

   (c) $\csc \theta = 2$, $\sec \theta = 1.2$, $\cot \theta = 1.7$

   (d) $\csc \theta = \dfrac{10}{y}$, $\sec \theta = \dfrac{10}{x}$, $\cot \theta = \dfrac{x}{y}$

   (e) $\csc \theta = \dfrac{r}{y}$, $\sec \theta = \dfrac{r}{x}$, $\cot \theta = \dfrac{x}{y}$

   (f) $\csc \theta = \dfrac{c}{b}$, $\sec \theta = \dfrac{c}{a}$, $\cot \theta = \dfrac{a}{b}$

2. **(a)** $\sin B = \dfrac{3}{5}$, $\cos B = \dfrac{4}{5}$, $\tan B = \dfrac{3}{4}$, $\csc B = \dfrac{5}{3}$, $\sec B = \dfrac{5}{4}$, $\cot B = \dfrac{4}{3}$

   $\sin C = \dfrac{4}{5}$, $\cos C = \dfrac{3}{5}$, $\tan C = \dfrac{4}{3}$, $\csc C = \dfrac{5}{4}$, $\sec C = \dfrac{5}{3}$, $\cot C = \dfrac{3}{4}$

   (b) $\sin A = \dfrac{3}{5}$, $\cos A = \dfrac{4}{5}$, $\tan A = \dfrac{3}{4}$, $\csc A = \dfrac{5}{3}$, $\sec A = \dfrac{5}{4}$, $\cot A = \dfrac{4}{3}$

   $\sin C = \dfrac{4}{5}$, $\cos C = \dfrac{3}{5}$, $\tan C = \dfrac{4}{3}$, $\csc C = \dfrac{5}{4}$, $\sec C = \dfrac{5}{3}$, $\cot C = \dfrac{3}{4}$

   (c) $\sin A = \dfrac{12}{13}$, $\cos A = \dfrac{5}{13}$, $\tan A = \dfrac{12}{5}$, $\csc A = \dfrac{13}{12}$, $\sec A = \dfrac{13}{5}$,

   $\cot A = \dfrac{5}{12}$

$$\sin B = \frac{5}{13}, \cos B = \frac{12}{13}, \tan B = \frac{5}{12}, \csc B = \frac{13}{5}, \sec B = \frac{13}{12},$$

$$\cot B = \frac{12}{5}$$

3. $\sin B = 0.8$, $\cos B = 0.6$, $\tan B = 1.33$, $\sec B = 1.67$, $\cot B = 0.75$

4. (a) $\dfrac{1}{\sqrt{2}}$ (b) $\sqrt{2}$ (c) $\sqrt{2}$ (d) 1

5. (a) $\sin B = \dfrac{5}{13}$, $\cos B = \dfrac{12}{13}$, $\tan B = \dfrac{5}{12}$,

     $\csc B = \dfrac{13}{5}$, $\sec B = \dfrac{13}{12}$, $\cot B = \dfrac{12}{5}$

Exercise 12-4

1. (a) 0.5736   (b) 1.235   (c) 1.390   (d) 0.4695
    (e) 0.9563   (f) 0.4695   (g) 9.514   (h) 3.864

2. (a) 25°   (b) 70°   (c) 83°   (d) 33°
    (e) 55°   (f) 28°   (g) 72°   (h) 68°

3. (a) 0 to 1   (b) 1 to 0   (c) 0 to arbitrarily large values
    (d) arbitrarily large values to 1
    (e) 1 to arbitrarily large values
    (f) arbitrarily large values to 0

4. (a) 1.42   (b) 0.942   (c) 52.6   (d) 12.3
    (e) 16.5   (f) 84.0

5. (a) 36°   (b) 52°   (c) 20°   (d) 30°

6. (a) $\angle B = 36°$, $\angle C = 54°$, $c = 9.75$
    (b) $\angle C = 60°$, $a = 5.2$, $c = 4.50$
    (c) $\angle B = 50°$, $a = 84$, $b = 100$
    (d) $\angle B = 55°$, $a = 21.4$, $b = 26.1$
    (e) $\angle A = 19°$, $b = 69.7$, $c = 73.7$
    (f) $\angle A = 34°$, $\angle C = 56°$, $b = 36.1$

Exercise 12-5

1. 6.34 m   2. 367 m   3. 87.2
4. 36°, 4.7 m   5. 746 m   6. 160 m
7. 5°   8. 11°   9. 4.33 m
10. 0.541 cm   11. 76°   12. 17°
13. (a) 81 m   (b) 90 m
14. (a) 303 m   (b) 195 m
15. 70 m   16. 8.6 m   17. 178 m

Review Exercise

1. (a) 3.05   (b) 721   (c) 179
2. (a) 55°   (b) 56°   (c) 53°

3. **(a)** $a = 4.2$, $\angle A = 53°$, $\angle C = 37°$
(b) $\angle B = 48°$, $a = 2.4$, $c = 3.6$
(c) $\angle C = 22°$, $a = 41$, $c = 16$
(d) $\angle B = 56°$, $\angle C = 34°$, $a = 18$
(e) $\angle M = 54°$, $\ell = 17$, $k = 30$
(f) $\angle P = 22°$, $q = 45$, $r = 48$

4. 30 m

5. 743 m

6. **(a)** 18 m   **(b)** 9.2 m

7. 126 m

8. 3186 m

REVIEW AND PREVIEW TO CHAPTER 13

Exercise 1
1. 62.8 cm, 314 cm²   2. 31.4 cm, 78.5 cm²
3. 44.0 cm, 154 cm²   4. 36.6 cm, 89.1 cm²
5. 55.7 cm, 111 cm²   6. 357 m, 6963 m²

CHAPTER 13

Exercise 13-1
1. **(a)** [4, 2]   **(b)** [6, −2]   **(c)** [−2, 3]   **(d)** [6, 0]
2. **(a)** (2, 5)   **(b)** (2, 11)   **(c)** (3, 3)   **(d)** (−1, 3)
3. **(a)** [−3, −2]   **(b)** [−1, 5]   **(c)** [5, 3]   **(d)** [0, −5]
5. **(a)** (6, 8)   **(b)** (0, 0)   **(c)** (4, 1)   **(d)** (7, 11)   **(e)** (−1, 1)
6. (*b*) and (*c*)
7. **(a)** [5, 9]   **(b)** [3, 7]   **(c)** [4, −1]   **(d)** [8, 6]
8. **(a)** 5   **(b)** 13   **(c)** 13   **(d)** 17
  (e) 25   **(f)** 17   **(g)** 10   **(h)** 5

Exercise 13-2
1. **(a)** [3, 4], [3, 5], [3, 4], [3, 5], [3, 5]
  (b) $\overrightarrow{AB} = \overrightarrow{EF}$, $\overrightarrow{BC} = \overrightarrow{GH} = \overrightarrow{KL}$
3. $\overrightarrow{AB} = [5, -2]$, $\overrightarrow{BA} = [-5, 2]$, $\overrightarrow{BC} = [-10, -8]$, $\overrightarrow{CD} = [8, 5]$
  $\overrightarrow{DA} = [-3, 5]$, $\overrightarrow{AC} = [-5, -10]$, $\overrightarrow{DB} = [2, 3]$
4. **(a)** parallelogram   **(b)** $\overrightarrow{PQ} = [-2, 8]$, $\overrightarrow{QR} = [11, 6]$,
                                   $\overrightarrow{SR} = [-2, -8]$, $\overrightarrow{PS} = [11, 6]$
5. $D(6, 3)$
6. **(a)** $D(-1, -6)$ **(b)** $E(-1, -6)$
7. **(a)** $S(0, 14)$ **(d)** no

8. (a)

$[a, b]$	$\sqrt{a^2 + b^2}$	$\dfrac{b}{a}$
$[1, 2]$	$\sqrt{5}$	2
$[3, -4]$	5	$-\frac{4}{3}$
$[2, 4]$	$2\sqrt{5}$	2
$[3, -4]$	5	$-\frac{4}{3}$
$[1, 2]$	$\sqrt{5}$	2
$[1, 2]$	$\sqrt{5}$	2
$[3, -4]$	5	$-\frac{4}{3}$
$[-1, -2]$	$\sqrt{5}$	2

(b) $\overrightarrow{CD} = \overrightarrow{GH} = \overrightarrow{MN}$
$\overrightarrow{AB} = \overrightarrow{IJ} = \overrightarrow{KL}$

9. (a) $a = 5, b = 3$ **(b)** $a = c, b = d$
10. (a) same direction   **(b)** magnitude
     (c) multiply the magnitude by $\frac{6}{5}$
11. (c) 447, N63°W
12. 13 kn
13. (a) $[0, 500]$ **(b)** $[100, 0]$ **(c)** $[-173, -100]$
14. (b) east, 8.7 units

Exercise 13-3

1. (a) $[7, 10]$ **(b)** $[1, 7]$ **(c)** $[3, -1]$ **(d)** $[7, -3]$
    (e) $[-5, -7]$ **(f)** $[7, 13]$ **(g)** $[0, 0]$ **(h)** $[0, 0]$
    (i) $[3, 6]$ **(j)** $[0, 9]$
2. (a) $[-2, 5]$ **(b)** $[0, 8]$ **(c)** $[0, 0]$ **(d)** $[2, 10]$
    (e) $[-1, -1]$ **(f)** $[2, 5]$
3. magnitudes   **(a)** 13 km   **(b)** 33.5 km   **(c)** 10.4 km   **(d)** 15.6 km
4. (a) $[7, 5]$ **(b)** $[9, 4]$ **(c)** $[5, 2]$ **(d)** $[-1, 1]$
    (e) $[1, 0]$ **(f)** $[-6, 1]$ **(g)** $[1, 3]$ **(h)** $[3, 4]$
5. (a) $[2, 3]$, a vector   **(b)** $[a + c, b + d]$, a vector
    (c) yes, closure
6. (a) $=$ **(b)** $=$ **(c)** yes
7. (a) $=$ **(b)** $=$ **(c)** yes
8. (a) **(i)** $[3, 2]$ **(ii)** $[-2, -6]$ **(iii)** $[-4, 3]$ **(iv)** $[-2, -4]$
    (b) **(i)** $[a, b]$ **(ii)** $[a, b]$
    (c) **(i)** $[0, 0]$ **(ii)** $[0, 0]$
9. (a) $[-3, -4]$ **(b)** $[-3, -11]$ **(c)** $[5, -3]$ **(d)** $[4, 7]$
    (e) $[-a, -b]$ **(f)** $[-a, -b]$
10. (c) **(i)** same magnitude **(ii)** opposite direction

Exercise 13-4

1. (a) $\vec{a} + \vec{b}$ **(b)** $\vec{a} + \vec{c}$ **(c)** $\vec{a} + \vec{b}$
2. (a) $\vec{c}$ **(b)** $\vec{e}$ **(c)** $\vec{d}$
    (d) $\overrightarrow{DB}$ **(e)** $\overrightarrow{AD} = \overrightarrow{BC}$ **(f)** $\overrightarrow{CA}$

3. (a) $\overrightarrow{AC}$ **(b)** $\overrightarrow{BD}$ **(c)** $\overrightarrow{AD}$
5. $\overrightarrow{AB}+\overrightarrow{BC}=\overrightarrow{AC}=\overrightarrow{AD}+\overrightarrow{DC}$
6. (a) $\overrightarrow{AE}$ **(b)** $\overrightarrow{CA}$ **(c)** $\overrightarrow{CA}$ **(d)** $\overrightarrow{EC}$
(e) $\overrightarrow{AC}$ **(f)** $\overrightarrow{CB}$
7. (a) $\overrightarrow{AC}$ **(b)** $\overrightarrow{AD}$ **(c)** $\overrightarrow{CE}$ **(d)** $\overrightarrow{BE}$ **(e)** $\overrightarrow{AE}$

Exercise 13-5

1. (a) $[6, 15]$ **(b)** $[18, -6]$ **(c)** $[2, 4]$ **(d)** $[6, 9]$
(e) $[-2, 4]$ **(f)** $[0, 0]$ **(g)** $[0, -6]$ **(h)** $[-2, 8]$
(i) $[10, 20]$

2. (a) $[10, 9]$ **(b)** $[2, 7]$ **(c)** $[2, 7]$ **(d)** $[1, 4]$
(e) $[-10, -7]$ **(f)** $[18, 3]$ **(g)** $[20, 5]$ **(h)** $[0, -20]$

3. (a) $[14x, 8y]$ **(b)** $[9x, 7y]$ **(c)** $[20x, 4y]$
(d) $[24x, -3y]$

Exercise 13-6

1. (a) $[1, 2]$ **(b)** $[9, -1]$ **(c)** $[2, 2]$
(d) $[12, 18]$ **(e)** $[0, 0]$ **(f)** $[-4, 7]$
(g) $[2x, b]$ **(h)** $[2a, -4b]$ **(i)** $[-3a, 6b]$
(j) $[p-m, q-n]$

2. (a) $\vec{c}$ **(b)** $\vec{c}$ **(c)** $-\vec{c}$ **(d)** $\vec{c}$
(e) $-\vec{c}$ **(f)** $\vec{d}$

3. (a) $\vec{a}=\vec{b}-\vec{c},\ \vec{b}=\vec{a}+\vec{c},\ \vec{c}=\vec{a}-\vec{b}$
(b) $\vec{a}=-(\vec{b}+\vec{c}),\ \vec{b}=-(\vec{a}+\vec{c}),\ \vec{c}=-(\vec{a}+\vec{b})$
(c) $\vec{x}=\vec{z}-\vec{y},\ \vec{y}=\vec{z}-\vec{x},\ \vec{z}=\vec{x}+\vec{y}$

4. (a) $[8, 1]$ **(b)** $[14, -20]$ **(c)** $[-2, 0]$ **(d)** $[-21, 5]$
(e) $[-11, 8]$ **(f)** $[-40, 40]$ **(g)** $[6, -18]$ **(h)** $[6, 21]$

5. $[0, 0]$

6. (a) $[3, 3]$ **(b)** $[-5, 19]$ **(c)** $[10, -31]$
(d) $[5, 20]$ **(e)** $[5, -5]$ **(f)** $[3, -15]$
(g) $[21, -21]$ **(h)** $[8, -4]$ **(i)** $[13, 36]$
(j) $[-21, 14]$

7. (a) $\overrightarrow{DB}$ **(b)** $\overrightarrow{EB}$ **(c)** $\overrightarrow{BE}$ **(d)** $\overrightarrow{AD}$ **(e)** $\overrightarrow{O}$ **(f)** $\overrightarrow{BD}$
8. (a) $\overrightarrow{AC}$ **(b)** $\overrightarrow{BD}$ **(c)** $\overrightarrow{AD}$ **(d)** $\overrightarrow{DA}$

Exercise 13-7

1. (a) $\overrightarrow{BA}=\overrightarrow{BC}+\overrightarrow{CA},\ \overrightarrow{BC}=\overrightarrow{BA}-\overrightarrow{CA},\ \overrightarrow{CA}=\overrightarrow{BA}-\overrightarrow{BC}$
(b) $\overrightarrow{AB}=-\overrightarrow{CA}-\overrightarrow{BC},\ \overrightarrow{BC}=-\overrightarrow{AB}-\overrightarrow{CA},\ \overrightarrow{CA}=-\overrightarrow{AB}-\overrightarrow{BC}$
(c) $\vec{w}=\vec{v}+\vec{u},\ \vec{u}=\vec{w}-\vec{v},\ \vec{v}=\vec{w}-\vec{u}$

2. (a) $\vec{x}$ **(b)** $\vec{y}$ **(c)** $-\vec{x}$ **(d)** $\vec{z}$ **(e)** $-\vec{x}$
(f) $\vec{y}-\vec{x}$ **(g)** $\vec{x}-\vec{y}$ **(h)** $\vec{z}$ **(i)** $\frac{1}{2}\vec{z}$ **(j)** $\vec{z}$
(k) $\vec{y}-\vec{x}$ **(l)** $\frac{1}{2}(\vec{y}-\vec{x})$ **(m)** $\frac{1}{2}(\vec{y}-\vec{x})$ **(n)** $\frac{1}{2}(\vec{x}-\vec{y})$

3. $\overrightarrow{AD}=\overrightarrow{AB}+\frac{1}{2}\overrightarrow{BC}$

Exercise 13-8
1. (a) (60°, 100) (b) (210°, 200)
   (c) (315°, 50)   (d) (135°, 30)
2. (a) 4 cm (b) 6 cm (c) 3 cm
   (d) 5 cm (e) 1.6 cm (f) 3.6 cm
4. (59°, 583)   5. (293°, 1300)
6. (104°, 20.6)   7. (354°, 402)
8. (7°, 605)   9. (101°, 25.5)
10. (276°, 403)   11. (236°, 361)
12. (190°, 304)   13. (275°, 402)
14. (8°, 350), 346   15. ·(100°, 300), 296

Review Exercise
1. (a) (7, −1) (b) (4, −6) (c) (2, −3) (d) (−1, −1)
2. (a) [12, 13] (b) [4, −9] (c) [1, −6] (d) [−14, 9]
3. (a) 5 (b) 5 (c) 13 (d) 17
   (e) 13.0 (f) 8.6 (g) 17 (h) $\sqrt{m^2+n^2}$
4. (a) (90°, 200) (b) (180°, 100) (c) (270°, 150)
   (d) (0°, 200) (e) (45°, $10\sqrt{2}$) (f) (135°, $5\sqrt{2}$)
   (g) (225°, $3\sqrt{3}$) (h) (315°, $7\sqrt{2}$)
5. $\overrightarrow{AE}=\overrightarrow{EC}$, $\overrightarrow{BE}=\overrightarrow{ED}$, $\overrightarrow{AD}=\overrightarrow{BC}$, $\overrightarrow{BA}=\overrightarrow{CD}$
6. (a) $\vec{x}$ (b) $\vec{y}$ (c) $\vec{a}$
7. (a) [12, 6] (b) [8, −1] (c) [13, 23]
   (d) [5, −3] (e) $2\sqrt{5}$ (f) $\sqrt{58}$
   (g) $2\sqrt{5}+\sqrt{26}$ (h) [−6, −19]
8. (a) [2, 10] (b) [12, 15] (c) [6, 4]
   (d) [6, −2] (e) $\sqrt{65}+2\sqrt{10}+3$ (f) $2\sqrt{26}$
9. (b) $\overrightarrow{OA}=[4, 2]$, $\overrightarrow{AB}=[3, 3]$, $\overrightarrow{BC}=[−5, −5]$
   $\overrightarrow{CD}=[−8, 1]$, $\overrightarrow{OD}=[−6, 1]$
10. (b) $P(2, 6)$, $Q(6, 8)$
    $R(13, 13)$, $S(15, 13)$
11. $\overrightarrow{AB}=\overrightarrow{CD}$
12. (16°, 25.7)
13. (a) (6, 0) (b) [2, 5], [8, 2], [8, 2], [2, 5]
    (c) parallelogram
14. (b) [2, −1]
15. (a) (81°, 253) (b) (99°, 253)
16. (b) parallelogram

REVIEW AND PREVIEW TO CHAPTER **14**

Exercise 1
1. $a = 55°$ 2. $b = 145°$ 3. $c = 130°$, $d = 130°$
4. $e = 40°$ 5. $f = 30°$, $g = 70°$ 6. $h = 90°$

Exercise 2
1. $x = 6\frac{2}{3}$ 2. $a = 4\frac{1}{2}$ 3. $6\frac{2}{3}$ 4. $x = 18$, $y = 21$
5. $a = 8\frac{1}{3}$ 6. $a = 16\frac{4}{5}$, $m = 8\frac{4}{7}$ 7. $x = 6\frac{2}{3}$
8. $x = 2\frac{5}{8}$ 9. $y = 4\frac{1}{5}$

CHAPTER 14

Exercise 14-1

1. (a) $(2, 10)$ **(b)** $(-2, 2)$ **(c)** $(-5, 3)$ **(d)** $(0, 0)$ **(e)** $(-2, 8)$
(f) $(-3, -4)$ **(g)** $(-8, -2)$ **(h)** $(-5, -2)$
2. (a) $(7, 2)$ **(b)** $(0, -3)$ **(c)** $(1, 3)$ **(d)** $(4, -4)$
(e) $(-1, 1)$ **(f)** $(6, -5)$ **(g)** $(5, 5)$ **(h)** $(1, -5)$
3. (a) $[4, 3]$ **(b)** $[10, 8]$ **(c)** $[5, -1]$ **(d)** $[7, 9]$
(e) $[3, 9]$ **(f)** $[2, -6]$ **(g)** $[5, 6]$ **(h)** $[4, 0]$
(i) $[-3, \frac{1}{2}]$
4. (a) $[2, 7]$ **(b)** $(5, 7), (1, 8), (2, 7)$
5. (b) $A'(6, 3)$, $B'(5, 8)$, $C'(7, 7)$
(d) $\sqrt{26}, \sqrt{5}, \sqrt{17}, \sqrt{26}, \sqrt{5}, \sqrt{17}$
(f) $-5, -\frac{1}{2}, 4, -5, -\frac{1}{2}, 4$
6. (b) $A'(-2, 1)$, $B'(3, 2)$, $C'(0, 5)$
(d) $\sqrt{26}, 3\sqrt{2}, 2\sqrt{5}, \sqrt{26}, 3\sqrt{2}, 2\sqrt{5}$
(f) $\frac{1}{5}, -1, 2, \frac{1}{5}, -1, 2$
7. yes, no
10. $2x + y = 6$

Exercise 14-2

2. (a) $(4, -7)$ **(b)** $(-2, -9)$ **(c)** $(6, 0)$ **(d)** $(0, 5)$
(e) $(-1, 1)$ **(f)** $(6, 3)$ **(g)** $(8, -1)$ **(h)** $(0, 0)$
3. (a) $(-2, 5)$ **(b)** $(-4, 3)$ **(c)** $(8, 6)$ **(d)** $(1, 2)$
(e) $(-7, 11)$ **(f)** $(0, -4)$ **(g)** $(-6, 0)$ **(h)** $(1, -1)$
4. The points on the mirror line are unchanged.
The mirror line, and lines perpendicular to it, are unchanged.
7. (a) $P'(-2, 4)$, $Q'(3, -8)$ **(b)** $13, 13$
8. (a) $A'(1, -3)$, $B'(3, 2)$ **(b)** $\sqrt{29}, \sqrt{29}$
9. (b) $A'(-1, -1)$, $B'(5, -2)$, $C'(3, -4)$
(d) $\sqrt{37}, 2\sqrt{2}, 5, \sqrt{37}, 2\sqrt{2}, 5$
(f) $A'(1, 1)$, $B'(-5, 2)$, $C'(-3, 4), \sqrt{37}, 2\sqrt{2}, 5$
10. (a) $A'(-1, 1)$, $B'(6, 1)$, $C'(6, -5)$ **(b)** $21, 21$
11. (a) $(1, 2)$ **(b)** $(7, 6)$
12. (a) $(2, 7)$ **(b)** $(-2, -7)$
13. (b, a)

Exercise 14-3

1. (a) $90°, -270°$ **(b)** $270°, -90°$ **(c)** $135°, -225°$ **(d)** $180°, -180°$
2. (a) $-300°$ **(b)** $-350°$ **(c)** $330°$
(d) $90°$ **(e)** $40°$ **(f)** $-260°$
3. The centre of rotation. (All points if the angle is $0°$ or $360°$)
4. (a) $180°, 360°$ **(b)** $90°, 180°, 270°, 360°$
(c) any angle **(d)** $120°, 240°, 360°$
(e) $180°, 360°$ **(f)** $60°, 120°, 180°, 240°, 300°, 360°$

7.

	90°	180°	270°
$A(1, 0)$	$(0, 1)$	$(-1, 0)$	$(0, -1)$
$B(2, 1)$	$(-1, 2)$	$(-2, -1)$	$(1, -2)$
$C(3, 4)$	$(-4, 3)$	$(-3, -4)$	$(4, -3)$
$D(-1, 3)$	$(-3, -1)$	$(1, -3)$	$(3, 1)$
$P(x, y)$	$(-y, x)$	$(-x, -y)$	$(y, -x)$

8. (a) $(0, 6)$ **(b)** $(1, 1)$ **(c)** $(6, 2)$

9. $O'(0, 0)$, $P'(\sqrt{2}, \sqrt{2})$, $Q'(0, 2\sqrt{2})$

Exercise 14-4

4.

	$A(1, 2)$	$B(3, 0)$	$C(-2, 5)$	$P(x, y)$
$T \circ T$	$(-3, 8)$	$(-1, 6)$	$(-6, 11)$	$(x - 4, y + 6)$
R	$(-1, -2)$	$(-3, 0)$	$(2, -5)$	$(-x, -y)$
$F \circ G$	$(-1, -2)$	$(-3, 0)$	$(2, -5)$	$(-x, -y)$
$G \circ F$	$(-1, -2)$	$(-3, 0)$	$(2, -5)$	$(-x, -y)$
$T \circ R$	$(-3, 1)$	$(-5, 3)$	$(0, -2)$	$(-x - 2, y + 3)$
$R \circ T$	$(1, -5)$	$(-1, -3)$	$(4, -8)$	$(-x + 2, -y - 3)$
$T \circ F$	$(-1, 1)$	$(1, 3)$	$(-4, -2)$	$(x - 2, -y + 3)$
$F \circ T$	$(-1, -5)$	$(1, -3)$	$(-4, -8)$	$(x - 2, -y - 3)$

5. $F \circ G = G \circ F = R$

6. (a) (i) $(6, 7)$ (ii) $(3, 9)$ (iii) $(11, 10)$ (iv) $(x + 5, y + 6)$
    (b) Translation defined by $\vec{a} + \vec{b}$

7. Translation

8. (a) R_{90} **(b)** R_{115} **(c)** $R_{\ominus + \alpha}$

9. all

Exercise 14-5

1. (a) 4, 4   **(b)** 2, 2   **(c)** 0, 1   **(d)** 2, 2   **(e)** 0, 2   **(f)** 1, 1
    (g) 0, 1   **(h)** 5, 5   **(i)** 6, 6   **(j)** 8, 8   **(k)** infinite   **(l)** 2, 2
    (m) 1, 1   **(n)** 1, 1   **(o)** 5, 5   **(p)** 0, 1   **(q)** 3, 3   **(r)** 0, 3

2. (a) $A\ H\ I\ M\ O\ T\ U\ V\ W\ X\ Y$
    (b) $B\ C\ D\ E\ H\ I\ K\ O\ X$

(c) *H I X*
(d) *H I N O S X Z*

Exercise 14-6

1. (a) $(3, 3)$ **(b)** $(9, -3)$ **(c)** $(0, 6)$
  (d) $(-15, -6)$ **(e)** $(-3, 1)$ **(f)** $(3a, 3b)$
2. (a) $(3, 1)$ **(b)** $(-1, 0)$ **(c)** $(-4, -2)$
  (d) $(\frac{1}{2}, \frac{9}{2})$ **(e)** $(1, -\frac{3}{2})$ **(f)** $(\frac{1}{2}a, \frac{1}{2}b)$
3. (a) $(-5, -5)$ **(b)** $(0, -30)$ **(c)** $(10, -45)$
  (d) $(-30, -4)$ **(e)** $(35, 5)$ **(f)** $(-5a, -5b)$
4. The centre of dilatation.
  Any line through the centre of dilatation.
  (If $K = 1$, all points and lines are unchanged)
6. (a) $A'(-2, -2)$, $B'(0, 2)$, $C'(6, 4)$
  (b) $AB = \sqrt{5}$, $BC = \sqrt{10}$, $CA = 5$, $A'B' = 2\sqrt{2}$, $B'C' = 2\sqrt{10}$, $C'A' = 10$
7. (a) $A'(3, 3)$, $B'(18, 3)$, $C'(18, 15)$
  (b) $AB = 5$, $BC = 4$, $CA = \sqrt{41}$
    $A'B' = 15$, $B'C' = 12$, $C'A' = 3\sqrt{41}$
  (c) $90, 10$
  (d) 9
8. (a) $\frac{1}{3}$ **(b)** 3 **(c)** $\frac{4}{3}$
9. (a) $A'(4, 8)$, $B'(6, 12)$, $C'(8, 10)$
  (b) $A'(3, 5)$, $B'(5, 9)$, $C'(7, 7)$
  (c) $A'(2, -2)$, $B'(4, -6)$, $C'(6, -4)$
  (d) $A'(-2, -2)$, $B'(-4, -6)$, $C'(-6, -4)$

Review Exercise

1. (a) translation
  (b) reflection in *x*-axis
  (c) dilatation
  (d) translation
  (e) rotation (or dilatation)
  (f) reflection in *y*-axis
2. (i) **(a)** $(0, 0)$ **(b)** $(3, -4)$ **(c)** $(-2, -1)$ **(d)** $(-6, 6)$
       (e) $(0, -5)$ **(f)** $(1, 1)$ **(g)** $(6, -\frac{1}{2})$ **(h)** $(a, -b)$
  (ii) **(a)** $(0, 0)$ **(b)** $(9, 12)$ **(c)** $(-6, 3)$ **(d)** $(-18, -18)$
       (e) $(0, 15)$ **(f)** $(3, -3)$ **(g)** $(18, \frac{3}{2})$ **(h)** $(3a, 3b)$
  (iii) **(a)** $(2, -4)$ **(b)** $(5, 0)$ **(c)** $(0, -3)$ **(d)** $(-4, -10)$
       (e) $(2, 1)$ **(f)** $(3, -5)$ **(g)** $(8, -3\frac{1}{2})$ **(h)** $(a+2, b-4)$
  (iv) **(a)** $(0, 0)$ **(b)** $(-3, 4)$ **(c)** $(2, 1)$ **(d)** $(6, -6)$
       (e) $(0, 5)$ **(f)** $(-1, -1)$ **(g)** $(-6, \frac{1}{2})$ **(h)** $(-a, b)$
  (v) **(a)** $(0, 0)$ **(b)** $(-3, -4)$ **(c)** $(2, -1)$ **(d)** $(6, 6)$
       (e) $(0, -5)$ **(f)** $(-1, 1)$ **(g)** $(-6, -\frac{1}{2})$ **(h)** $(-a, -b)$
3. translation, reflection, rotation
4. (a) $3, 3$ **(b)** $8, 8$ **(c)** $1, 1$
5. (a), (b), (c)
7. (b) $\sqrt{26}$, $2\sqrt{5}$, $\sqrt{10}$
  (i) $\sqrt{26}$, $2\sqrt{5}$, $\sqrt{10}$
  (ii) $\sqrt{26}$, $2\sqrt{5}$, $\sqrt{10}$
  (iii) $3\sqrt{26}$, $6\sqrt{5}$, $3\sqrt{10}$

9.

	$A(-2, -2)$	$B(4, 6)$	$C(2, 8)$	$P(x, y)$
F	$(-2, 2)$	$(4, -6)$	$(2, -8)$	$(x, -y)$
R	$(2, 2)$	$(-4, -6)$	$(-2, -8)$	$(-x, -y)$
T	$(0, -3)$	$(6, 5)$	$(4, 7)$	$(x+2, y-1)$
D	$(-1, -1)$	$(2, 3)$	$(1, 4)$	$(\frac{1}{2}x, \frac{1}{2}y)$
$T \circ D$	$(1, -2)$	$(4, 2)$	$(3, 3)$	$(\frac{1}{2}x+2, \frac{1}{2}y-1)$
$D \circ T$	$(0, -\frac{3}{2})$	$(3, \frac{5}{2})$	$(2, \frac{7}{2})$	$(\frac{1}{2}x+1, \frac{1}{2}y-\frac{1}{2})$
$F \circ R$	$(2, -2)$	$(-4, 6)$	$(-2, 8)$	$(-x, y)$
$D \circ F$	$(-1, 1)$	$(2, -3)$	$(1, -4)$	$(\frac{1}{2}x, -\frac{1}{2}y)$
$F \circ D$	$(-1, 1)$	$(2, -3)$	$(1, -4)$	$(\frac{1}{2}x, -\frac{1}{2}y)$
$D \circ D$	$(-\frac{1}{2}, -\frac{1}{2})$	$(1, \frac{3}{2})$	$(\frac{1}{2}, 2)$	$(\frac{1}{4}x, \frac{1}{4}y)$
$D \circ R$	$(1, 1)$	$(-2, -3)$	$(-1, -4)$	$(-\frac{1}{2}x, -\frac{1}{2}y)$
$F \circ T$	$(0, 3)$	$(6, -5)$	$(4, 7)$	$(x+2, -y+1)$

10. (c) $2, \frac{3}{2}, \frac{1}{3}, \frac{1}{2}$

REVIEW AND PREVIEW TO CHAPTER 15

Exercise 1
1. $\frac{1}{4}$, 0.25 **2.** $\frac{3}{4}$, 0.75 **3.** $\frac{1}{3}$, 0.$\dot{3}$ **4.** $\frac{1}{10}$, 0.1
5. $\frac{13}{20}$, 0.65 **6.** $\frac{6}{5}$, 1.2 **7.** $\frac{17}{20}$, 0.85 **8.** $\frac{9}{4}$, 2.25
9. $\frac{1}{20}$, 0.05 **10.** $\frac{3}{200}$, 0.015 **11.** $\frac{21}{200}$, 0.105 **12.** $\frac{2}{3}$, 0.$\dot{6}$
13. $\frac{1}{8}$, 0.125 **14.** $\frac{3}{8}$, 0.375 **15.** $\frac{5}{8}$, 0.625

Exercise 2
1. 40% **2.** 75% **3.** 70% **4.** 15%
5. 6% **6.** 25% **7.** 175% **8.** 57.5%
9. 34.5% **10.** 202.5% **11.** 62.5% **12.** 12.5%
13. 37.5% **14.** 125% **15.** 387.5%

Exercise 3
1. 1 **2.** 4.32 **3.** 7.38 **4.** 750
5. 1.44 **6.** 0.1875 **7.** 8 **8.** 55.5
9. 14 **10.** 630 **11.** 3.6 **12.** 1.1
13. 117 **14.** 1100 **15.** 325 **16.** 12.5
17. 116 **18.** $6826.75 **19.** $1948.24 **20.** $337.50

Exercise 4

1. 37.5%   **2.** 17.14%   **3.** $133\frac{1}{3}$%   **4.** $33\frac{1}{3}$%
5. 20%   **6.** $166\frac{2}{3}$%   **7.** 58%   **8.** 7%
9. 5.7%   **10.** 700%

CHAPTER 15

Exercise 15-1

1. (a) Bullets are consumed when tested.
   (b) Testing all the ore results in actual mining.
   (c) Time and expense requires sampling only.
   (d) Wine is consumed when tested.
   (e) Impossible to tag all geese.
2. automobile brakes, television sets, water craft.
3. (a) biased, inaccurate   **(b)** expensive
   (c) bias
4. (a) 37   **(b)** 82   **(c)** 25
5. (a) 25   **(b)** 38   **(c)** 2   **(d)** 1

Exercise 15-3

1. (a) median   **(b)** mode   **(c)** mean   **(d)** mean
   (e) median   **(f)** mode   **(g)** mean   **(h)** median
2. (a) 26; 53; 49.3   **(b)** 20; 12; 12.1
   (c) 5; 4.5; 4.4   **(d)** 8; 8.5; 10.4
   (e) 3 and 4; 4; 4.3
3. 17; 17; 17.4
4. $31 000; $31 000; $31 029.41
5. (b) 51   **(c)** 62   **(d)** 63.6
6. (a) $55.75   **(b)** $56.75   **(c)** $56.66

Exercise 15-4

1. (a) 24   **(b)** 75   **(c)** 304   **(d)** 150   **(e)** 50
2. (a) 34%   **(b)** 82%   **(c)** 84%
3. (a) 16%   **(b)** 96%   **(c)** 16%
4. (a) 68%   **(b)** 98%   **(c)** 160   **(d)** 20
5. (a) 84%   **(b)** 1360   **(c)** 40   **(d)** 320
6. (a) 82%   **(b)** 480   **(c)** 1500
7. (a) 16%   **(b)** 80   **(c)** 420
8. (a) 16%   **(b)** 960   **(c)** 4920
9. range: 12, mean: 179, standard deviation: 3.35
10. range: 9, mean: 50, standard deviation: 2.51

Exercise 15-5

1. (a) 6   **(b)** 3   **(c)** $\frac{1}{2}$ **(d)** $\frac{1}{2}$ **(e)** $\frac{1}{3}$

2. (a) 12   **(b)** 3   **(c)** $\frac{1}{4}$ **(d)** $\frac{1}{3}$ **(e)** $\frac{3}{4}$

3. (a) $\dfrac{1}{4}$ **(b)** $\dfrac{1}{4}$ **(c)** $\dfrac{1}{2}$

5. (a) $\dfrac{3}{5}$ **(b)** $\dfrac{2}{5}$

6. (a) $\dfrac{1}{4}$ **(b)** $\dfrac{3}{4}$ **(c)** $\dfrac{1}{13}$ **(d)** $\dfrac{12}{13}$ **(e)** $\dfrac{1}{2}$ **(f)** $\dfrac{1}{26}$ **(g)** $\dfrac{1}{52}$

7. (a) $\dfrac{1}{2}$ **(b)** $\dfrac{1}{10}$ **(c)** $\dfrac{1}{4}$

8. (a) $\{(1,1),(1,2),(1,3),(1,4),(1,5),(1,6),(2,1),(2,2),\ldots,(5,4),(5,5),(5,6),$
$(6,1),(6,2),(6,3),(6,4),(6,5),(6,6)\}$

(b) $0, \dfrac{1}{36}, \dfrac{1}{18}, \dfrac{1}{12}, \dfrac{1}{9}, \dfrac{5}{36}, \dfrac{1}{6}, \dfrac{5}{36}, \dfrac{1}{9}, \dfrac{1}{12}, \dfrac{1}{18}, \dfrac{1}{36}$

(c) $\dfrac{5}{18}$ **(d)** $\dfrac{1}{4}$

9. (a) 0 **(b)** $\dfrac{1}{216}$ **(c)** $\dfrac{1}{36}$

10. (a) $\dfrac{1}{8}$ **(b)** $\dfrac{3}{8}$ **(c)** $\dfrac{7}{8}$

11. (a) $\dfrac{3}{8}$ **(b)** $\dfrac{1}{4}$ **(c)** $\dfrac{11}{16}$

12. (a) $\dfrac{1}{4}$ **(b)** $\dfrac{1}{4}$ **(c)** $\dfrac{1}{2}$ **(d)** $\dfrac{1}{16}$ **(e)** $\dfrac{1}{2704}$ **(f)** $\dfrac{1}{52}$

13. (a) $\dfrac{25}{102}$ **(b)** $\dfrac{13}{51}$ **(c)** $\dfrac{26}{51}$ **(d)** $\dfrac{13}{204}$ **(e)** 0 **(f)** 0

Review Exercise

1. (a) 27   **(b) (i)** 15 **(ii)** 11 **(iii)** 22
2. (b) 6   **(c)** 136   **(d)** 135.5   **(e)** 1.45
3. (a) 82%   **(b)** 2%   **(c)** 1600   **(d)** 1600
4. (a) 84%   **(b)** 840   **(c)** 480

5. (a) $\dfrac{1}{4}$ **(b)** $\dfrac{3}{4}$ **(c)** $\dfrac{3}{10}$ **(d)** $\dfrac{7}{10}$ **(e)** $\dfrac{9}{20}$ **(f)** $\dfrac{11}{20}$

6. (a) $\dfrac{1}{6}$ **(b)** $\dfrac{2}{9}$ **(c)** $\dfrac{1}{2}$

7. (a) $\dfrac{1}{4}$ **(b)** $\dfrac{1}{52}$ **(c)** $\dfrac{3}{4}$ **(d)** $\dfrac{12}{13}$ **(e)** $\dfrac{3}{13}$ **(f)** $\dfrac{2}{13}$

8. (a) $\dfrac{1}{1296}$ **(b)** $\dfrac{5}{1296}$ **(c)** $\dfrac{1291}{1296}$ **(d)** $\dfrac{1}{1296}$

Trigonometric Ratios

$\theta°$	$\sin \theta$	$\cos \theta$	$\tan \theta$
0	.0000	1.0000	.0000
1	.0175	.9999	.0175
2	.0349	.9994	.0349
3	.0523	.9986	.0524
4	.0698	.9976	.0699
5	.0872	.9962	.0875
6	.1045	.9945	.1051
7	.1219	.9926	.1228
8	.1392	.9903	.1405
9	.1564	.9877	.1584
10	.1737	.9848	.1763
11	.1908	.9816	.1944
12	.2079	.9782	.2126
13	.2250	.9744	.2309
14	.2419	.9703	.2493
15	.2588	.9659	.2680
16	.2756	.9613	.2868
17	.2924	.9563	.3057
18	.3090	.9511	.3249
19	.3256	.9455	.3443
20	.3420	.9397	.3640
21	.3584	.9336	.3839
22	.3746	.9272	.4040
23	.3907	.9205	.4245
24	.4067	.9136	.4452
25	.4226	.9063	.4663
26	.4384	.8988	.4877
27	.4540	.8910	.5095
28	.4695	.8830	.5317
29	.4848	.8746	.5543
30	.5000	.8660	.5774
31	.5150	.8572	.6009
32	.5299	.8481	.6249
33	.5446	.8387	.6494
34	.5592	.8290	.6745
35	.5736	.8192	.7002
36	.5878	.8090	.7265
37	.6018	.7986	.7536
38	.6157	.7880	.7813
39	.6293	.7772	.8098
40	.6428	.7660	.8391
41	.6561	.7547	.8693
42	.6691	.7431	.9004
43	.6820	.7314	.9325
44	.6947	.7193	.9657
45	.7071	.7071	1.0000

Trigonometric Ratios

$\theta°$	$\sin \theta$	$\cos \theta$	$\tan \theta$
46	.7193	.6947	1.0355
47	.7314	.6820	1.0724
48	.7431	.6691	1.1106
49	.7547	.6561	1.1504
50	.7660	.6428	1.1918
51	.7772	.6293	1.2349
52	.7880	.6157	1.2799
53	.7986	.6018	1.3270
54	.8090	.5878	1.3764
55	.8192	.5736	1.4281
56	.8290	.5592	1.4826
57	.8387	.5446	1.5399
58	.8481	.5299	1.6003
59	.8572	.5150	1.6643
60	.8660	.5000	1.7321
61	.8746	.4848	1.8041
62	.8830	.4695	1.8807
63	.8910	.4540	1.9626
64	.8988	.4384	2.0503
65	.9063	.4226	2.1445
66	.9136	.4067	2.2460
67	.9205	.3907	2.3559
68	.9272	.3746	2.4751
69	.9336	.3584	2.6051
70	.9397	.3420	2.7475
71	.9455	.3256	2.9042
72	.9511	.3090	3.0777
73	.9563	.2924	3.2709
74	.9613	.2756	3.4874
75	.9659	.2588	3.7321
76	.9703	.2419	4.0108
77	.9744	.2250	4.3315
78	.9782	.2079	4.7046
79	.9816	.1908	5.1446
80	.9848	.1737	5.6713
81	.9877	.1564	6.3138
82	.9903	.1392	7.1154
83	.9926	.1219	8.1444
84	.9945	.1045	9.5144
85	.9962	.0872	11.4301
86	.9976	.0698	14.3007
87	.9986	.0523	19.0811
88	.9994	.0349	28.6363
89	.9999	.0175	57.2900
90	1.0000	.0000	————

INDEX